statistical analysis
for business
and economics

Leonard J. Kazmier

Associate Professor of Management
Arizona State University

McGraw-Hill Book Company

New York   Toronto   St. Louis   San Francisco   London   Sydney

to my parents

preface This book covers the methods of description and inference typically included in a one-semester course in business and economic statistics. It is different from other books in this field in that it is programmed to enhance student comprehension by the application of instructional principles developed in recent research on the learning process. As such, the presentation method used in this book is intended not to replace classroom discussion and practice, but to make such participation more meaningful by helping the student to identify more clearly areas in which he needs additional practice and help.

In terms of content, both the traditional and modern approaches to the use of statistical analysis are represented in the units that comprise this book. Following a coverage of basic definitions and the methods of statistical description in the first four units, probability theory and its use in the principal methods of statistical inference are considered in Units 5 through 11, as indicated in the table below. All discussion of Bayesian inference and decision theory has been deferred until Unit 12, so that these methods can be presented after a thorough coverage of the classical methods of inference. The placement of this material as well as that on time-series analysis and index numbers gives the instructor the option of including or eliminating these statistical methods without any loss of continuity.

Major topics	*Units*
Statistical description	1 to 4
Probability theory and methods of inference	5 to 11
Bayesian inference and decision theory (optional)	12
Regression and correlation analysis	13 to 14
Time-series analysis and index numbers (optional)	15 to 16

The method of presenting the material in this book is novel by the standards of classical textbooks in at least two respects. First, though every author gives attention to the appropriate sequencing of material in his book, the methodology of programming requires that the frame-by-frame sequencing be tested and modified on the basis of the performance of representative student groups. Second—and this is perhaps the most visible difference— the student is requested to indicate his developing knowledge by answering key questions and doing short sample problems as he progresses through each unit. His own continuing performance thus serves as feedback regarding his comprehension of the material being presented. The student can of course look at the answers in the margin before attempting to answer them on his own, thus depriving himself of the opportunity for independent practice and feedback. The choice is his.

This book is *not* intended to be self-instructional for the majority of students, although advanced students and graduate students will find the methodology better suited for self-review than is the presentation method of the traditional textbook. For the typical undergraduate student, the book helps him to ask more meaningful questions during class discussion because of his ability to identify the precise material that he needs to have clarified. Thus the instructor is able to use the management principle of *exception* during the class session, for his role is not that of lecturing on the book but of discussing and elaborating in the specific areas of student difficulty and expanding upon the basic core of material presented.

Some early versions of programmed material have been criticized for being slow-moving and boring for the superior student. The use of "small steps" was one price that some programmers were willing to pay for making instructional material relatively easy. The programmed material in this book is not easy. However, it has been designed to be fast-moving, comprehensive, and effective.

The author owes a debt of gratitude to the numerous reviewers who generously responded with helpful and pointed suggestions regarding the test version of this book. Along these lines I owe special thanks to Professor Edward Trubac of the University of Notre Dame, who served as a consulting reviewer throughout the development of the original manuscript. Without the exceptional performance of Marcia Zirbes, who typed the entire final manuscript, timely completion of the book would certainly have been impossible. Since the development of effective programmed material is particularly dependent on student feedback and review, I would like to thank the students at Notre Dame and Arizona State who bore up nobly under this task and, indeed, seemed rather to enjoy it.

Finally, I am indebted to the literary executor of the late Sir Ronald A. Fisher, F.R.S., Cambridge, and to Oliver & Boyd Ltd., Edinburgh and London, for their permission to reprint Tables III, IV, and V-A from their book *Statistical Methods for Research Workers*.

Leonard J. Kazmier

instructions for the student

In addition to being made up of a tested sequence of material, this book is different from the typical textbook in that you are requested to answer key questions and do short sample problems as you progress through each unit of material. The answers to these questions and problems are given along the left margin of each page. Please cover these answers until after you have responded to each question, and then check your answer against the one given in the margin.

By following this recommended procedure you will gain two advantages that will increase your effectiveness in learning, that of using the opportunity for independent practice and of having continual feedback to inform *yourself* of your progress and understanding in each topic area.

The development of the material in this book is relatively fast-moving and comprehensive with little repetition as such, and so you will find that close attention on your part is necessary. When you experience difficulty, as indicated by your inability to answer key questions or do sample problems, put a check mark in the margin as a reminder to ask for a clarification of the concept or technique during class.

A review section is included at the end of each unit. You can use this as an overall self-test after completing the unit as well as for later review. As indicated, the solutions to the first group of problems at the end of each unit are presented in the back of the book.

For reference purposes the Glossary of Formulas, just preceding the Index, provides the basis for quickly locating needed formulas.

contents

Two Population Means. Confidence Intervals for Proportions and Differences between Proportions.

9 ▪ hypothesis testing   168

Hypothesis Testing and the Null Hypothesis. The Level of Significance and Type I and Type II Errors. Hypotheses Concerning Population Means. Hypotheses Concerning the Difference between Two Means. Hypotheses Concerning Proportions (Using the Binomial Distribution). Hypotheses Concerning Proportions (Using the Normal Distribution).

10 ▪ the use of student's t distribution   189

Characteristics of the t Distribution. Estimation Using the t Distribution. Hypothesis Testing Using the t Distribution. The Use of the Normal, Binomial, and t Distributions.

11 ▪ the chi-square test   206

Introduction. Comparing Observed Frequencies to Expected Frequencies. Contingency Tables. Interpretation of the χ^2 Test. An Alternative Formula for Computing χ^2 and the Correction for Continuity.

12 ▪ bayesian inference and decision theory   226

Objective, Subjective, and Conditional Probability. Bayesian Inference. Decision Making under Conditions of Risk: Expected Payoff. Decision Making under Conditions of Uncertainty: Further Decision Criteria. Decision Making under Conditions of Conflict: Game Theory.

13 ▪ linear-regression analysis   254

The Graphic Analysis of Simple Linear Regression. The Least-squares Criterion in Fitting a Straight Line. Use of the Regression Equation. The Standard Error of Estimate.

14 ▪ correlation   276

The Meaning of the Correlation Coefficient. Development of the Pearson Correlation Coefficient r. Computations in Simple Correlation Analysis. Rank Correlation. Multiple and Partial Correlation and the Meaning of Correlation Values.

15 ▪ time-series analysis   296

The Components of a Time Series. Trend Analysis. Seasonal Variation.

Estimation of Cyclical and Irregular Variations. The Use of Time-series Analysis in Forecasting.

unit 1 ▪ the use of statistical analysis

For the purpose of either effective managerial decision making or economic analysis, quantitative data have to be collected, analyzed, and interpreted. On the one hand, the analysis of the data may be directed entirely toward describing and interpreting only the information actually collected; this is referred to as statistical description. On the other hand, the analysis may be directed toward describing and interpreting a whole class of phenomena of which the information collected is merely a sample; this is referred to as statistical inference. In this unit we introduce the important distinctions between descriptive statistics and inferential statistics, consider the ways in which inductive and deductive reasoning are represented in statistical analysis, discuss the kinds of numerical data that can be analyzed, and present some rules to follow in determining the number of significant digits included in computations and the appropriate rounding of the results of these computations.

1.a ▪ descriptive and inferential statistics

As indicated above, the tools of statistical analysis can be used either for summarizing and interpreting a set of measurements as such or for making inferences regarding the attributes of a larger set of data, of which the obtained measurements are just a part. In recent years the techniques of statistical inference have become particularly important in the analysis of economic and business data, and hence these techniques constitute a major portion of this book.

1 The methods of statistical analysis can be directed toward either statistical description or statistical inference. When the methods of statistics are used to summarize the information that has been collected or to organize it so that comprehension of the information is made easier, then the methods are being used for

description

the purpose of statistical (description / inference).

2 For example, grouping a large number of measurements and presenting the results in tables or graphs involves the use of

description

statistical techniques for the purpose of statistical _description_ .

3 On the other hand, when we arrive at some conclusions regarding the characteristics of a larger set of variables than those actually measured, the techniques of statistical analysis are being applied

inference

for the purpose of statistical (description / inference).

4 For example, on the basis of interviews conducted with 5,000 of 50,000 families residing in a metropolitan area, an economist comes to certain conclusions regarding planned consumer expenditures in that area. In this case the analytic techniques are being

inference

used for the purpose of statistical _infence_ .

5 In the following list, post a D for the situations in which statistical techniques are used for the purpose of description and an I for those in which the techniques are used for the purpose of inference.

I

(a) The price movements of 30 issues of stock are analyzed to determine whether stocks in general have gone up or down during a certain period of time.

D

(b) A statistical table is constructed for the purpose of presenting the passenger-miles flown by various commercial airlines in the United States.

D

(c) The average of a group of test scores is computed so that each score in the group can be classified as being either above or below average.

I

(d) Several manufacturing firms in a particular industry are surveyed for the purpose of anticipating industry-wide investment in capital equipment.

6 In statistical analysis the term _population_, or universe, is used to designate all of the elements that conform to a certain definition; the term _sample_ designates some portion of the population. In the accompanying diagram, in which the x's represent individual elements, the population is designated by the letter ____, and the sample taken from that population is designated by the letter ____.

A

B

7 The methods of statistical description can be used to describe the characteristics of either a sample or an entire population of elements, whereas the methods of inference are used only when (sample / population) data are known.

sample

8 Or, to put it another way, the application of statistical techniques for the purpose of statistical description suggests that the characteristics of (some / all / either some or all) elements in the population have been measured.

either some or all

9 On the other hand, the application of statistical techniques for the purpose of statistical inference suggests that the characteristics of (some / all / either some or all) of the elements in the population have been measured.

some

10 What constitutes a statistical population is entirely a matter of definition. Thus, if a statistician is interested in determining average family income in the United States, then the population of values is made up of the incomes of all families residing in _The_ _____, whereas the incomes of families residing in Detroit would constitute a _sample_ taken from this population.

11 A statistical population need not be made up of a large number of elements, nor need it have geographic boundaries. For example, a study of the construction characteristics of all buildings more than 40 stories in height would include (a great number of / ~~relatively few~~) buildings in the statistical population.

12 No matter how few elements are included in a statistical population, however, a sample taken from that population (can / cannot) be larger than the population itself.

13 On the other hand, a sample taken from one population (can / cannot) contain more elements than are included is *some other* statistical population.

14 For example, in a study of retail-store sales the number of retailing establishments surveyed as a sample in order to estimate statewide sales volume (can / cannot) be greater than the total number of retail stores in a particular community.

15 Furthermore the same set of measurements can be considered as a statistical population for one purpose and as a statistical sample for another purpose. When a "test of mathematical knowledge" is given to a group of college freshmen in order to come to some conclusions regarding the mathematical competence of college freshmen in general, then the scores constitute a (sample / population); when the scores are used only for the purpose of making course decisions for the particular students who took the test, the scores constitute a (sample / population).

16 When the characteristics of a population are measured, the process is called a *census*; measuring the characteristics of a sample is called *sampling*. Thus the national census carried out every 10 years in the United States includes an attempt to enumerate (all / a sample) of the people in the country.

17 In terms of an analogy, measuring the characteristics of a portion of a population is to sampling as measuring the characteristics of an entire population is to _census_.

18 Therefore the process of taking a census in order to collect, analyze, and interpret the characteristics of a population is directly related to statistical (description / inference), and the process of sampling is always involved in statistical _inference_.

19 The characteristics, or attributes, of a population are also designated differently from the attributes of a sample. Descriptive measures of a population are called *population parameters*, but descriptive measures of a sample are called *sample statistics.* If 55 percent of a sample of registered voters who respond to a mailed questionnaire indicate favor for a particular tax proposal, this 55 percent figure is a (population parameter / sample statistic).

sample statistic

20 Thus any descriptive measurement of a population is considered to be a (statistic / parameter), and a descriptive measurement of a sample is a sample ___*statistic*___

parameter
statistic

21 Average family income computed for a sample of the families in a community is a sample _____; average family income based on a complete census of the families in the community is a population _____.

statistic
parameter

22 At this point it might be useful to highlight the fact that the word "statistics" has at least three distinct meanings, depending on the context in which it is used. It may refer to:

(a) the procedure of statistical analysis
(b) descriptive measures of a sample
(c) the individual measurements, or elements, that make up either a sample or a population

When one becomes "an accident statistic" by being included in some count of accident frequency, the term is used in the sense of definition **(a / b / c).**

c

23 According to the definitions in Frame 22, in a course of study called Business Statistics the term "statistics" is usually used in the sense of definition **(a / b / c).**

a

24 According to the definitions in Frame 22, when such sample statistics as the proportion of a sample in favor of a proposal and the average age of those in the sample are determined, the term "statistics" is being used in the sense of definition **(a / b /c).**

b

summary

description
inference

25 The two major applications of the tools of statistical analysis are directed toward the purposes of statistical _____ and statistical _____.

population
sample

26 The set of elements that includes all elements that belong to that group is called a statistical _____; a group of elements that includes a portion, but not all, of the elements that belong to the overall set is called a statistical _____.

census

27 When all the elements in a statistical population are measured, the process is referred to as taking a _____. If only a portion of the elements included in a statistical population are

sampling	measured, the process is called _____.

28 A descriptive measurement of a population, such as calculation

parameter	of the average value, is designated as a population _____.
	A similar descriptive measurement determined for a sample of
statistic	values is designated as a sample _____.

29 We have discussed three distinct meanings that the term "statistics" may have. See how many of these you can give below (in any order):

methods of statistical analysis	**(a)** _____
descriptive measures of a sample	**(b)** _____
the individual measurements in a sample or population	**(c)** _____

1.b ▪ inductive and deductive reasoning, sampling, and probability

Whenever the characteristics of a population, or general truths, are determined by observing the characteristics of a number of the elements that make up that population, the process of inductive reasoning, or *induction*, is involved. This has also been referred to as the process of reasoning from the *particular to the general*. On the other hand, when we begin with the characteristics of the population of elements known, and thereby conclude what the characteristics of an element that belongs to this population must be, the process of deductive reasoning, or *deduction*, is involved. Deduction can also be viewed as the process of reasoning from the *general to the particular*. In this section we shall explore the relationship of these two categories of reasoning with the descriptive and inferential uses of statistics, the requirements associated with "good" sampling, and the role of probability theory in statistical analysis.

deduction	**30** The process of reasoning from the general to the particular describes (induction / deduction).

induction	**31** The process of reasoning from the particular to the general describes (induction / deduction).

deduction	**32** The method of reasoning which is based on the application of a known population description or general principle is _____.

33 Therefore, given the information that all stocks in a particular product field have increased in price by $1 to $3 on a particular day, give an example of the use of this information in a deductive way.

Given any stock in this group, we can conclude that its price went up by at least $1 on this day.	_____
	_____

34 When an economist attempts to discover the relationship between tax structure and the pattern of consumer spending by observing the effects of different tax policies in several specific

induction	locations, he is utilizing the reasoning process of _____.

35 Since the classical development of mathematics has been founded on beginning with basic assumed truths, or axioms, and deriving other mathematical principles based entirely on these axioms, the system is primarily (inductive / deductive).

deductive	

36 The scientific method places particular emphasis on the importance of controlled and verifiable observations of particular events as a basis for discovering general truth. Because of this, the scientific method is largely (inductive / deductive).

inductive	

37 The complete cycle of scientific activity includes the processes of both induction and deduction. When a scientist discovers or verifies the existence of specific principles by observing results under controlled conditions, he is reasoning from the _____ to the _____. When he is able to develop subsidiary principles, or when he applies known principles for the purpose of predicting the outcomes of specific events, he is reasoning from the _____ to the _____.

particular	
general	
general particular	

38 In using the inductive method, it is rarely the case that all the elements that belong to a particular population can be observed. Therefore conclusions arrived at by the process of induction are typically based on having observed, or measured, a _____ of elements taken from the population.

sample (or portion)	

39 But because the sample characteristics are used to describe not only the elements that make up the sample but also the entire population from which the elements were selected, the statistical methods that are used in conjunction with the process of induction are always directed toward the objective of statistical (description / inference).

inference	

40 Thus the application of the methods of statistics for the purpose of inference directly represents the reasoning process of _____.

induction	

41 Because both the process of induction and the use of quantitative tools are integral parts of the scientific method, statistical inference is an extremely important branch of statistics and is today relatively more important than the application of statistical methods for the purpose of statistical _____.

description	

42 When a description is based on observing and/or measuring a sample of elements rather than the entire population of elements, can we ever be sure that the description is correct for all elements in the population? (yes / no)

no	

43 Therefore the process of statistical inference invariably involves the application of probability theory, which we shall introduce in greater detail in later units. When probability theory is used in statistical inference, the risk involved in accepting a quantitative description of a population based on sample data is (eliminated / identified as to amount).

identified as to amount

44 In statistical inference based on sample data, risk cannot be eliminated. But the amount of risk can be specifically identified by the application of _____ theory.

probability

45 In the area of hypothesis testing, for example, the decision maker faces the choice of accepting or not accepting a description as being representative of a population. If he accepts the hypothesis as being true, he runs the risk that it is actually _____. On the other hand, if he adopts a conservative strategy and rejects a tentative description unless it is very clearly supported by sample data, he runs the risk that the description is actually _____.

false (untrue)

true (correct)

46 Frame 45 suggests that in the process of statistical inference risk (can / cannot) be avoided but the kind of risk that is taken (is / is not) under the decision maker's control.

cannot

is (since he is the one who chooses to accept or reject a tentative description)

47 The preceding comments on the role of probability theory in statistical inference are of course introductory in nature; they will be expanded later, beginning with Unit 5. Consider now the relationship between sampling and the use of probability theory; if a number of samples are taken from a population, would every sample be equally representative of the population? (yes / no)

no

48 Ideally, we should like to use a sampling procedure such that the representativeness of the sample would be guaranteed. Unfortunately no such procedure has been discovered or devised. Thus we can (always / sometimes / never) be sure that a particular sample is actually representative of a particular population.

never

49 Instead of guaranteeing that a sample is representative, the best that a "good" sampling procedure can do is to make certain that known sources of bias are not introduced in the sampling procedure. Such a sample is called a *probability sample*, which we shall discuss further in Unit 7. In terms of the discussion above, we know that a probability sample (is / is not) necessarily representative of the population.

is not

50 Even though it does not guarantee representativeness, a probability sample has the distinct advantage that the extent to which it is likely to be representative can be stipulated by means of a specific probability statement, thus making possible the application of _____ theory for the purpose of statistical _____.

probability   inference

51 Thus the only type of sample that makes it possible to apply statistical methods for the purpose of inference is the _____ sample.

52 Since there are a number of sampling procedures that conform to the requirements of probability sampling, some of which are discussed in Unit 7, the need to have a probability sample when one wishes to use statistical methods for the purpose of inference is not so restrictive as it sounds. However, if a sample includes a known source of bias, or does not conform to one of the accepted techniques of probability sampling, the methods of statistical in-

ference (can / cannot) be legitimately used.

53 One of the requirements of a probability sample is that every element in the statistical population have a known, and usually equal, chance of being included in the sample. On this basis an investigator who chooses a sample of stock issues that, in his

judgment, looks representative (does / does not) have a probability sample.

54 A political poll taker stops a number of people at a downtown

intersection to get their views. Can the methods of statistical inference be applied to this sample for the purpose of determining the political beliefs of all residents of the community? (yes / no)

summary

55 The type of reasoning that highlights the application of *known general principles* and the development of subsidiary principles that

are consistent with these is _____.

56 The type of reasoning that is dependent on observation or measurement of actual elements or events for the purpose of

discovering general principles is _____.

57 Inductive reasoning is directly involved when the methods of

statistics are applied for the purpose of statistical _____.

58 Many of the statistical methods which we shall cover in the first few units of this book are applicable for the purposes of both description and inference. However, the additional mathematical ingredient which is included when the methods of statistics are

applied for the purpose of inference is the use of _____ theory.

59 For the appropriate application of the methods of statistical inference, the statistical sample must be so chosen that it can be

considered a _____ sample.

1.c ▪ discrete and continuous variables

Statistical data may be either discrete or continuous. Because some of the methods of statistical analysis are specifically oriented toward just one of these categories of data, it is particularly important that we distinguish these two types of variables in this introductory unit. The possible values of a discrete variable can be only integers, or whole numbers, but a continuous variable can assume any fractional or integer value within the specified range of values. Thus discrete data are generated whenever the elements in a sample or population are counted, and continuous data are generated whenever the elements are measured.

discrete continuous	**60** The two types of variables, or data, that can be subjected to statistical analysis are termed _____ and _____.
continuous discrete	**61** The kind of numbers that can take on any fractional or integer value between specified limits are categorized as _____, whereas values that can appear only as whole numbers are called _____.
measuring counting	**62** The form of the data is related to whether the operation of counting or measuring has been carried out. Continuous data are generated whenever the operation of _____ is performed; discrete data are generated whenever the operation of _____ is performed.
discrete	**63** Thus, if we identify the number of people who use each of several brands of tooth paste, the data generated must be _____.
continuous	**64** If we determine the heights and weights of a group of college men, the data generated are _____.
5.7; 2.3; 7.6 (all the fractional values)	**65** Given the following numbers which are assumed to be independent of one another, and given no information as to their source, circle the numbers which *must* represent variables that are continuous. 5 5.7 9 2.3 8 7.6
5; 5.7; 9; 2.3; 8; 7.6 (all the values, since integers are possible in continuous data)	**66** Of the values in Frame 65, list those that represent or *could* represent data measured on a continuous scale:_____
5; 9; 8 (all the integers)	**67** Which of the values in Frame 65 *could* represent discrete variables? _____
continuous	**68** Because various fractional values are possible, the average selling price for a stock issue during a specified time period is an example of a (discrete / continuous) category of values.
discrete	**69** A daily quotation of the number of shares of stock traded on a stock exchange is an example of a (discrete / continuous) category of values.

1.d ▪ significant figures and the rounding of numbers

For the student unaccustomed to manipulating statistical data, two types of decisions can be rather troublesome: determining how many of the digits in a computed result represent accurate information, as contrasted to constituting a remainder; and determining how the rounding of a remainder should be carried out if it is exactly halfway between the digit preceding it and the next higher digit. In order to consider these problems, we need first to identify the number of significant digits contained in individual values. In turn, this depends on whether the data are discrete or continuous.

70   The significant digits in a number are those that represent accurate and meaningful information. Another way of putting it is that the accurate digits are the significant digits of a number. Thus the value 21, when it applies to a continuous variable, has _____ (number) significant digits.

two

71   The location of the decimal point does *not* have an effect on the number of significant digits contained in a number. Thus the numbers 215, 21.5, and .215, if on the continuous scale, would all have three _____ digits.

significant

72   The greater the number of significant digits, the greater the accuracy in measurement. Accordingly, circle the most accurate of the following numbers.

(a) 12.1
(b) 12.125
(c) 12.12

12.125

73   Suppose, however, we have a *count* of 12 and that this value is discrete. If we assume that the count is correct, is there any way that this value can be improved in accuracy? (yes / no).

no

74   Because the accuracy of correct discrete numbers cannot be improved, the number of significant digits contained in discrete numbers is considered limitless. Therefore the rules for determining the number of significant digits contained in numbers apply only to continuous variables. Accordingly, a correct count of 25 means (about 25 / exactly 25).

exactly 25

75   On the continuous scale, however, a measurement of 25 inches means "about 25 inches" (i.e., closer to 25 inches than to either 24 or 26 inches). This indicates that the accuracy of data measured on a continuous scale can, at least theoretically, (always / sometimes / never) be improved.

always

76   For the following unrelated values, indicate the number of significant digits in each number or indicate "limitless" where appropriate.

significant ⟶ Continuous.

3	_____ 13.3
2	_____ 19 (a measurement)
3	_____ .395
limitless	_____ 5 (a count)

77 Now that we have disposed of discrete numbers, the only important question remaining is whether zeros contained in continuous numbers should be considered as significant digits. If the zeros are "leading zeros," they are never considered significant, whether they occur before or after the decimal point. Accordingly, indicate the number of significant digits in each of the following numbers.

3	____ .737
2	____ .0095
2	____ 0.56
1	____ 0.08

78 Zeros that are contained within a series of significant digits are always considered significant. Accordingly, indicate the number of significant digits in each of the following numbers representing continuous data.

3	____ 0.509
5	____ 30,905
6	____ 255.095

79 Finally, "trailing zeros" are always significant when they are located to the right of the decimal point, but may or may not be significant when located entirely to the left of the decimal point, since in the latter case they may not represent measurement but may be used simply to locate the decimal point. In the case of trailing zeros all of which are located just before a decimal point, more information about the data is needed to determine whether any or all of these zeros are significant in each particular instance. For the following continuous numbers, indicate the number of significant digits when these can be definitely specified. Otherwise indicate "indefinite."

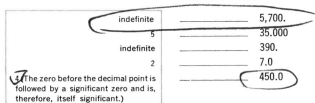

indefinite	_____ 5,700.
5	_____ 35.000
indefinite	_____ 390.
2	_____ 7.0
4 (The zero before the decimal point is followed by a significant zero and is, therefore, itself significant.)	_____ 450.0

80 Indicate the number of significant digits in each of the following continuous numbers, which include all varieties of the placement of zeros (use "indefinite" where appropriate).

indefinite	———————	50.
indefinite	———————	050.
5	———————	5,000.0
4	———————	5005
indefinite	———————	05,050.
2	———————	0.050

81 If a number with an indefinite number of significant digits must be interpreted without the availability of further information, only the minimum number of significant digits that it can contain is assumed. Thus 500 would be conservatively interpreted as containing one significant digit, which would suggest that the number is closer to 500 than it is to either 400 or 600. It is possible, however, that this number may contain as many as three significant digits; this would mean that the measurement is closer to 500 than it is to either 499 or _____ (number).

501

82 The identification of the number of significant digits is particularly important for the interpretation of numerical information, since it indicates the level of accuracy at which measurements have been made. Indicate the level of accuracy for each of the following measurements.

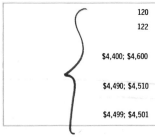

120
122
$4,400; $4,600
$4,490; $4,510
$4,499; $4,501

(a) 121 means closer to 121 than to either _____ (number) or _____ (number).
(b) $4,500, with two significant digits, means closer to $4,500 than to either _____ or _____.
(c) $4,500, with three significant digits, means closer to $4,500 than to either _____ or _____.
(d) $4,500, with four significant digits, means closer to $4,500 than to either _____ or _____.

83 In order to carry the correct number of significant digits in computational results, two rules, one pertaining to addition and subtraction and the other pertaining to multiplication and division, are useful. The rule pertaining to addition and subtraction states that all *digit positions* that are not significant in *any* of the values being added or subtracted are not significant in the total or difference. Thus, although $73.0 + 0.03 = 73.03$, appropriate rounding of this answer results in a sum of _____ (number).

73.0

84 Therefore, when adding or subtracting, decimal position *is* important. Accordingly, underline the significant-digit positions in the following sums and differences.

236.37 (= 236)
9,655.
9,655. (= 10,000)
49.50 (= 49.5)

(a) 231. + 5.37 = 236.37
(b) 10,000. (5 sig. dig.) − 345. = 9,655.
(c) 10,000. (2 sig. dig.) − 345. = 9,655.
(d) 50.00 − 0.5 = 49.50

85 The number of significant digits in a sum or difference is governed by the number of digit positions included in the (least / most) accurate number included in the calculations, *based on decimal location.*

least

86 The rounding rule for multiplication and division concerns the *number* of significant digits rather than digit positions in respect to the decimal point. This rule states that the number of significant digits in a product or quotient is determined by the value with the smallest number of significant digits that enters into the calculations. In applying this rule, the product of 16. × 4.0 would be written as _____ (number), whereas the product of 16. × 4. would be appropriately rounded as _____ (number), assuming continuous data.

64.

60.

64. (since the 4 has a limitless number of significant digits in this case)

87 On the other hand, if the 4 is a discrete number, then 16. × 4 = _____ (number) appropriately rounded.

88 For the following products and quotients, underline the significant digits. Assume that all values are continuous unless otherwise indicated.

1,221.

1,221. (= 1,000)

4.56 (= 5.) (0.08 has just one significant digit)

303.

(a) 2,442 ÷ 2 (discrete) = 1,221.
(b) 2,442 ÷ 2 = 1221.
(c) 57. × 0.08 = 4.56
(d) 101. × 3 (discrete) = 303.

89 Whenever a number is to be rounded, it is rounded "up" if the entire remainder following the significant digits is greater than "--500--," and, conversely, it is not rounded up when the entire remainder is "less than half." Thus 39.8751 rounded to four significant digits (or "to the second decimal place") would be written as _____ (number); 39.8749 rounded to four significant digits would be written as _____ (number).

39.88

39.87

90 Similarly, round all the following numbers to five significant digits.

393.66

700.06

0.11800

0.079831 (Since the leading zeros are not significant, there are just five significant digits in this value.)

(a) 393.658 =
(b) 700.059 =
(c) 0.118000 =
(d) 0.079831 =

91 When the remainder to be eliminated is exactly --500--, or an even half, then the usual practice by statisticians is to increase the value of the last significant digit by 1 if it is an odd number, but to leave it as it is if it is an even number. In this way, errors in rounding tend to be counterbalanced in the long run. Thus 0.375 rounded to two significant digits is 0.38, and 0.385 rounded to two significant digits is also 0.38. Similarly, round the following numbers to three significant digits each.

(a) 397.50 =

(b) 45.85 =

(c) 0.1995 =

92 For additional practice, round the following continuous data to four significant digits each.

(a) 21.21505 =

(b) 397.05001 =

(c) 0.003599499 =

(d) 0.07000555 =

93 The rules for identifying significant digits and rounding numbers which we have presented should be applied to final results of statistical calculations, and not to intermediate results, where unnecessary rounding error would thereby be introduced. Thus during calculations we usually carry (fewer / more) digits in our intermediate results than are actually significant.

94 The rules for determining significant digits and rounding numbers are particularly important because they have an effect on the (statistical calculations / interpretation of statistical data).

review

95 (Sec. 1.a, Introduction; Frames 1–15) When the methods of statistics are directed toward organizing either population or sample data and making them more understandable, then they are being used for the purpose of statistical _____. When the methods are directed toward analyzing sample data in order to make decisions about the population, they are being used for the purpose of statistical _____.

96 (Frames 16–18) When the characteristics of an entire population are measured, typically for the purpose of statistical description, this process is referred to as a _____, whereas the process of measuring the characteristics of a portion of a population is referred to as _____.

97 (Frames 19–21) The attributes or characteristics of a population, such as the number of elements in the population or the average of all the values, are referred to as population _____, whereas similar data for samples are referred to as sample _____.

98 (Frames 22–29) The word "statistics" can be used to refer to the attributes of a sample; give two other distinct meanings that this word can have:

(a) _____

(b) _____

induction	
deduction	

99 (Sec. 1.b, Introduction; Frames 30–41) The reasoning process of arriving at general principles or conclusions by observing specific instances, often with the associated use of statistical inference, is termed _____; the use of known principles for the purpose of deriving other principles or making predictions describes the process of _____.

probability	
identifying	

100 (Frames 42–46) In addition to the quantitative methods that are useful also for the purpose of statistical description, statistical inference always involves the application of _____ theory for the purpose of (eliminating / identifying) risk.

probability	

101 (Frames 47–59) A sample so chosen that every element in the population has a known, and usually equal, chance of being chosen, and which makes possible the use of the techniques of statistical inference, is the _____ sample.

counting	cannot
measuring	can

102 (Sec. 1.c, Introduction; Frames 60–69) Statistical data may be either *discrete* or *continuous.* Discrete data are generated by the operation of _____ and therefore (can / cannot) take on fractional values. Continuous data are generated by the operation of _____ and therefore (can / cannot) take on fractional values.

discrete	

103 (Frames 70–76) The number of significant digits is considered to be limitless for _____ data.

never	
always	
sometimes	
always	

104 (Frames 77–80) In continuous data leading zeros are (always / sometimes / never) significant; zeros contained within a series of significant digits are (always / sometimes / never) significant; trailing zeros entirely to the left of the decimal point are (always / sometimes / never) significant; and trailing zeros to the right of the decimal point are (always / sometimes / never) significant.

1,199	1,201

105 (Frames 81–82) If the number 1,200 is considered to have four significant digits, this means that its measured value is closer to 1,200 than it is to either ____ (number) or ____ (number).

decimal point	

106 (Frames 83–85) The rule for determining the number of significant digits in *sums* and *differences* states that the element with the least number of digit positions, based on the location of the _____, determines the number of digit positions included in the result.

fewest	

107 (Frames 86–88) For products and quotients, the position of the decimal point as such is not of primary importance. Rather, the number of significant digits carried in the result is equal to the quantity entering the calculations that has the (fewest / most) significant digits.

108 (Frames 89–94)   In the borderline rounding situation in which the remainder is exactly 5 (possibly with trailing zeros attached), we increase the value of the last significant digit by a value of 1 when that digit is an _____ number, but we simply drop the remainder when the last significant digit is an _____ number.

odd

even

problems
(solutions given
on page 346)

1   For each of the following five terms, indicate whether the term is most closely related to working with samples or with populations by posting an S or P in front of it, and briefly give the reason for your classification.

—— **(a)** statistical inference
—— **(b)** deduction
—— **(c)** parameter
—— **(d)** probability theory
—— **(e)** census

2   What are discrete data? By what process are they typically obtained, or generated?

3   In the following list, post a D for those numbers that must be discrete, a D or C for those numbers that could be either discrete or continuous, and a C for those numbers that must be continuous.

—— **(a)** 171
—— **(b)** 89.9
—— **(c)** 0.89
—— **(d)** 0
—— **(e)** 1.5
—— **(f)** 5.

4   Carry out the following arithmetic operations and round your answers to the appropriate number of digits or digit positions. Assume that the values are continuous unless otherwise indicated.

(a) 333.00 + 22
(b) 333.00 + 22 (discrete)
(c) 333.00 − 22
(d) 333.00 − 22 (discrete)
(e) 333.00 × 22
(f) 333.00 × 22 (discrete)
(g) 333.00 ÷ 22
(h) 333.00 ÷ 22 (discrete)

5   Indicate the number of significant digits in each of the following numbers, and then round each number to three significant digits.

(a) 612.5001
(b) 612.5000
(c) .06125

(d) 0.06125
(e) 0.06010205
(f) 0.613500

additional problems   **6**   For each of the following five terms, indicate whether the term is most closely related to working with samples or with populations by posting an S or P in front of it, and briefly give the reason for your classification.

_____ **(a)** induction
_____ **(b)** uncertainty
_____ **(c)** statistic
_____ **(d)** universe
_____ **(e)** general to particular

7   What are continuous data? By what process are they typically obtained, or generated?

8   In the following list, post a D for those numbers that must be discrete, a D or C for those numbers that could be either discrete or continuous, and a C for those numbers that must be continuous.

_____ **(a)** 17
_____ **(b)** 21.3
_____ **(c)** 14.1
_____ **(d)** 49.
_____ **(e)** 0.33
_____ **(f)** 5.0

9   Carry out the following arithmetic operations and round your answers to the appropriate number of digits or digit positions. Assume that the values are continuous unless otherwise indicated.

(a) 18.9 + 9
(b) 18.9 + 9 (discrete)
(c) 18.9 − 9
(d) 18.9 − 9 (discrete)
(e) 18.9 × 9
(f) 18.9 × 9 (discrete)
(g) 18.9 ÷ 9
(h) 18.9 ÷ 9 (discrete)

10   Indicate the number of significant digits in each of the following numbers, and then round each number to two significant digits.

(a) 13.5
(b) 12.5
(c) 0.13499
(d) 0.10501
(e) 12.5000
(f) 0.00125001

unit 2 • frequency distributions and methods of graphical description

Frequency distributions are typically discussed early in the study of statistical methods because they provide both a method for organizing data for easier comprehension and a basis for simplifying the computation of certain sample statistics or population parameters. The use of frequency distributions in conjunction with statistical computations will be included in Units 3 and 4. In this unit we shall discuss the elements of the frequency distribution, the related construction of histograms, frequency polygons, and frequency curves, and other methods of graphical description used in presenting quantitative data.

2.a • the frequency distribution

A frequency distribution consists of a listing of several measurement categories, or classes, with an indication of the number of observed measurements, or frequency, associated with each class. The difference between class limits and class boundaries and the determination of class interval and midpoint will be covered in this section. Unless otherwise specified, our discussion always concerns continuous, rather than discrete, data.

1 Throughout the following discussion of the grouping of data into classes the assumption is made that the data are (discrete / continuous).

continuous

2 When a number of classes of measurements are listed along with an indication of the frequency of observed measurements falling within each class, the listing is called a _____ _____.

frequency distribution

3 Table 2.1 lists the heights of a sample of 50 students at a men's university. Since each individual measurement is separately listed in this table, the data are considered to be (grouped / ungrouped).

ungrouped

table 2.1 • heights of 50 men students measured to the nearest inch (ungrouped)

67	73	71	74	61	68	70	70	66	73
68	67	72	69	71	69	76	70	72	71
77	69	71	74	66	68	70	72	72	70
71	70	64	65	70	69	72	75	66	67
70	72	67	70	71	68	66	73	69	67

4 In contrast, data that have been entered in a frequency distribution are considered to be _____ data.

grouped

5 Table 2.2 is the frequency distribution for the measurements presented in Table 2.1. By organizing the measurements into classes, a frequency distribution makes it (easier / more difficult) to interpret a group of measurements.

easier

Height	Number of students
60–62	1
63–65	2
66–68	13
69–71	20
72–74	11
75–77	3

6 However, there is a price paid for grouping data in a frequency distribution. If we refer to Table 2.1 alone, can we determine the value of each of the measurements included in this table, at least to the nearest inch? (yes / no)

yes

7 On the other hand, can we determine the value of each of the 50 measurements by reference to Table 2.2 alone? (yes / no)

no

8 Although we lost some of the precision in our data through grouping, this disadvantage is offset by the fact that the interpretation of the data is made easier. Using Table 2.1, for example, it would be difficult to give an estimate of the height of most of the students, but Table 2.2 clearly indicates that the size category of _____ to _____ inches contains the greatest frequency of measurements.

69; 71

9 Thus use of a frequency distribution to organize data leads to interpretation that is (easier / more difficult) and data that are (more / less) precise.

easier

less

10 In terms of the structural properties of classes, each class of measurements in a frequency distribution has lower and upper limits, lower and upper boundaries, an interval, and a midpoint. Each of these values will be needed in carrying out the computations described in Units 3 and 4. The class limits are the numbers that typically serve to identify the classes in a listing of a frequency distribution. Thus, for the class whose frequency is 20 in Table 2.2, the *lower class limit* is _____ (number) and the *upper class limit* is _____ (number).

69

71

11 Similarly, for the class whose frequency is 11, 72 is the lower _____ and 74 is the _____.

class limit

upper class limit

12 Are the class limits typically inclusive; i.e., would observed measurements that correspond exactly to the lower class limit or upper class limit be included in that class? (Note the values of adjoining class limits in Table 2.2.) (yes / no)

yes

72; 73; 74

13 Therefore what are the measured heights, to the nearest inch, that would be included in the class whose lower and upper limits are 72 and 74, respectively? _____, _____, and _____

14 As contrasted to a class limit, a *class boundary* is the precise point that separates one class from another, rather than being a value included in one of the classes. A class boundary is typically located midway between the upper limit of a class and the lower limit of the next higher class adjoining it. Therefore the class boundary separating the class 63–65 and the class 66–68 is halfway between 65 and 66, or at the point _____ (number).

65.5

15 The precise point separating two classes is called a class _____.

boundary

16 Of course, every class typically has a lower and an upper boundary, just as it has lower and upper limits. Using the adjoining classes 69–71 and 72–74 as an example, and getting back to limits for a minute, we find that the values of the upper *limit* of one class and the lower *limit* of the next higher class adjoining it (are / are not) the same.

are not

17 Still referring to the adjoining classes 69–71 and 72–74, we find that the values of the upper *boundary* of one class and the lower *boundary* of the next higher class adjoining it (are / are not) the same.

are

18 Some statisticians use the term "nominal limits" to refer to the inclusive values identifying a class and "exact limits" to refer to the precise points separating the class from adjoining classes. Exact limits are therefore the same as class _____, and nominal limits are what we have called class _____.

boundaries
limits

19 For the classes of Table 2.2, enter the missing lower and upper boundaries in the table below.

62.5–65.5
65.5–68.5

Class limits	Class boundaries
60–62	59.5–62.5
63–65	_____–_____
66–68	_____–_____
69–71	68.5–71.5
72–74	71.5–74.5
75–77	74.5–77.5

20 Suppose that the heights of the students had been measured to the nearest half inch, instead of the nearest inch. Indicate the class boundaries of the two adjoining classes below.

Class limits	Class boundaries

Class limits	Class boundaries
60.0–62.5	_____–_____
63.0–65.5	_____–_____

21 If you had any difficulty in Frame 20, remember that we always consider the size of the gap between adjoining class limits, set the boundary midway in this gap, and set similar boundaries for the classes at the two ends of the distribution whose lower or upper limits do not adjoin any class. Thus the numerical value of a class boundary (does / does not) necessarily end in .5.

22 If an obtained measurement falls precisely on a class boundary, in which class should it be placed? Though this question appears to be an important one, it refers to a situation which should never occur. Consider the description given in the heading of Table 2.2. Can the measurement 65.5 be listed? (yes / no)

23 Boundaries are always defined more precisely than the level of measurement being used for the collection of data, and so the rounding of any fractional values would take place as part of the measurement process and *before* entry of the data into the frequency distribution. For measurement of height to the nearest inch, for example, a height of 65.5 would have been rounded as part of the original measurement process to _____ (number).

24 Occasionally it is somewhat difficult to decide whether the particular values identifying the classes of a frequency distribution are class limits or class boundaries. Consider the classes:

At least 20 but less than 30
At least 30 but less than 40

Assuming that measurement is to the nearest unit, the actual inclusive limits for the first class are _____ and _____, and the lower and upper boundaries of the first class are _____ and _____.

25 Finally, an open-end distribution is one in which either one or both of the classes at the two ends of the frequency distribution have no stated limits and therefore do not have associated boundaries. For the following abridged example of an open-end distribution, enter the class boundaries, indicating "none" where appropriate.

Class limits	Class boundaries
Under 30	_____
30–49	_____
50–69	_____
70+	_____

26 When a definite boundary cannot be set at one or both ends of a frequency distribution, it is called a(n) _____ distribution.

27 Having discussed class limits and class boundaries, let us now consider the class interval i. The length, or size, of the class interval is determined by subtracting the lower boundary of a class from its upper boundary. This operation can be represented by the formula $i = B_U - B_L$. For the following data,

$i = $ _____ $-$ _____ $= $ _____

Class limits	Class boundaries
15–19	14.5–19.5
20–24	19.5–24.5

28 The size of the class interval being used in a frequency distribution can be determined also by subtracting the lower boundary of a class from the lower boundary of the adjacent higher class, the lower limit of a class from the lower limit of the adjacent higher class, and similarly for adjacent upper boundaries and adjacent upper limits. Using the data of Frame 27, determine the size of the class interval by subtracting the lower boundaries of adjacent classes and by subtracting the lower limits of adjacent classes.

$i = B_{L(2)} - B_{L(1)} = $ _____ $-$ _____ $= $ _____

$i = L_{L(2)} - L_{L(1)} = $ _____ $-$ _____ $= $ _____

29 On the other hand, it is *incorrect* to subtract the lower limit of a class from its upper limit in attempting to identify interval size. That is, $i \neq L_U - L_L$. For the data of Frame 27,

$L_U - L_L = $ _____ $-$ _____ $= $ _____

30 According to the formula $i = B_U - B_L$, the size of the class interval being used in Table 2.2 is $i = $ _____ $-$ _____ $= $ _____ .

31 As the name implies, the midpoint of a class is the point dividing the class into equal halves, on the basis of interval size. This point can be identified by adding the lower and upper limits of a class, or the lower and upper boundaries, and dividing by two. The formulas that we could construct to represent these operations are

$$\text{Midpt} = \frac{L_L + L_U}{2} \quad \text{and} \quad \text{Midpt} = \frac{B_L + B_U}{2}$$

respectively. Using either of these formulas, determine the values of the midpoints for the following data, and verify that either procedure yields the same result.

	Class limits	Class boundaries	Class midpoint

Sum / 2

		Class limits	Class boundaries	Class midpoint
	17	15–19	14.5–19.5	_____
	22	20–24	19.5–24.5	_____

32 The class midpoint is often also called the *class mark*, and it is used to represent all values in the class for the purpose of certain calculations. In the table below list the class marks for the first three classes of Table 2.2.

	Height	Class mark
61	60–62	_____
64	63–65	_____
67	66–68	_____

33 The location of the class midpoint, or class mark, can be determined also by adding one-half of the interval size to the lower boundary of a class. Symbolically, this could be represented as midpt = $B_L + \frac{1}{2}i$. Using this approach, recompute the midpoints determined in Frame 32.

59.5 + 1.5 = 61
62.5 + 1.5 = 64
65.5 + 1.5 = 67

1st midpt = _____ + _____ = _____
2d midpt = _____ + _____ = _____
3d midpt = _____ + _____ = _____

34 Now that we have discussed class midpoints, we can observe that the size of the class interval being used in a frequency distribution can be determined also by subtracting the midpoint of a class from that of the adjoining higher class. Symbolically, $i = \text{midpt}_{(2)} - \text{midpt}_{(1)}$. Thus, given the data below,

22 – 17 = 5 (which corresponds to the value determined by the other methods in Frames 27 and 28)

i = _____ − _____ = _____

Class	Class midpoint
15–19	17
20–24	22

35 Circle the identifying letter of each formula listed below which does *not* represent a valid computational procedure for determining the size of the class interval being used in a frequency distribution.

(a) $i = B_U - B_L$
(b) $i = L_U - L_L$
(c) $i = B_{U(2)} - B_{U(1)}$
(d) $i = L_{U(2)} - L_{U(1)}$
(e) $i = \text{midpt}_{(2)} - \text{midpt}_{(1)}$

b

36 Of course, the identification of the class limits, boundaries, midpoint, and interval is done for a frequency distribution that has already been constructed. In respect to the formation of a frequency distribution in the first place, there are no fixed rules concerning the appropriate number of classes to be defined or the size of the class interval to be used. It does follow, however, that for a given range of values to be grouped the smaller the size of the class interval, the (smaller / larger) the number of classes in the frequency distribution.

37 Although it is usually considered appropriate to construct between six and fifteen classes for a frequency distribution, the actual number of classes and the related size of the class interval depend on the requirements of the particular problem. In any event, we might observe that since grouping always results in some loss of precision of the data, or grouping error, the larger the size of the class interval, the (smaller / larger) is this error.

38 The first step in forming a frequency distribution is to subtract the lowest obtained measurement in the data to be grouped from the highest measurement to obtain the range R of the measurements. For the ungrouped measurements listed in Table 2.3, $R =$ _____ — _____ = _____.

table 2.3 ▪ **a set of ungrouped measurements**

32	26	16	44	28
40	30	31	17	30
37	32	42	31	36
49	35	21	25	40
27	25	33	34	27

39 The next step in forming a frequency distribution is to decide on the number of classes to be used and to divide the range by this number to obtain the appropriate size of the class interval to be used. For fractional results, the interval size is typically defined at the next higher whole number. If we wish to have seven classes in the frequency distribution for the data of Table 2.3, whose range of values is 33, the appropriate size of the class interval is _____ (number).

40 Using the class interval of 5, construct the classes to be used in conjunction with the data of Table 2.3, beginning the first class in the frequency distribution with the lower limit of 16.

Class limits

Class limits	
16–20	_____
21–25	_____
26–30	_____
31–35	_____
36–40	_____
41–45	_____
46–50	_____

20.5

25.5   23

41 For the class whose lower and upper limits are 21 and 25, respectively, the lower boundary is _____ (number), the upper boundary is _____ (number), and the class mark is _____ (number).

42 The final step in constructing a frequency distribution is to tally the number of obtained measurements falling into each of the defined classes, so that the frequency associated with each class can be determined. For the data of Table 2.3, complete the tally below and post the frequency associated with each class.

Class limits	Tally	Number of measurements, f
16–20	_____	_____
21–25	_____	_____
26–30	_____	_____
31–35	_____	_____
36–40	_____	_____
41–45	_____	_____
46–50	_____	_____

//	2
///	3
𝚮𝚮 /	6
𝚮𝚮 //	7
////	4
//	2
/	1

43 Since we have consistently referred to the grouping of measurements, rather than to counts of objects, throughout this section we have assumed that the data being grouped are (continuous / discrete).

continuous

44 If data are discrete, they can also be grouped. In this case the concept of a class boundary is unrealistic, in that with the values being discrete there can be no point at which adjoining classes meet; discrete data can carry only integer values. However, the methods of grouping are often applied to discrete data in the same way as for continuous data. Although this practice leads to identifying values for class boundaries that could not occur, no matter how precise the count, it is convenient to use these values for computational purposes. Thus, for the following grouped discrete data, the class boundaries of the last class are _____ (number) and _____ (number), the midpoint of the class is _____ (number), and the size of the class interval is _____ (number).

Number of days absent	Number of employees
0–3	3
4–7	7
8–11	2
12–15	1

2.b ▪ histograms, frequency polygons, and frequency curves

In addition to their presentation in tabular form, the measurements included in a frequency distribution can be presented by several graphic methods. The main objective for developing graphic illustrations for the information contained in a frequency distribution is to make the interpretation of the information easier. In this section we shall illustrate the use of histograms, frequency polygons, and frequency curves for presenting the data contained in frequency distributions.

45 The *histogram* is one of the ways of graphically presenting a frequency distribution. Figure 2.1 is a histogram for the frequency distribution given in Table 2.2. Notice that the values listed along the horizontal axis of the histogram are class (limits / boundaries / midpoints).

figure 2.1 ▪ histogram: heights of 50 men students.

Number of students

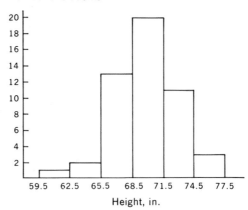

Height, in.

46 The values listed along the vertical axis of the graph on which the histogram is constructed indicate the possible _____ _____ associated with each class.

frequency distributions and graphical description ▪ 26

interval

47 The width of the rectangles that make up the histogram indicates the size of the class _____.

frequency

48 When all class intervals are the same, the height of each rectangle directly represents the _____ associated with each class of measurements.

histogram

49 Thus "a series of rectangles whose bases are marked off by class boundaries and whose heights are indicative of the frequency of measurements associated with each class" is a description of the graphic device called the _____.

50 Construct a histogram for the following frequency distribution taken from Frame 42.

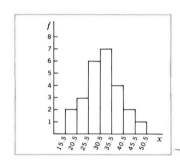

Class	f
16–20	2
21–25	3
26–30	6
31–35	7
36–40	4
41–45	2
46–50	1

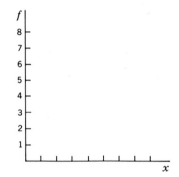

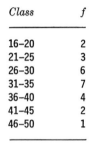

51 Another way of graphically portraying a frequency distribution is by means of a *frequency polygon*. Figure 2.2 is the frequency polygon associated with the data of Table 2.2. The dimension of the graph that has types of values identical to those posted on the histogram is the (vertical / horizontal) axis.

vertical

figure 2.2 ■ frequency polygon: heights of 50 men students.

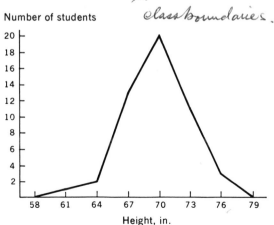

Class boundaries.

Number of students

Height, in.

52 Whereas the histogram lists class boundaries along the horizontal axis, the frequency polygon contains a listing of class _____.

midpoints (or marks)

53 "A line graph of class frequencies plotted against class midpoints" is a description of the _____.

frequency polygon

54 Since a polygon is a many-sided *closed* figure, it is necessary to add "extra" class midpoints at the lower and upper extremes of the distribution for the adjacent nonexistent classes whose frequencies are zero, so that the polygon does form a closed figure with the horizontal axis of the graph. In Fig. 2.2 these two additional class midpoints are _____ (number) and _____ (number).

58; 79

55 Construct a frequency polygon for the following grouped data, for which you previously constructed a histogram.

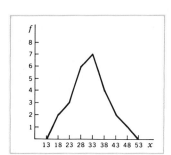

Class	f
16–20	2
21–25	3
26–30	6
31–35	7
36–40	4
41–45	2
46–50	1

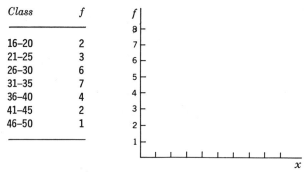

56 Since the histogram and frequency polygon are closely related, it might be useful to enter both on the same graph for purposes of comparison. Each point of the frequency polygon is located at the midpoint of the top side of each of the rectangles that make up the histogram, and these midpoints are connected to form the polygon. Accordingly, complete the construction of the frequency polygon on the graph below.

Complete the polygon by joining appropriate midpoints; the resulting figure should resemble the frequency polygon in Frame 55.

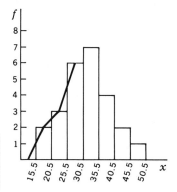

frequency distributions and graphical description ▪ **28**

57 If the frequency polygon is smoothed, or if a curve is fitted to a frequency distribution, the obtained curve is called a frequency curve. Superimpose the approximate form of the frequency curve on the frequency polygon below.

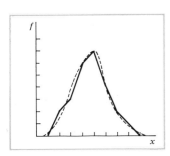

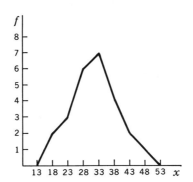

58 A curve constructed on a graph on which the horizontal axis represents various possible values of a variable and the vertical axis represents various possible frequencies, or relative frequencies, of occurrence is called a _____.

59 The form of a frequency curve can be described in two ways: in terms of its *departure from symmetry*, which is called *skewness*, and in terms of its *degree of peakedness*, which is called *kurtosis*. In later units we shall have frequent occasion to use these concepts in applying statistical tests and to consider how the extent of skewness and kurtosis can be determined. For the present our objective is to develop the capability to identify correctly the form of a frequency curve. When we look at a frequency curve to observe whether the first half of the curve looks like the mirror image of the second half, we are giving attention to the concept of (skewness / kurtosis).

60 A distribution of measurements whose frequency curve is not symmetrical is said to be skewed. In a skewed distribution there are extreme values at one end of the distribution that are not counterbalanced by extreme values at the other end of the distribution. Which of the following frequency curves represent distributions of measurements that are clearly skewed? (Circle the identifying letters.)

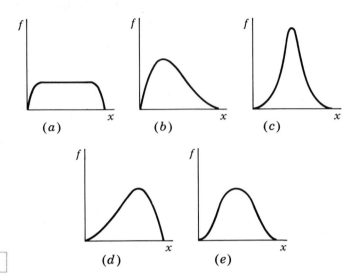

(a)   (b)   (c)

(d)   (e)

b and d

61 When only a few of the measurements of the distribution are in the direction of the higher values of the variable, thus forming a tail to the right, the distribution is said to be *positively skewed.* In Frame 60 the frequency curve which is positively skewed is _____ (identifying letter).

b

62 On the other hand, when the tail of the distribution is in the direction of the lower values of the variable, and thus toward the origin of the graph, the distribution is said to be *negatively skewed,* or skewed to the left. The frequency curve in Frame 60 which is negatively skewed is _____ (identifying letter).

d

63 Thus, of the two curves below, frequency curve a is _____ skewed and curve b is _____ skewed.

negatively
positively

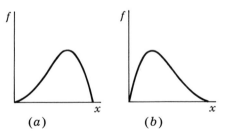

(a)   (b)

64 In terms of kurtosis, a frequency curve that is very flat, indicating a wide dispersion of measurements, is said to be *platykurtic;*

a curve with a high peak, indicating a concentration of measurements about some particular value, is said to be *leptokurtic;* one with an intermediate degree of dispersion and peakedness is said to be *mesokurtic.* Which form of frequency curve represents a distribution in which the obtained measurements are bunched up and vary only by small amounts from one another? (platykurtic / mesokurtic / leptokurtic)

leptokurtic

65 Of the three curves below, the one which appears to be meso-kurtic is _____ (identifying letter) and the one that appears to be platykurtic is _____ (identifying letter).

a
c

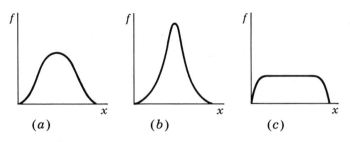

66 The three kinds of frequency curves in terms of peaked-ness, progressing from "flat" to "extremely peaked," are the _____, _____, and _____ curves.

platykurtic; mesokurtic; leptokurtic

67 Of course, frequency curves simultaneously vary in terms of both skewness and kurtosis. Of the curves below, the one which is both positively skewed and leptokurtic is _____ (identifying letter), and the one which is both negatively skewed and meso-kurtic is _____ (identifying letter).

c
e

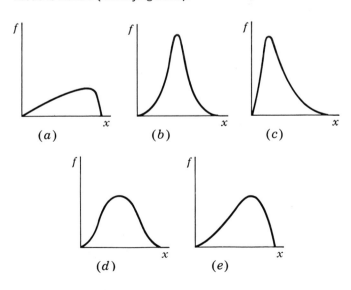

68 As applied to frequency curves, the term "skewness" refers to _____; the term "kurtosis" refers to _____.

68 As applied to frequency curves, the term "skewness" refers to _____; the term "kurtosis" refers to _____.

departures from symmetry

degree of peakedness

69 In terms of skewness a frequency curve can be _____ _____, _____, or _____ _____. In terms of kurtosis it can be _____ _____, _____, or _____ _____.

negatively skewed; symmetrical; positively skewed

platykurtic; mesokurtic; leptokurtic

70 For the purpose of carrying out certain statistical calculations, we often need to identify the *cumulative frequency* associated with each class, as well as the frequency itself. The cumulative frequency for a class is obtained by summing the frequency for the class with the frequencies of all classes "below" it, i.e., with all classes with smaller midpoints. Accordingly, complete the cumulative-frequency (cf) column for the following data taken from Table 2.2.

Height	f	cf
60–62	1	1
63–65	2	3
66–68	13	16
69–71	20	_____
72–74	11	_____
75–77	3	_____
	Sum = 50	

36

47

50

71 To provide a convenient arithmetic check on the accuracy of the cumulative frequencies, it is useful to note that, as in Frame 70, the cumulative frequency of the last (highest-valued) class is the same as _____.

the sum of all frequencies in the distribution

72 Determine the cumulative frequencies for the following data.

Class	f	cf
16–20	2	_____
21–25	3	_____
26–30	6	_____
31–35	7	_____
36–40	4	_____
41–45	2	_____
46–50	1	_____
	Sum = 25	

2

5

11

18

22

24

25

73 A cumulative-frequency distribution can be graphically represented by a cumulative-frequency polygon, which is more popularly called an *ogive*. Because the frequencies associated with each class are understood to extend right up to the upper boundary of the class, these boundaries are the values posted along the horizontal axis of the ogive. For the data of Table 2.2, complete the following ogive.

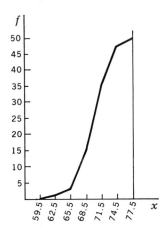

Height	cf
60–62	1
63–65	3
66–68	16
69–71	36
72–74	47
75–77	50

Enter the cumulative frequencies for the classes whose upper boundaries are 74.5 and 77.5. The resulting diagram should resemble that of Frame 75.

74 Thus the polygon representing the total number of frequencies, or observed measurements, up to the upper boundary of each class of a frequency distribution is called a _____ _____ polygon, or an _____.

cumulative-frequency

ogive

75 Just as a frequency polygon can be smoothed or fitted with a frequency curve, so also can an ogive be smoothed, resulting in an ogive curve. On the graph below indicate the approximate shape of the ogive curve by superimposing it over the ogive.

The resulting curve can be described as an S-shaped curve.

2.c ▪ other methods of graphical description

The construction of histograms, frequency polygons, frequency curves, ogives, and ogive curves is associated with graphically portraying continuous data that have been grouped in a frequency distribution. In addition to these, the column chart, bar chart, pictogram, line chart, stratum chart, and pie chart are other graphic methods that can be used whenever obtained data can be classified into a number of categories.

76 Because frequency distributions and the methods of graphic description are used for organizing statistical information that has already been collected, the methods that have been and continue to be discussed in ths unit can be described as being primarily in the category of (statistical description / statistical inference).

statistical description

77 As contrasted to the methods of graphic description that were discussed in Sec. 2.b, the methods to be discussed in this final section can be used whenever data have been classified into categories, and therefore they are not dependent on having data that have been grouped in a _____ as such.

frequency distribution

table 2.4 ▪ domestic automobile production of the four major automobile manufacturers in the United States, 1961 to 1965, in millions of units

	1961	1962	1963	1964	1965	Total 1961–1965
American Motors	0.37	0.45	0.48	0.39	0.35	2.04
Chrysler	0.65	0.72	1.05	1.24	1.47	5.13
Ford	1.69	1.94	1.96	2.15	2.57	10.31
General Motors	2.73	3.74	4.08	3.96	4.95	19.46
Total	5.44	6.85	7.57	7.74	9.34	36.94

Source of data: *Automobile Facts and Figures,* Automobile Manufacturers Association, 1966.

78 Table 2.4 presents an analysis of the domestic automobile production of the four major automobile manufacturers in the United States between 1961 and 1965. On the following graph a *column chart* has been partially constructed presenting the total automobile production during this five-year period. In appearance this chart resembles a _____.

histogram

Production, millions of units

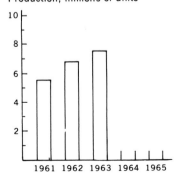

79 Unlike a histogram, the column chart represents categories of data and not classes of a frequency distribution; the labels for the categories rather than class boundaries are posted along the horizontal axis; the vertical axis can signify amount as well as frequency; the rectangles do not touch one another; and the rectangles can be made any convenient, though uniform, width. With these differences in mind, complete the column chart in Frame 78 by referring to Table 2.4 for needed totals.

The other two totals, which can be only approximately indicated on this small column chart, are 7.74 and 9.34 million units.

80 Thus a chart that depicts amounts against categories with the amounts represented by a series of vertical columns of appropriate height and uniform width is called a _____.

column chart

81 The *bar chart* is very similar to the column chart except that the identification of the two axes is interchanged, resulting in a series of bars rather than columns, as illustrated in the partially completed bar chart below. Some authors refer to either type of diagram as a bar chart, whether the bars are vertical, as in Frame 78, or horizontal, as in this frame. Using the data from Table 2.4, complete the bar chart.

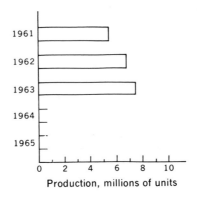

Production, millions of units

The remaining two bars should indicate 7.74 and 9.34 million units.

82 When associated categories of data are to be posted on the same bar chart, two methods are available. If we wish to present the two or more categories of data in a cumulative fashion, the use of a *component bar chart* is appropriate. In the partially completed chart below notice that the component categories that make up each bar are identified. In business reports a color coding is often used to differentiate the components. Complete the component bar chart, using the appropriate data from Table 2.4, with G for General Motors, F for Ford, C for Chrysler, and A for American Motors.

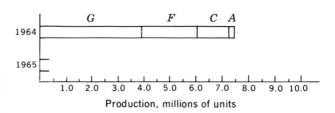

Production, millions of units

Of the 9.34 million units produced in 1965, G = 4.95, F = 2.57, C = 1.47, and A = 0.35.

83 A bar chart in which each bar represents the cumulation of two or more identified categories of data is a _____ bar chart.

component

84 When we wish to highlight the comparison rather than the cumulation of the several categories of data to be included on the same bar chart, a *grouped bar chart* is appropriate. Accordingly, complete the construction of the grouped bar chart below, using data from Table 2.4.

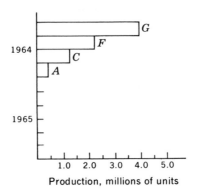

Production, millions of units

For 1965, G = 4.95, F = 2.57, C = 1.47, and A = 0.35.

85 Thus two types of bar charts can be used to identify simultaneously amounts in two or more categories: comparison of the categories is highlighted by the use of a _____ bar chart, and the cumulation of the categories is highlighted by the use of a _____ bar chart.

grouped

component

86 The *pictogram*, or picture diagram, is similar to the column or bar chart except that symbolic figures are used in place of the enclosed columns or bars. In the pictogram below, for example, each small figure of a car represents the production of 1 million autos. Complete this pictogram, using the data of Table 2.4.

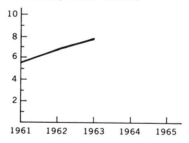

1964

1965

Production of automobiles
(each figure represents 1 million autos)

Production for 1965 would be represented by 9⅓ vehicles.

87 Pictograms are very popular in financial reports directed at the general public because of their concreteness and ease of interpretation. The example in Frame 86 involves a simple bar chart transformed into a pictogram. How could a component bar chart be presented in this form? _____.

by using different colors for the autos manufactured by different companies

88 When small symbolic figures are used to represent the quantities associated with each category of data, the resulting display is called a _____.

pictogram

89 Whenever the categories being tabulated represent time, as in the data of Table 2.4, they can also be graphically portrayed by means of a *line chart*. Complete the line chart below, using the data of Table 2.4.

Production, millions of units

The appearance of the line chart should be similar to the top line of the chart in Frame 91.

90 A graph on which a single line represents the relationship between time, plotted on the horizontal axis, and amounts, plotted on the vertical axis, is a _____.

line chart

91 As contrasted to a line chart, a *stratum chart* graphically presents an analysis of two or more categories of data, or strata, which are accumulated in the chart. The figure below is an illustration of a stratum chart, again using the data of Table 2.4. In terms of how quantities of two or more variables are presented, the stratum chart is similar to the (grouped / component) bar chart.

component

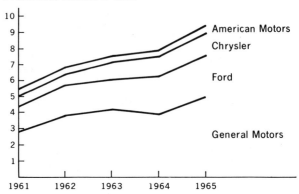

Production, millions of units

92 Thus a line chart that indicates subdivision of the amount or quantity tabulated against time into two or more classifications is called a _____.

stratum chart

93 Finally, another widely used graphic device for indicating division of a whole into various parts is the *pie chart.* The figure below is the pie chart representing the division of total automobile manufacturing for the five-year period among the major manufacturers. In the blank pie chart alongside, complete a similar analysis for automobile-manufacturing activity in the year 1965, using the data of Table 2.4.

Domestic automobile production, millions of units

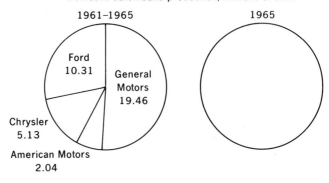

For 1965, $G = 4.95$, $F = 2.57$, $C = 1.47$, and $A = 0.35$. Of course, without use of some mathematical instrument like a protractor, the areas you indicate can be only approximately proportional to the amounts.

94 The column chart, bar chart, pictogram, line chart, and stratum chart could all be used to study changes in amount or quantity over time. Can a single pie chart be used for this purpose? (yes / no)

no (though changes could be shown by a series of pie charts)

frequency distributions and graphical description ▪ 38

95 As a variation of the usual pie chart, the *percentage pie chart* indicates the division of a whole into percentages. Complete the percentage pie chart below for the analysis of automobile manufacturing during 1965.

Domestic automobile production
1965

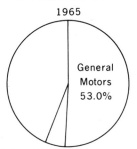

General Motors 53.0%

American Motors 3.7%

The remaining two percentages are $F = 27.5\%$ and $C = 15.7\%$.

review

96 (Sec. 2.a, Introduction; Frames 1–4) When data are categorized according to a series of classes of measurements and the associated frequency of each class is indicated, the resulting listing is called a _____.

frequency distribution

97 (Frames 5–9) Aside from its use in simplifying certain computations, the primary advantage of a frequency distribution as a descriptive tool is that it simplifies _____, although the price that is paid for its use is that some _____ is lost through the process of grouping.

interpretation of data

precision (or accuracy)

98 (Frames 10–18) In terms of the structural properties of the classes that make up a frequency distribution, the inclusive measurements that serve to identify a class and differentiate it from other classes are called class _____, whereas the precise points that separate a class from other classes are called class _____.

limits

boundaries

99 (Frames 19–26) Indicate the class boundaries for the following classes, which indicate that time was measured to the nearest tenth of a second.

Time, seconds	*Class boundaries*
11.0–11.9	_____
12.0–12.9	_____
13.0+	_____

10.95–11.95

11.95–12.95

12.95–none

100 (Frames 25–26) Because no upper boundary can be set for the last class of the frequency distribution given in Frame 99, the distribution of measurements is called an _____ distribution.

open-end

boundary boundary	**101** (Frames 27–30, 34–35) When the limits and boundaries of a *single class* are identified, the class interval can be determined by subtracting the lower _____ from the upper _____. When the limits and boundaries of *two adjoining classes* are known, the size of the class interval being used in the frequency distribution can be determined by comparing the appropriate boundaries,
midpoints	limits, or _____ of the adjoining classes.
boundary	**102** (Frames 31–33) The midpoint of a class can be determined by adding half of the interval size to the lower _____ of the class.
smaller larger	**103** (Frames 34–44) In forming a frequency distribution, the use of relatively small rather than large class intervals results in a grouping error that is (smaller / larger) and a (smaller / larger) number of classes.
histogram	**104** (Frames 45–50) A graph on which class boundaries are located along the horizontal axis and rectangles are constructed over this axis to represent the frequency of measurements associated with each class is called a _____.
frequency polygon	**105** (Frames 51–56) A graph on which midpoints of classes are posted along the horizontal axis, the height of the point entered on the graph above each midpoint represents class frequency, and the points are joined, thus forming a closed figure with the horizontal axis, is called a _____.
departure from symmetry degree of peakedness	**106** (Frames 57–63) In the description of frequency curves, skewness refers to _____, and kurtosis refers to _____.
negatively skewed; symmetrical; positively skewed platykurtic; mesokurtic; leptokurtic	**107** (Frames 64–69) In terms of skewness a frequency curve can be described as being _____, _____ _____, or _____. In terms of kurtosis it can be _____, _____, or _____.
ogive	**108** (Frames 70–75) The polygon that graphically represents the cumulative frequency up to the upper boundary of each class of a frequency distribution is called the cumulative-frequency polygon, or, more popularly, the _____.
column chart	**109** (Frames 76–80) A chart that can be used for any classified data and depicts amounts by a series of vertical columns related to the categories identified along the horizontal axis is called a _____.
	110 (Frames 81–87) With reference to the two kinds of bar charts used to analyze amounts by subcategories, cumulation of the sub-

component

grouped

categories is highlighted by the _____ bar chart, and comparison of the categories is facilitated by the _____ bar chart.

111 (Frames 86–88)   When small symbolic figures are used in place of the bars in a bar chart (or in place of the columns in a column chart), the resulting display is called a _____.

pictogram

112 (Frames 89–92)   A line chart that portrays the subdivision of amounts into two or more categories in a composite manner is called a _____.

stratum chart

113 (Frames 93–95)   The most popular pictorial device used for indicating the sources, or parts, that make up a whole amount is the _____.

pie chart

problems
(solutions given
on page 346)

1   Given the following data presumed to be on the continuous scale of measurement:

Class limits	f
3–5	1
6–8	2
9–11	2
12–14	5
15–17	4

(a) Identify the class boundaries for each class.
(b) Determine the size of the class interval being used.
(c) Construct the histogram for this frequency distribution.
(d) Construct the associated frequency polygon.
(e) Describe the frequency curve in terms of skewness.
(f) Construct the ogive for this frequency distribution.

2   Given the following simplified data which report the dollar sales of three products according to region, in thousands of dollars:

Product	East	Region Midwest	West	Total
A	50	55	70	175
B	70	40	80	190
C	30	40	20	90
Total	150	135	170	455

(a) Construct a column chart depicting total sales by region.
(b) Construct a component bar chart to illustrate the product breakdown of sales, by region.
(c) Construct a pie chart illustrating total sales by product.

3 Given the following data for sales, to the nearest $1,000:

		Year			
Product	1964	1965	1966	1967	Total
A	120	170	160	175	625
B	160	160	180	190	690
C	10	30	60	90	190
Total	290	360	400	455	1,505

(a) Construct a line chart illustrating total sales by year.
(b) Construct a stratum chart.

additional problems **4** Given the following data presumed to be on the continuous scale of measurement:

Wages	Number of employees
$100.00–$109.99	8
$110.00–$119.99	10
$120.00–$129.99	16
$130.00–$139.99	14
$140.00–$149.99	10

(a) Identify the class boundaries for each class.
(b) Determine the size of the class interval being used.
(c) Construct a histogram for these data.
(d) Construct the associated frequency polygon.

5 For the following data indicating a farm's production of wheat and corn in terms of thousands of bushels:

Year	Wheat	Corn	Total
1964	16.5	11.0	27.5
1965	17.5	9.5	27.0
1966	20.0	12.5	32.5
1967	23.5	15.5	39.0

(a) Construct a bar chart depicting total production of grain by year.
(b) Construct a grouped column chart illustrating the type of grain production by year.
(c) Construct a percentage pie chart for the 1967 production figures.
(d) Construct a stratum chart.

unit 3 ▪ measures of central tendency

A numerical average is a value that typifies, or is representative of, a whole range of values. Because an average is numerically located within the range of values that it represents, the various types of averages are often referred to as measures of central tendency. In this unit we shall consider the calculation and characteristics of the arithmetic mean, the median, and the mode. Because quartiles, deciles, and percentiles are computationally similar to the median, these position measures will also be briefly discussed. Though other measures of central tendency are important for certain specialized applications, the three types of averages discussed at length in this unit and the mathematical criteria that they satisfy are of general importance in statistical analysis.

3.a ▪ the arithmetic mean

The arithmetic mean, which we shall often simply call the mean, corresponds to the generally accepted meaning of the word "average." As such, its value is determined by taking the sum of a set of measurements and dividing this sum by the number of measurements. In presenting the statistical formulas for the mean, we shall have the opportunity to become acquainted with some of the essentials of statistical notation and to consider how the mean can be computed for measurements that are grouped in a frequency distribution.

1 For ungrouped data the value of the mean is determined by summing all measurements and dividing by _____ _____.

the number of measurements

2 In general, sample statistics are designated by Roman letters, and population parameters are designated by Greek letters. The arithmetic mean of a sample is represented by the symbol $\bar{X}$ (read: "X bar"), whereas the mean of a population is represented by the symbol μ (mu), which is a (Roman / Greek) letter.

Greek

3 Thus, in order to distinguish the sample mean from the population mean, the sample mean is represented by _____, and the population mean is represented by _____.

$\bar{X}$

μ

4 The statistical formula for computing a sample mean is

$$\bar{X} = \frac{\Sigma X}{n}$$

The general symbol X in the formula above denotes any of the n values that can be assumed by the variable. Thus, if we have the market price for each of five stock issues, the values can be represented by the symbols X_1, X_2, _____, _____, and _____.

X_3; X_4; X_5

5 In the statistical formula in Frame 4, n represents the total number of values of X. In the stock-issue example of the same frame, $n = $ _____ (number).

6 In the statistical formula for the sample mean, Σ is the upper-case Greek letter sigma, which can be read as "sum of." In this case, then, the letter designates not a population parameter but an arithmetic operation. ΣX would be read as _____ _____.

7 Given the following values for a variable, make the appropriate substitutions in the formula and solve for the value of the sample mean: $X = $ 8, 6, 2, and 4.

$$\bar{X} = \frac{\Sigma X}{n} =$$

8 Throughout the preceding discussion we have been careful to specify that the formula is used to compute the value of a sample mean, rather than a population mean. However, when the population mean μ is being computed, the only difference in the formula is that N, which signifies number of measurements in the population, is substituted for n, which signifies the number of sample elements. Thus the formula for computing the population mean is

 $\mu =$

9 When data are grouped in a frequency distribution, each class midpoint, or class mark, which is represented by the symbol X_c, is taken to be representative of all measurements included in the class. The value of each class midpoint is multiplied by the frequency of measurements included in that class in order to determine the sum of the measurements included in a class. For grouped data the formula for the sample mean is thus

$$\bar{X} = \frac{\Sigma f X_c}{\Sigma f} \qquad \text{or, more simply,} \qquad \bar{X} = \frac{\Sigma f X}{\Sigma f}$$

In this formula, which we shall apply in a few frames, what term is equal to n (or N, if the population mean μ is being computed)?

10 Thus, whenever an f is included in the formula for the arithmetic mean, this indicates that the formula is to be used with (ungrouped / grouped) data.

11 We can also take this opportunity to present some additional rules regarding the appropriate use of the summation sign. Two operations which students sometimes confuse with one another are that of summing a group of squared values, designated by ΣX^2, and that of squaring the sum of a group of values, designated by $(\Sigma X)^2$. When the formula reads ΣX^2, we square the value of each variable (before / after) summing; for the formula $(\Sigma X)^2$ we square (each variable / the sum).

before

the sum

12 Therefore, if X has the vaues 2, 4, and 6, then

$$\Sigma X =$$
$$\Sigma X^2 =$$
$$(\Sigma X)^2 =$$

$12 \ (= 2 + 4 + 6)$

$56 \ (= 4 + 16 + 36)$

$144 \ (= 12^2)$

13 Similarly, if a formula indicates that two terms following a summation sign are to be multiplied by one another or divided one by the other, this arithmetic operation must be carried out *before* the summation is done. Thus the expression ΣXY indicates that summation should be carried out (before / after) the value of each X variable is multiplied by the corresponding value of a Y variable.

after

14 If we wish to sum the values of two variables first, and then multiply the sums, the correct symbolic expression for this operation is $\Sigma X \Sigma Y$ and is read as _____.

sum of X times sum of Y

15 If we wish to multiply the sum of a set of variables X by a constant a, what is the best symbolic way of representing this operation? _____

$a\Sigma X$ (Entering the a after the summation sign would indicate that each value of X is multiplied by a before summation.)

16 If we are simply summing a constant a, the arithmetic result is the same as if we had multiplied a by the number of elements (n or N). That is, $\Sigma a = na$ (or Na). For example, complete the following summation and related calculation.

$$a$$

$$7$$
$$7$$
$$7$$
$$7$$

$$\Sigma a = \text{_____}$$

$$na = \text{_____} \times \text{_____} = \text{_____}$$

28

$4 \times 7 = 28$

17 Because of the placement of the summation sign in the numerator of the formula $\bar{X} = \Sigma fX / \Sigma f$, summation should be carried out (before / after) multiplication of each class midpoint by its associated frequency.

after

18 Complete the following table as the first step toward computing the arithmetic mean for these grouped data.

Class limits	X_c	f	fX_c
6–8	7	3	21
9–11	10	6	60
12–14	13	7	91
15–17	16	4	_____
18–20	19	2	_____
		$n = \Sigma f = 22$	$\Sigma fX_c =$ _____

19 Indicate the simplest form of the formula used to compute the arithmetic mean for grouped data and use it to determine the value of the mean for the data in Frame 18, carrying your answer to the first decimal place.

$\bar{X} =$

3.b ▪ the median

A set of measurements that is arranged in sequential order according to the magnitude of the measurements, either lowest to highest or highest to lowest, is called an array. For ungrouped measurements the median is simply the middle measurement in an array of measurements. For grouped data it is necessary to locate the class containing the median and then to locate the median within this class by a process of interpolation.

20 Does the set of values 7, 8, 5, 10, 3 constitute an array? (yes / no) Why or why not? _____

21 Arrange the values 7, 8, 5, 10, 3 in an array and identify the value of the median. Array = _____;
med = _____.

22 What is the value of the median for the numbers 5, 8, 12, 3, 9?
_____

23 When there is an even number of measurements rather than an odd number of measurements, there is no one middle value. In such cases the median is assumed to be located midway between the two middle values. Accordingly, what is the value of the median for the numbers 7, 9, 2, 2, 8, 11? _____

24 What is the median for the numbers 3, 5, 6, 6, 8, 9? _____

25 Particularly when a large number of measurements is involved, it is convenient to use a position rule for locating the value representing the median of an array of measurements. When a set of measurements is arranged in order of magnitude, from X_1 to X_n, the median can be located by dividing n by 2 and adding $\frac{1}{2}$. Symbolically, med $= X_{n/2+\frac{1}{2}}$. Using this formula, if five measurements are arranged in order of magnitude, which term represents the value of the median?

$X_{\frac{5}{2}+\frac{1}{2}} = X_3$ (which corresponds to the elements you identified in Frames 21 and 22)

Med $= X_{n/2+\frac{1}{2}} =$

---

26 Similarly, which sequentially numbered term represents the median when 135 measurements are arranged in order?

$X_{n/2+\frac{1}{2}} = X_{135\frac{1}{2}+\frac{1}{2}} = X_{68}$

Med $=$

27 When there is an even number of measurements, the formula indicates that the median is located between two measurements. Thus, if there are 70 measurements,

$X_{70\frac{1}{2}+\frac{1}{2}} = X_{35\frac{1}{2}}$

Med $=$

Since fractional sequence numbers for terms do not exist, this sequence number indicates that the median is midway between the values of the _____ th and _____ th terms in the array.

35th; 36th

28 For grouped, as contrasted to ungrouped, data, the first step in locating the median is to identify the class in which the median is located. Since the median is at the middle of an array of measurements, it is useful to compute the cumulative frequency for each class in the frequency distribution so that the class containing the midpoint of the distribution of frequencies can be identified. The cumulative frequency for a class includes not only the number of measurements in that class but also the frequencies of all classes "below" that class. Accordingly, complete the cumulative-frequency (cf) column in the table below.

Class limits	f	cf
6–8	4	4
9–11	6	10
12–14	7	17
15–17	4	_____
18–20	3	_____
	$\Sigma f = 24$	

21
24

29 The class containing the median is the first class whose cumulative frequency cf is equal to or exceeds the sum of the frequencies divided by 2. Thus, for the data in Frame 28, we identify the median class by observing which class is the first to have a cumulative frequency equal to or greater than _____ (number).

12 (which is 24 divided by 2)

30 For the data in Frame 28 the class containing the median is the class whose limits are _____ (number) and _____ (number).

12; 14

31 In determining the position of the median within the class containing it, two assumptions are made. The first is that the measurements included in a class are equally dispersed in it, and the second is that measurement is continuous rather than discrete. Since we are suggesting that interpolation should be used to locate the median, using the midpoint of the median class as automatically representing the value of the median (is / is not) a common practice.

is not

32 The formula used for interpolation in determining the value of the median from grouped data is

$$\text{Med} = B_L + \frac{n/2 - \text{cf}_B}{f_c} i \qquad \text{where } n = \Sigma f$$

In this formula B_L is the lower *boundary* of the class containing the median. For the data of Table 3.1, therefore, $B_L = $ _____ (number).

11.5

table 3.1 ▪ a frequency distribution for continuous data

Class limits	Class boundaries	X_c	f	cf
6–8	5.5–8.5	7	4	4
9–11	8.5–11.5	10	6	10
12–14	11.5–14.5	13	7	17
15–17	14.5–17.5	16	4	21
18–20	17.5–20.5	19	3	24

33 In the formula in Frame 32, cf_B is the cumulative frequency of the class below the median class. By "below" we mean the adjacent class whose midpoint has a lower value than that of the median class. For the data of Table 3.1, $\text{cf}_B = $ _____ (number).

10

34 In the formula

$$\text{Med} = B_L + \frac{n/2 - \text{cf}_B}{f_c} i$$

the frequency of the median class is designated f_c. For the data of Table 3.1, $f_c = $ _____ (number).

7

35 Finally, i in the formula for determining the value of the median for grouped data indicates the size of the class interval containing the median. In Table 3.1, $i = $ _____ (number).

3

36 Determine the value of the median for the data of Table 3.1, carrying your answer to the first decimal place.

$$\text{Med} = B_L + \frac{n/2 - \text{cf}_B}{f_c} \, i \ =$$

37 Similarly, determine the value of the median for the data in the following frequency distribution.

Class limits	*Class boundaries*	X_c	f	cf
1–2	0.5–2.5	1.5	2	2
3–4	2.5–4.5	3.5	5	7
5–6	4.5–6.5	5.5	15	22
7–8	6.5–8.5	7.5	10	32
9–10	8.5–10.5	9.5	5	37

$$\text{Med} = B_L + \frac{n/2 - \text{cf}_B}{f_c} \, i \ =$$

summary

38 The median is the middle value of a set of measurements that is listed in an _____.

39 Using the position rule for locating the measurement taken as the value of the median, determine the median for the measurements 5, 8, 7, 4, 9, 3, 1.

$$\text{Med} = X_{n/2 + \frac{1}{2}} \ =$$

40 For grouped data entered in a frequency distribution, the fact that we interpolate within the median class to find the value of the median suggests that we assume that the measurements in that class (are / are not) equally distributed in it and that the measurements are on a (discrete / continuous) scale of measurement.

41 Compute the value of the median for the following simplified data.

Class limits	f
4–6	3
7–9	5
10–12	10

$$\text{Med} = B_L + \frac{n/2 - \text{cf}_B}{f_c} \, i \ =$$

3.c ▪ the quartiles and other position measures

Though they are not measures of central tendency as such, quartiles, deciles, and percentiles are similar to the median in that they also divide a total distribution of measurements into equal portions based on the distribution of frequencies. Whereas the median divides a distribution into two halves, the quartiles divide it into four quarters, the deciles divide it into ten tenths, and the percentile points divide it into 100 parts. Because of this similarity, the values of these positional measures can be determined by using only slightly modified versions of the formulas for computing the median. In this section we shall address our attention primarily to the computation of the quartiles.

42 For the median, as for other measures of position, it is important to remember that the distribution of measurements is divided into equal portions not in terms of the number of score points on either side of the median but in terms of the actual frequency of measurements on either side of the median. Thus, if the lowest observed value of a measurement is 20 and the highest observed value is 80, the median (would / would not) necessarily be located at 50.

> would not (Half of the total frequency of measurements could be located within the first 20 measurement units, for example.)

43 Similarly, the quartiles divide a distribution into four quarters not in terms of the number of possible units of measurement included in each portion but in terms of the _____ _____ of measurements in each portion of the distribution.

> frequency (or actual number)

44 If the one point that corresponds to the median divides the distribution into two equal halves, how many points need to be identified in order to divide a distribution into four quarters containing equal numbers of observed measurements? _____ (number)

> 3

45 Accordingly, the first, second, and third quartiles are represented by the symbols Q_1, Q_2, and Q_3, respectively. Twenty-five percent of the measurements are located below the point of Q_1, 50 percent of the measurements are located below Q_2, and _____ percent of the measurements are located below Q_3.

> 75

46 Since 50 percent of the measurements are located below Q_2, to what measure of central tendency does the value of Q_2 correspond? _____

> the median

47 The modification of the usual formulas for the median in order to compute the values of the quartiles is relatively simple. For ungrouped data, where med $= X_{n/2+\frac{1}{2}}$,

$$Q_1 = X_{n/4+\frac{1}{2}} \qquad Q_2 = X_{n/2+\frac{1}{2}} \qquad Q_3 =$$

> $X_{3n/4+\frac{1}{2}}$

48 For the array of measurements 3, 5, 6, 7, 7, 8, 9, 11, compute the values of the median and the three quartiles.

$$Med = X_{n/2+\frac{1}{2}} =$$
$$Q_1 = X_{n/4+\frac{1}{2}} =$$
$$Q_2 = X_{n/2+\frac{1}{2}} =$$
$$Q_3 = X_{3n/4+\frac{1}{2}} =$$

> $X_{4\frac{1}{2}} = 7$
> $X_{2\frac{1}{2}} = 5.5$
> $X_{4\frac{1}{2}} = 7$
> $X_{6\frac{1}{2}} = 8.5$

75

49 Referring to the values of the quartiles just computed, even if you did not have the original data available, what would you conclude is the percentage of measurements in the array with a value of 8.5 or less? _____ percent

$B_L + \dfrac{3n/4 - cf_B}{f_c} i$

50 For grouped data the usual formula for the median is similarly modified in order to compute the quartiles. Thus

$$Q_1 = B_L + \frac{n/4 - cf_B}{f_c} i \qquad Q_2 = B_L + \frac{n/2 - cf_B}{f_c} i$$

$$Q_3 =$$

12.4 (No additional computation is necessary, since $Q_2 = $ med.)

51 For the data of Table 3.1, if the value of the median is 12.4, what is the value of Q_2, the second quartile?

$$Q_2 =$$

52 In computing the values of Q_1 and Q_3, we of course interpolate within the classes in which the respective quartiles are located, rather than within the class containing the median. For the data of Table 3.1 compute the value of Q_1.

$8.5 + \left(\dfrac{6 - 4}{6}\right) 3 = 8.5 + \left(\dfrac{2}{6}\right) 3 = 9.5$

$$Q_1 = B_L + \frac{n/4 - cf_B}{f_c} i =$$

table 3.1 ▪ **a frequency distribution for continuous data**

Class limits	Class boundaries	X_c	f	cf
6–8	5.5–8.5	7	4	4
9–11	8.5–11.5	10	6	10
12–14	11.5–14.5	13	7	17
15–17	14.5–17.5	16	4	21
18–20	17.5–20.5	19	3	24

53 For the data of Table 3.1 compute the value of Q_3.

$14.5 + \left(\dfrac{18 - 17}{4}\right) 3 = 14.5 + \dfrac{3}{4}$
$= 15.25 = 15.2$

$$Q_3 = B_L + \frac{3n/4 - cf_B}{f_c} i =$$

54 Given the fact that deciles are the points that divide a distribution of measurements into 10 equal portions, what is the formula for locating the position of the fourth decile in an array of ungrouped measurements when med $= X_{n/2 + \frac{1}{2}}$?

$X_{4n/10 + \frac{1}{2}}$ (or $X_{2n/5 + \frac{1}{2}}$)

$$D_4 =$$

55 Similarly, indicate the formula for determining the value of the fourth decile for grouped data, where

$$\text{Med} = B_L + \frac{n/2 - cf_B}{f_c} i$$

$B_L + \dfrac{4n/10 - cf_B}{f_c} i$

$$D_4 =$$

$$8.5 + \left(\frac{9.6 - 4}{6}\right) 3 = 8.5 + \left(\frac{5.6}{6}\right) 3$$
$$= 11.3$$

56 Using the formula developed in Frame 55, compute the value of the fourth decile for the data of Table 3.1.

$$D_4 = B_L + \left(\frac{4n/10 - cf_B}{f_c}\right) i =$$

3.d ▪ the mode

A third measure of central tendency is the mode. The mode is that value which occurs with the greatest frequency in a set of measurements. When one value occurs more frequently than any other value, the distribution of measurements is called *unimodal*. If it happens that two different values have equal and maximum frequencies associated with them, the distribution is called *bimodal*. When all values of the measurements are nonrepetitive, or unique, no mode exists. For ungrouped data calculation of the mode simply involves identifying the value which is most frequently represented in the measurements. For grouped data calculation of the mode involves identifying the class of values with the highest frequency and then locating the position of the mode within that class by interpolation.

57 What is the mode of the measurements 3, 5, 6, 9, 11, 12, 13?

There is no mode.

58 What is the mode for the measurements 3, 3, 3, 4, 4, 6, 7, 9, 9?

3

59 Since a single mode exists for the data of Frame 58, these measurements can be described as following a ——————— distribution.

unimodal

60 On the other hand, the measurements 5, 6, 6, 6, 8, 9, 9, 9, 11, 12 can be described as following a ——————— distribution.

bimodal

61 For grouped data one possible approach for locating the mode is to accept the midpoint of the modal class as the best estimate. Rather than following this procedure, however, we shall determine the location of the mode by interpolation on the basis of the frequencies of measurements in the two classes adjoining the modal class. The formula used is

$$\text{Mode} = B_L + \frac{D_1}{D_1 + D_2} i$$

Since B_L in this formula is the lower boundary of the class containing the mode, for the data of Table 3.1, B_L = —————— (number).

11.5

62 In the formula for the mode, D_1 is the difference between the frequency of the modal class and that of the adjacent *lower* class (i.e., the adjacent class with the smaller class midpoint). For Table 3.1, D_1 = —————— (number).

1 (= 7 − 6)

$3 \, (= 7 - 4)$	**63** In the formula for the mode used with grouped data, D_2 is the difference between the frequency of the modal class and that of the adjacent *higher* class. For Table 3.1, $D_2 =$_____ (number).
class interval	**64** Similarly to the formula for the median, i indicates the size of the _____ in which the mode is located.
$11.5 + \left(\dfrac{1}{1+3}\right) 3 = 12.25 = 12.2$	**65** Calculate the value of the mode for the data of Table 3.1. $\text{Mode} = B_L + \dfrac{D_1}{D_1 + D_2} i =$

66 Similarly, determine the value of the mode for the following frequency distribution.

Class	f
1–2	2
3–4	5
5–6	15
7–8	10
9–10	5

$4.5 + \left(\dfrac{10}{10+5}\right) 2 = 5.8$

$$\text{Mode} = B_L + \frac{D_1}{D_1 + D_2} i$$

$$\text{Mode} =$$

$15 - 5 = 10$

$15 - 10 = 5$

3.e ▪ relationship among the mean, median, and mode

In this section we shall consider the relationship among the mean, median, and mode from both the mathematical and empirical points of view. First we shall consider the mathematical criterion, or objective, that is satisfied by each of these measures of central tendency. Then we shall consider how the values of the mean, median, and mode differ systematically from one another for various types of distributions of measurements.

67 The mean, median, and mode satisfy different mathematical criteria as to what constitutes the typical or average value. For a group of measurements, suppose that we wish to guess at the value of each measurement in turn. Which of the measures of central tendency, when used as the one best guess each time, would lead to the greatest number of guesses being exactly correct? (*Hint:* Consider which type of average indicates the "most popular" measurement.) (the mean / the median / the mode)

the mode

68 Or, turning the statement about, we can say that the measure of central tendency which results in the *fewest number* of errors when it is used as the one best estimate for every measurement in the group is the (mean / median / mode).

mode

69 Symbolically, the mathematical criterion of a "good" average that is satisfied by the mode can be expressed as $N_e = \min$. That is, when the mode is used as the best estimate of the value of

number	every measurement in a distribution of measurements, the _____ of errors is minimized.

70 However, we might take the *magnitude* of each error into consideration in the mathematical criterion. Given that e is the amount of error without regard to its direction, or arithmetic sign, then if we wish to minimize the sum of the errors that are made in estimating the value of each measurement, the mathematical criterion can be symbolically represented by (Σe^2 = min / Σe = min / N_e = min).

(margin: Σe = min)

71 The measure of central tendency that satisfies the criterion that the *sum of the errors* be minimized is the median. Thus, if we take any other value in the distribution and use it as the best estimate of every measurement, the arithmetic sum of the absolute values of the errors would be (less / greater) than the sum of the errors when the median is used as the estimate.

(margin: greater)

72 Symbolically, the mathematical criterion satisfied by the median can be represented by _____ = min.

(margin: Σe)

73 Finally, the third major criterion that can be satisfied is that the *sum* of the *errors squared* be minimized. This criterion is satisfied by the arithmetic mean and can be represented symbolically by _____ = min.

(margin: Σe^2)

74 When it is used as the basis for estimating the value of every measurement in a distribution, the mean is that value which results in a minimum sum of _____.

(margin: errors squared)

75 The objective of minimizing the sum of squared errors is an important one in statistical analysis, and one that we shall refer to again in later units. It is usually referred to as the *least-squares criterion*. For measures of central tendency the least-squares criterion is satisfied by the (mean / median / mode).

(margin: mean)

76 Thus there are three major mathematical criteria for determining the location of an average, and the mean, median, and mode are the three values in a distribution of measurements that correspond to the requirements of each criterion. Symbolically expressed, the mode satisfies the criterion _____.

(margin: N_e = min)

77 The median satisfies the symbolic criterion _____.

(margin: Σe = min)

78 The mean satisfies the symbolic criterion _____.

(margin: Σe^2 = min)

79 The criterion indicating that the sum of the squared deviations should be minimized is popularly referred to as the _____

least-squares	_____ criterion.

80 Which measure of central tendency would have its value most affected by the addition of a few very high *or* very low measurements to the distribution being described? (*Hint:* It would have to be one of the two measures of central tendency whose criteria take the magnitude of error, and not just the number of errors, into

the mean	consideration.) (the mean / the median / the mode)

81 Since the mathematical criterion satisfied by the arithmetic mean concerns not just the sum of the errors, but the sum of the

errors squared	_____, it is most affected by the addition

of a few measurements that are extremely high or low in relation to the general distribution of measurements.

82 On the other hand, which measure of central tendency is unaffected by the addition of a few measurements at the extreme low or high end of the distribution; i.e., which measure satisfies the mathematical criterion which does not take magnitude of error

the mode	into account? _____

83 By elimination, since the mode is unaffected by extreme measurements, and since the mean is most affected, the measure of central tendency that is somewhat affected by the addition of measurements to one end of the distribution, but not to the same

median	extent as the arithmetic mean, is the _____.

84 Let us now illustrate the nature of the effect that we have been discussing. Given the following set of ungrouped measurements, determine the values of the mean, median, and mode: $X = 3, 5, 6, 6, 7,$ and 9.

$\frac{36}{6} = 6$	$\bar{X} = \dfrac{\Sigma X}{n} =$
$X_{3.5} = 6$	$\mathrm{Med} = X_{n/2+\frac{1}{2}} =$
6 (most frequent measurement)	$\mathrm{Mode} =$

85 Though the above example in Frame 84 does not, of course, constitute a mathematical proof, it indicates that when the distribution of measurements is symmetrical, the values of the mean,

are equal to one another	median, and mode (differ markedly / are equal to one another).

86 Now suppose we add a few measurements to the distribution of six measurements given in Frame 84 and, further, let us give these relatively high values to observe the differential effect on the three measures of average. Given the following eight measure-

ments, compute the values of the mean, median, and mode:
X = 3, 5, 6, 6, 7, 9, 16, and 20.

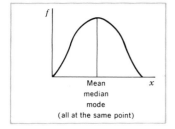

$\frac{72}{8} = 9$

$X_{4.5} = 6.5$

6

$\bar{X} = \dfrac{\Sigma X}{n} =$

Med $= X_{n/2+\frac{1}{2}} =$

Mode $=$

87 Thus, comparing the measures of central tendency for the simplified data of Frames 84 and 86, we find that the measure of average which is most affected by the addition of extreme measurements is the _____; the measure which is only somewhat affected is the _____; the measure which is unaffected is the _____.

mean

median

mode

88 We can also illustrate these differential effects graphically. For the following symmetrical frequency curve, enter and label the vertical lines indicating the expected relative locations of the mean, median, and mode of the distribution.

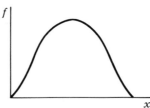

Mean
median
mode
(all at the same point)

89 On the following frequency curve representing a positively skewed distribution of measurements, label the vertical lines representing the relative values of the mean, median, and mode.

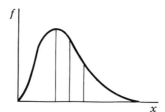

mode; median; mean (from left to right)

90 Similarly, for the following negatively skewed distribution, indicate the relative locations of the mean, median, and mode.

mean; median; mode (from left to right)

91 Therefore the relationship among the values of the three principal measures of central tendency is indicative of the direction and extent of departure from symmetry for the distribution of measurements. When the values of the mean, median, and mode are all identical, the distribution is _____. When the mean is the largest in value (and the median is larger than the mode), the distribution is _____. When the mode is largest in value (and the median is larger than the mean), the distribution is _____.

92 Which measure of central tendency represents the best average depends on whether or not the distribution of measurements is skewed and on the intended use of the average. For example, given the following distribution of per-family income in a small community, which measure of central tendency would be most representative if we wish to use average family income as one basis for deciding whether or not to locate a retail outlet in the community? (mean / median / mode) Why? _____

_____

_____

Annual family income	Number of families
Under $2,000	25
$2,000–$3,999	75
$4,000–$5,999	50
$6,000–$7,999	30
$8,000–$9,999	3
$10,000–$14,999	2
$15,000–$24,999	0
$25,000–$49,999	0
$50,000–$99,999	15
$100,000+	5

review **93** (Frames 1–19) Below, post the formulas for computing (a) the sample mean for ungrouped data; (b) the population mean for ungrouped data; and (c) the arithmetic mean for grouped data, whether for a sample or a population.

(a) $\bar{X} =$

(b) $\mu =$

(c) $\bar{X}$ (or μ) $=$

94 (Sec. 3.b, Introduction; Frames 20–27) The position rule for locating the median in an array of ungrouped measurements can be symbolically represented as med = _____.

95 (Frames 28–31) In determining the value of the median for grouped data, the midpoint of the class containing the median (is / is not) used as the best estimate of the value of the median.

96 (Frames 32–41) In the formula

$$\text{Med} = B_L + \frac{n/2 - \text{cf}_B}{f_c} i$$

what is B_L? _____

_____

97 (Sec. 3.c, Introduction; Frames 42–43) Given a nonsymmetrical distribution in which the lowest-valued measurement equals 50 and the highest-valued measurement equals 100, the median of the distribution (would / would not) usually be located at 75.

98 (Frames 44–49, 54) For *ungrouped* measurements listed in an array, indicate below the formulas to be used for locating the position in the array of **(a)** Q_3 and **(b)** D_3.

(a) $Q_3 =$

(b) $D_3 =$

99 (Frames 50–53, 55–56) Given the formula for determining the value of the median for *grouped* data

$$\text{Med} = B_L + \frac{n/2 - \text{cf}_B}{f_c} i$$

indicate the formulas for computing **(a)** Q_1 and **(b)** D_3 for the same data.

(a) $Q_1 =$

(b) $D_3 =$

100 (Sec 3.d, Introduction; Frames 57–60) Identify the value of the mode for the ungrouped measurements: 75, 79, 79, 83, 87, 87, 94. Mode = _____.

101 (Frames 61–66) In using the formula for determining the value of the mode for grouped measurements,

$$\text{Mode} = B_L + \frac{D_1}{D_1 + D_2} i$$

Since D_1 and D_2 refer to the difference in frequencies between the modal class and the adjacent lower and upper classes, respectively, for the following data the mode would be located near the (lower / upper) boundary of the modal class.

Class boundaries	f
5.5–8.5	1
8.5–11.5	8
11.5–14.5	6

102 (Frames 67–78) In terms of the mathematical criteria satisfied by the three principal types of averages, for the mean: _____ = min; for the median: _____ = min; and for the mode: _____ = min.

Σe^2; Σe

N_c

103 (Frames 75, 79) The mathematical criterion satisfied by the arithmetic mean is popularly referred to as the _____ _____ criterion.

least-squares

104 (Frames 80–87) The average which is least affected by extreme scores on one "side" of the distribution is the _____; the one which is most affected is the _____.

mode

mean

105 (Frames 88–92) When the mean is larger in value than the median (and the median is larger than the mode), the frequency curve representing the data can be described as being _____ _____, and when the mean is smaller in value than the median, the distribution is _____. When all of the measures of central tendency have the same value, the distribution is _____.

positively skewed

negatively skewed

symmetrical

employee absence during a three-month period

Employee identification number	Number of days absent
001	5
002	0
003	1
004	7
005	1
006	2
007	9
008	5
009	1
010	3

problems
(solutions given on page 349)

1 For the data above, tabulating employee absence in a particular department during a three-month period, determine the following values:

(a) the arithmetic mean
(b) the median

(c) the mode

(d) Q_1, Q_2, and Q_3

2 Comment upon and interpret the differences in the values of the measures of central tendency computed in Prob. 1.

3 In an academic grading system in which $A = 4$, $B = 3$, $C = 2$, $D = 1$, and $E = 0$, a group of college juniors have the cumulative grade-point averages indicated in the following table:

Grade-point average	Number of students
1.0–1.4	0
1.5–1.9	2
2.0–2.4	10
2.5–2.9	9
3.0–3.4	6
3.5–3.9	3

(a) Compute the arithmetic mean for this distribution.

(b) Compute the median.

(c) Compute the mode.

(d) Compute Q_1 and Q_3 and interpret the meanings of these measures of location.

(e) Interpret the obtained differences in the values of the mean, median, and mode.

additional problems **4** Given the sample of test scores below, compute:

(a) the arithmetic mean

(b) the median

(c) the mode

(d) the third quartile

(e) the sixth decile

ten randomly selected scores on a short examination

8	5	10	10	10
8	7	10	8	12

5 Interpret the differences in the values of the mean, median, and mode computed in Prob. 4.

6 The following frequency distribution indicates the number of student errors in the responses written in a self-instructional unit.

Errors	f
0–4	4
5–9	12
10–14	17
15–19	6
20–24	3
25–29	2
30–34	0
35–39	1

(a) Compute the arithmetic mean.
(b) Compute the value of the median.
(c) Determine the value of the mode.
(d) Compute the location of the ninetieth percentile point.
(e) Describe the associated frequency curve in terms of its skewness.

unit 4 • measuring dispersion

In Unit 3 we considered the various types of averages that can be computed and the relationships among them. Collections of measurements differ also in the amount of dispersion, or variability, represented in the distribution. For example, two groups of examination scores might each have an arithmetic mean of 80, but the scores on one test might vary from a low of 65 to a high of 90, whereas the scores on the other test might vary from a low of 45 to a high of 98. These two distributions thus have a common arithmetic mean but differ in their dispersion. A number of methods are available for measuring the extent of dispersion in a collection of measurements, of which we shall discuss the *range, quartile deviation, mean deviation, standard deviation,* and *coefficient of variation.* The standard deviation, by far the most important of the measures of dispersion, is used in methods of statistical inference to be discussed later in this book. After considering the various methods of measuring dispersion, we shall return in Sec. 4.f to the topics of skewness and kurtosis in order to demonstrate how departure from symmetry and the degree of peakedness of a frequency curve can be statistically determined and defined.

4.a • the range

The measure of dispersion that is the easiest to compute and is the crudest measure of dispersion is the range. Represented by R, it is simply the difference between the highest value and the lowest value in a collection of ungrouped measurements.

$H - L$

1 L stands for the lowest value in a collection of measurements and H stands for the highest value. Since R is always a positive quantity, the formula that is used for computing the value of the range is $R =$ _____ $-$ _____ .

$14 - 2 = 12$

2 Compute the range for the following ungrouped measurements: 8, 10, 14, 2, 8, 12, 13.

$$R = H - L = \underline{\hspace{1cm}} - \underline{\hspace{1cm}} = \underline{\hspace{1cm}}$$

2

3 The range is a crude measure of dispersion in that it is unstable. Specifically, its value depends entirely on just the two extreme measurements in the group, and thus one unusually high or low measurement affects the value of the range markedly. For example, the value that is unusually different from the others in the group of measurements given in Frame 2 is _____ (number).

$6(= 14 - 8)$

4 If the 2 is removed from the group of measurements given in Frame 2, the resulting value of the range is _____ (number) instead of 12.

two
unstable

5 Thus the chief limitation to the use of the range as a measure of dispersion is that its value is determined by just _____ (number) measurements and thus tends to be _____ .

6 For grouped data that are organized in a frequency distribution, the range is the maximum number of measurement units included in the distribution. Thus the range is equal to the difference between the upper *boundary* of the highest class with any frequencies in it and the lower boundary of the lowest class with any tabulated frequencies. Accordingly the range for the data of the following frequency distribution is $R = $ _____ $-$ _____ $=$ _____.

Class	f
6–8	3
9–11	6
12–14	7
15–17	4
18–20	2

7 Similarly, the range for the following grouped data is

$R = $ _____ $-$ _____ $=$ _____

Class	f
4–6	10
7–9	5
10–12	3
13–15	0

8 Thus for ungrouped data the range is equal to the difference between the _____ and the _____ _____. For grouped data the range is equal to the difference between the _____ of the highest class with tabulated frequencies and the _____ _____ of the lowest class with tabulated frequencies.

4.b ▪ the quartile deviation

The quartile deviation, represented by QD, is a type of range and has in fact been called the "semi-interquartile range." In effect, its value represents half the range of the middle 50 percent of the measurements when they are listed as an array.

9 The formula for the quartile deviation is

$$QD = \frac{Q_3 - Q_1}{2}$$

Therefore, given that $Q_3 = 17.5$ and $Q_1 = 10.0$,

$QD = $

10 Thus the measure of variability that is based on determining the range between the values of the third and first quartile of the distribution and dividing this range by 2 is called the _____ _____.

11 Since the median (or Q_2) is located exactly in the middle of the range between Q_1 and Q_3 for *distributions of measurements that are symmetrical between these two points,* then adding the value of QD, which is one-half of this range, to the median is equal to the value of (Q_1 / med / Q_3).

12 Similarly, for symmetrical distributions, med $-$ QD $= \underline{\quad Q_1 \quad}$.

13 Or, to look at the same relationship among these values from another point of view, the intervals of measurement between Q_1 and the median and between the median and Q_3 each contain _____ percent of all measurements in the distribution.

14 Suppose we both subtract the value of QD from the median and add its value to the median, thus defining an interval "around" the median. For a symmetrical distribution, the interval with the limits med $\pm$ QD (read: "the median plus *and* minus QD") contains _____ percent of all of the measurements in the distribution.

15 The quartile deviation is not widely used as a measure of dispersion, but the approach of considering the percentage or proportion of measurements included within a certain distance of a central value is particularly important in interpreting the standard deviation, which we shall discuss shortly. One feature that the quartile deviation does have, however, is that when open-end distributions are involved, so that the lowest and/or highest possible score points cannot be identified, QD (can / cannot) be used as a measure of dispersion but the range (can / cannot) be used.

16 The formula for computing the quartile deviation is the same for either ungrouped or grouped data. What does differ is the procedure by which the values of Q_1 and Q_3 are determined in the first place. Recalling that med $= X_{n/2+\frac{1}{2}}$ for an ungrouped array of measurements, compute the values of Q_1, Q_3, and QD for the following array: 7, 7, 9, 11, 12, 15, 17, 21.

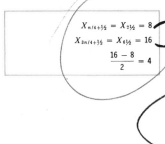

$$X_{n/4+\frac{1}{2}} = X_{2\frac{1}{2}} = 8$$
$$X_{3n/4+\frac{1}{2}} = X_{6\frac{1}{2}} = 16$$
$$\frac{16-8}{2} = 4$$

$Q_1 =$

$Q_3 =$

$\text{QD} = \dfrac{Q_3 - Q_1}{2} =$

17 Similarly, recalling that for grouped data

$$\text{Med} = B_L + \frac{n/2 - \text{cf}_B}{f_c} \, i$$

compute the values of Q_1, Q_3, and QD for the following data, carrying your answer to the first decimal place.

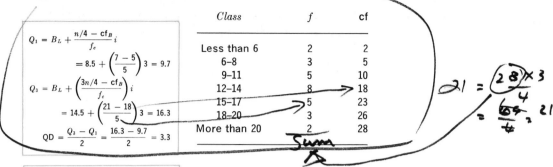

The table in the image:

Class	f	cf
Less than 6	2	2
6–8	3	5
9–11	5	10
12–14	8	18
15–17	5	23
18–20	3	26
More than 20	2	28

$$Q_1 = B_L + \frac{n/4 - cf_B}{f_e} \, i$$

$$= 8.5 + \left(\frac{7-5}{5}\right) 3 = 9.7$$

$$Q_3 = B_L + \left(\frac{3n/4 - cf_B}{f_e}\right) i$$

$$= 14.5 + \left(\frac{21-18}{5}\right) 3 = 16.3$$

$$QD = \frac{Q_3 - Q_1}{2} = \frac{16.3 - 9.7}{2} = 3.3$$

---

yes (The high point of the curve is at the class 12–14, with the other frequencies symmetrically distributed about this class.)

18 Look at the pattern of frequencies in the distribution given in Frame 17. Is the frequency curve for this distribution of measurements symmetrical? (yes / no)

19 Since the frequency distribution given in Frame 17 is symmetrical, the value of the quartile deviation can be used not only as a general measure of dispersion, but also with the median as a point of reference. Given that the median of this distribution is 13.0 and the quartile deviation is 3.3, we can conclude that the middle 50 percent of the measurements are included within the limits _____ (number) and _____ (number).

9.7; 16.3 (obtained by solving for med ± QD)

20 Look back at the data of Frame 17. Can we compute the range as a measure of dispersion for these measurements? (yes / no) Why or why not? _____

no; because it is an open-end distribution

4.c ▪ the mean deviation (average deviation)

The value of the range is based on the location of the two extreme measurements of a group, whereas the value of the quartile deviation is based on the dispersion of the middle 50 percent of the distribution; i.e., it is based on the values of Q_1 and Q_3. Computation of the value of the mean deviation, or MD, on the other hand, takes the value of every measurement in the group into consideration. The value of MD is based on the difference, or deviation, between the arithmetic mean of a group of measurements and each of the measurements in that group.

21 Before we introduce the procedure used to compute the value of the mean deviation, we shall first introduce the concept of a *deviation*. Unless otherwise indicated, this term always refers to the difference between a measurement and the mean of the group from which the measurement is taken. Furthermore it is always the mean that is subtracted from the individual value, and not the other way around. Thus a positive deviation always indicates that the variable in question is (smaller / larger) than the mean, and a negative deviation always indicates that the measurement is (smaller / larger) than the mean.

larger

smaller

22 In Unit 3 we introduced X as representing the value of a variable and $\bar{X}$ as representing the sample mean. A deviation, on the other hand, is represented by lowercase x (read: "small x"). Using these symbols, we can say $x =$ _____ $-$ _____.

$$X - \bar{X}$$

23 For population data the mean of the group is represented by the Greek letter μ. Therefore the formula used to determine the values of deviations for a group of measurements comprising a population is $x =$ _____.

$$X - \mu$$

24 Given the following array, indicate the value of the deviation associated with each measurement.

$$\left(\bar{X} = \frac{\Sigma X}{n} = \frac{30}{5} = 6 \right)$$

X	x
4	____
4	____
6	____
7	____
9	____
$\Sigma X = 30$	

$4 - 6 = -2$
$4 - 6 = -2$
$6 - 6 = 0$
$7 - 6 = +1$
$9 - 6 = +3$

25 As the name implies, the mean deviation is a kind of arithmetic mean of all of the deviation scores. What is the arithmetic mean of the deviation scores in Frame 24?

$$\frac{0}{5} = 0 \qquad \bar{x} = \frac{\Sigma x}{n} =$$

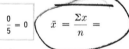

26 The sum of the deviations from the mean *always* equals zero, and therefore the mean deviation is computed somewhat differently from the way that we might at first suppose. In computing the value of the mean deviation, we sum the *absolute values* of the deviations without regard to sign, represented by $|x|$ (read: "absolute value of small x"), rather than the signed deviation values. Thus the formula that is used to compute the value of the mean deviation is

$$\frac{\Sigma |x|}{n} \qquad MD =$$

27 For the data of Frame 24 which are repeated below, complete the last column of the table and compute the value of MD, carrying your answer to the first decimal place.

X	x	$|x|$
4	-2	_____
4	-2	_____
6	0	_____
7	$+1$	_____
9	$+3$	_____
	$\Sigma|x| =$	_____

MD =

Left margin answer:

2
2
0
1
3
—
8

$\dfrac{\Sigma|x|}{n} = \dfrac{8}{5} = 1.6$

28 With grouped data the value of each class midpoint, or class mark, is taken to represent all of the measurements in the class, exactly as for the computation of the arithmetic mean for grouped measurements. Remembering that the formula for computing the arithmetic mean for grouped measurements is $\bar{X} = \Sigma fX/\Sigma f$, complete the corresponding formula for computing the mean deviation for grouped data.

MD =

Left margin answer:

$\dfrac{\Sigma f|x|}{\Sigma f}$

29 Using the formula $\bar{X} = \Sigma fX/\Sigma f$, determine the value of the mean for the grouped data below.

Class	f	X_c	fX
1–5	2	3	_____
6–10	5	8	_____
11–15	2	13	_____
16–20	1	18	_____
	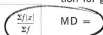 10		$\Sigma fX =$ _____

$\bar{X} =$

Left margin answer:

6
40
26
18
—
90

$90/10 = 9.0$

30 Now, using the value of 9.0 that was computed as the mean of the distribution, enter the values for $|x|$ and $f|x|$ in the table below.

Class	f	X_c	$|x|$	$f|x|$
1–5	2	3	_____	_____
6–10	5	8	_____	_____
11–15	2	13	_____	_____
16–20	1	18	_____	_____
	$\Sigma f = 10$			$\Sigma f|x| =$ _____

Left margin answer:

6 12
1   5
4   8
9   9
   34

31 Finally, compute the value of the mean deviation for the grouped data in Frame 30

$$\frac{\Sigma f|x|}{\Sigma f} = \frac{34}{10} = 3.4$$

MD =

32 Like the quartile deviation, the mean deviation as such is seldom used for comparing the extent of dispersion of sets of data in business and economics. We have taken the time to discuss this measure of dispersion for two reasons: first, because it is of historical importance and is found in early applications of statistical techniques to business data and, second, because it provides a good way of introducing and working with the concept of deviations from the mean. The understanding of deviations, in turn, is important in understanding the standard deviation, to be discussed next. In this context, a deviation value is represented by the symbol _____, and for sample data it can be determined by using the formula _____ — _____.

$$x$$
$$X - \bar{X}$$

4.d ▪ the standard deviation

As we indicated in the introduction to this unit, the standard deviation is the most important of the measures of dispersion because of its use in statistical inference. It is similar to the quartile deviation in that its use is typically directed at specifying the proportion of measurements that are located within a certain distance from a central point, and it is similar to the mean deviation in that its computation is based upon the deviations of individual measurements from a group mean. The standard deviation of a sample is represented by the lowercase letter s; the standard deviation of a population of measurements is represented by the lowercase Greek letter σ (sigma). Of course, the uppercase Greek letter Σ (sigma) is used to represent the process of summation.

33 Whereas the computation of the mean deviation requires the summation of the *absolute values* of the deviations, the computation of the standard deviation requires summation of the *squares* of the deviations. Therefore the fact that deviations can be positive or negative (does / does not) present a problem in the computation of the standard deviation.

does not (since the square of either a positive or a negative value is itself aways positive)

34 For an ungrouped sample of measurements the formula for the standard deviation is

$$s = \sqrt{\frac{\Sigma x^2}{n}}$$

Thus the standard deviation can be described as being the square root of the mean of the squared deviations. In Sec. 4.c the mean deviation for the following ungrouped measurements was found to be 1.6. Compute the value of the standard deviation, carrying your answer to the first place beyond the decimal. A table of squares and square roots is included in Table A.6.

X	x	x^2
4	-2	_____
4	-2	_____
6	0	_____
7	1	_____
9	3	_____
		$\Sigma x^2 =$ _____

$$s = \sqrt{\frac{\Sigma x^2}{n}} =$$

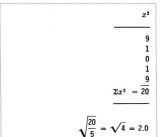

4
4
0
1
9
18

$\sqrt{\frac{18}{5}} = \sqrt{3.6} = 1.9$

35 Similarly, compute the standard deviation for the following sample of measurements, given that $\bar{X} = 8.0$ and $s = \sqrt{\Sigma x^2/n}$.

x^2	X
9	5
1	7
0	8
1	9
9	11
$\Sigma x^2 = 20$	

$\sqrt{\frac{20}{5}} = \sqrt{4} = 2.0$

$s =$

36 For grouped data the formula is modified just as the formulas for the arithmetic mean and mean deviation were modified for use with grouped data. Thus, instead of the formula $s = \sqrt{\Sigma x^2/n}$, we use the formula

$$s = \sqrt{\phantom{\frac{\Sigma fx^2}{\Sigma f}}}$$

$\sqrt{\frac{\Sigma fx^2}{\Sigma f}}$

with grouped data.

37 For the simplified grouped data previously used for illustrating the computation of the mean deviation, complete the column of information needed for computing the standard deviation.

Class	f	X_c	x	x^2	fx^2
1–5	2	3	-6	36	_____
6–10	5	8	-1	1	_____
11–15	2	13	4	16	_____
16–20	1	18	9	81	_____
	$\Sigma f = 10$				$\Sigma fx^2 =$ _____

72
5
32
81
190

38 Complete the computation of the value of the standard deviation for the grouped data in Frame 37.

$$\sqrt{\frac{190}{10}} = \sqrt{19} = 4.4$$

$$s = \sqrt{\frac{\Sigma f x^2}{\Sigma f}} =$$

39 Similarly, illustrate the values that have to be determined and compute the standard deviation for the following sample of grouped data, given that the mean equals 5.0.

X_c	x	x^2	fx^2
2	-3	9	18
5	0	0	0
8	$+3$	9	18
			$\Sigma fx^2 = 36$

$$\sqrt{\frac{\Sigma f x^2}{\Sigma f}} = \sqrt{\frac{36}{8}} = \sqrt{4.5} = 2.1$$

Class	f
1–3	2
4–6	4
7–9	2

$$s =$$

40 Before we discuss the way in which the value of the standard deviation is interpreted, let us review the two formulas for grouped and ungrouped data which we have already used and introduce an important variation for each of them. Remember that the standard deviation is the square root of the arithmetic average of the squared deviations; then the formula for the standard deviation of ungrouped sample data is

$$\sqrt{\frac{\Sigma x^2}{n}}$$

$$s =$$

and for grouped sample data it is

$$\sqrt{\frac{\Sigma f x^2}{\Sigma f}}$$

$$s =$$

41 Whether the standard deviation is being computed for a sample or for a population, essentially the same formulas are used. The only differences are that for population data $x = X - \mu$, N replaces n in the formula for ungrouped data, and the symbol representing the standard deviation is the lowercase Greek letter

sigma σ (_____).

42 The formulas that we have used thus far to compute the value of the standard deviation are referred to as the *deviation formulas.* In using these formulas, the first step in the computational procedure is that every observed measurement (or every class mid-

mean   point, for grouped data) has the value of the group _____ subtracted from it.

43 The arithmetic means of both the ungrouped and grouped sets of measurements that we have worked with in this section have all been integers (whole numbers). Is the arithmetic required in the computation of the standard deviation more involved when the

yes; because the deviations would be fractional values and each of these has to be squared

mean has a fractional value? (yes / no) Why or why not? _____
_____.

44 Because of the arithmetic difficulty typically involved in using the deviation formulas for the standard deviation, *computational formulas* have been derived to simplify the necessary calculations. For ungrouped sample data the computational formula is

$$s = \sqrt{\frac{\Sigma X^2}{n} - \left(\frac{\Sigma X}{n}\right)^2}$$

At first introduction, this formula may appear to be more complex than the formula $s = \sqrt{\Sigma x^2/n}$. But it is computationally easier to use because it does not require prior computation of the mean or determination of _____ from the mean.

deviations

45 Other than the value of n, the sample size, the only values that we need to substitute in the formula $s = \sqrt{\Sigma X^2/n - (\Sigma X/n)^2}$ are the sum of the _____ and the sum of the _____.

squared measurements (X^2)

measurements (X)

46 Using the sample of ungrouped data from Frame 34, complete the following table to obtain the values needed to use the computational formula for the standard deviation.

X	X^2
4	____
4	____
6	____
7	____
9	____
$\Sigma X =$ ____	$\Sigma X^2 =$ ____

	16
	16
	36
	49
	81
30	198

47 Now determine the value of the standard deviation for the data in Frame 46, using the computational formula.

$$s = \sqrt{\frac{\Sigma X^2}{n} - \left(\frac{\Sigma X}{n}\right)^2} =$$

$$\sqrt{\frac{198}{5} - \left(\frac{30}{5}\right)^2} = \sqrt{39.6 - 36.0}$$
$$= \sqrt{3.6} = 1.9 \text{ (which is the same as}$$
the previous solution in Frame 34)

48 Similarly, compute the standard deviation for the following sample of measurements, using the formula given in Frame 47.

X	X^2
5	25
7	49
8	64
9	81
11	121
$\Sigma X = 40$	$\Sigma X^2 = 340$

$s =$

$$\sqrt{\frac{340}{5} - \left(\frac{40}{5}\right)^2} = \sqrt{68 - 64} = \sqrt{4}$$
$$= 2.0$$

49 The formula for computing the standard deviation for un-grouped *population* data is again virtually identical, except that the equivalent parameter symbols are exchanged for the sample symbols. Accordingly, given the formula for ungrouped sample data $s = \sqrt{\Sigma X^2/n - (\Sigma X/n)^2}$, the equivalent formula for population data is

$$\sigma = \implies \text{population}.$$

50 For *grouped data* an X (or X_c) in any computational formula represents not individual scores but the _____

class midpoints _____.

51 Therefore the frequency of each class has to be taken into consideration in the computational formula for the standard deviation for grouped data. Given that the formula for ungrouped data is $s = \sqrt{\Sigma X^2/n - (\Sigma X/n)^2}$, the formula for computing the standard deviation for grouped sample data is

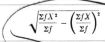

$$s = \quad \text{grouped data + mid-p.}$$

52 For the grouped data previously used, complete the following table in preparation for using the computational formula for the standard deviation.

Class	f	X_c	X^2	fX	fX^2
1–5	2	3	9	____	____
6–10	5	8	64	____	____
11–15	2	13	169	____	____
16–20	1	18	324	____	____
	$\Sigma f = 10$			$\Sigma fX =$ ____	$\Sigma fX^2 =$ ____

6	18
40	320
26	338
18	324
90	1,000

53 Now compute the standard deviation for the grouped data in Frame 52, using the computation formula

$$\sqrt{\frac{1,000}{10} - \left(\frac{90}{10}\right)^2} = \sqrt{100 - 81}$$
$$= \sqrt{19} = 4.4 \text{ (which is the same as the solution using the deviation formula in Frame 38)}$$

$$s = \sqrt{\frac{\Sigma fX^2}{\Sigma f} - \left(\frac{\Sigma fX}{\Sigma f}\right)^2} =$$

54 Similarly, construct the necessary table and compute the standard deviation for the following sample of grouped data.

Class	f	X_c
1–3	2	2
4–6	4	5
7–9	2	8
	$\Sigma f = 8$	

X^2	fX	fX^2
4	4	8
25	20	100
64	16	128
	$\Sigma fX = 40$	$\Sigma fX^2 = 236$

$$s = \sqrt{\frac{\Sigma f X^2}{\Sigma f} - \left(\frac{\Sigma f X}{\Sigma f}\right)^2} =$$

55 Thus we have discussed four basic varieties of the formula for the standard deviation. In the listing below, identify the appropriate formula by letter for each of the four types of situations involving sample data.

Deviation formula for ungrouped data: _____ *d*

Deviation formula for grouped data: _____ *b*

Computational formula for ungrouped data: _____ *a*

Computational formula for grouped data: _____ *c*

(a) $s = \sqrt{\dfrac{\Sigma X^2}{n} - \left(\dfrac{\Sigma X}{n}\right)^2}$

(b) $s = \sqrt{\dfrac{\Sigma f x^2}{\Sigma f}}$

(c) $s = \sqrt{\dfrac{\Sigma f X^2}{\Sigma f} - \left(\dfrac{\Sigma f X}{\Sigma f}\right)^2}$

(d) $s = \sqrt{\dfrac{\Sigma x^2}{n}}$

(margin: d, b, a, c)

56 With reference to the list in Frame 55, the formula that is generally the easiest to use in computing the standard deviation for grouped sample data is _____ (identifying letter).

(margin: c)

57 We shall have to wait until Unit 6 before we can fully illustrate the use of the standard deviation. By knowing the values of the mean and standard deviation for a set of measurements, we can often specify the percentage, or proportion, of measurements that are included within a specified distance from the mean. If we know the percentage of measurements included within a specified distance from the mean, we can also determine the percentage of measurements located outside of these limits by subtracting the known percentage from _____ (number).

(margin: 100 (since the total of the percentages equals 100))

58 For example, it is known that for a distribution of measurements whose frequency curve is both symmetrical and mesokurtic, 68 percent of the measurements are located within one standard deviation of the mean. Or, putting it another way, the limits that are defined by subtracting the value of the standard deviation from the mean and adding the value of the standard deviation to the mean include 68 percent of the measurements for such a distribution. Thus, if the mean of a set of measurements is 100 and the standard deviation is 15, 68 percent of the measurements would be included between the values of _____ (number) and _____ (number).

(margin: 85; 115 (Incidentally, these are the values of the population mean and standard deviation for many adult IQ tests.))

59 For a symmetrical and mesokurtic distribution, if 68 percent of the measurements are located between the limits of 100 ± 15, what percentage would be located outside of these limits? _____ percent What percentage would be located above 115? _____ percent

(margin: 32 (= 100% − 68%)
16 (The other 16 percent is below 85.))

60 The diagram below graphically illustrates the example that we have been discussing. On this frequency curve enter the percentages of measurements that would be located within the four intervals that are separated by the vertical lines on the curve, remembering that the interval $\mu \pm \sigma$ includes 68 percent of the measurements.

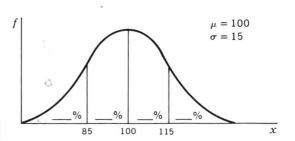

$\mu = 100$
$\sigma = 15$

____% ____% ____% ____%

85 100 115

x

16; 34; 34; 16

61 A frequency curve that is both symmetrical and mesokurtic is called a normal curve. It is the most important type of frequency curve from the standpoint of its use in statistical inference, and one which we shall discuss much more fully in Unit 6. As we have illustrated in the preceding frames, when we know that a distribution of measurements follows a normal curve, then we can designate the _____ of measurements included within a specified range of values.

percentage (or proportion or number)

62 In discussing the nature of the standard deviation, we can also take note of a mathematical similarity to the mean. As you may recall from Unit 3, the three principal measures of central tendency satisfy different mathematical criteria. The mathematical criterion satisfied by the mean can be symbolically represented by $(N_e = \min / \Sigma e = \min / \Sigma e^2 = \min)$.

$\Sigma e^2 = \min$

63 The mathematical criterion which results in a minimum sum of the errors squared is called the _____ criterion.

least-squares

64 Now, if we substitute the term "errors" for "deviations," the measure of dispersion which uses the sum of the errors squared in its computation is the _____.

standard deviation

65 For many advanced applications of statistics, the value $\Sigma x^2/n$ as a measure of dispersion is more useful than its square root, which we have defined as the _____.

standard deviation

66 The value $\Sigma x^2/n$, which is the arithmetic average of the squared deviations, is called the *variance* of the distribution. If we already know the value of the standard deviation, the value of the variance

squaring the value of the standard deviation	can be determined by _____ _____ .

67 Because of this computational fact, the variance for a sample of measurements is represented by the symbol s^2 and the variance for a population of values is represented by _____ .

σ^2 *variance*

68 Though it is mathematically correct to define it as "the standard deviation squared," the definition "the average of the squared deviations" is a more direct definition of the _____ .

variance

4.e ▪ the coefficient of variation

The range, quartile deviation, mean deviation, and standard deviation are all *absolute* measures of dispersion in that they are expressed in terms of the particular measuring units used in collecting a set of data. On the other hand, the *coefficient of variation*, represented by the symbol V, is a *relative* measure of dispersion. Its value is not expressed in terms of any particular unit of measurement, but as a ratio between two values. As such, it is very useful in comparing the dispersion of groups of measurements that are otherwise noncomparable.

69 For sample data the coefficient of variation is defined by $V = s/\bar{X}$. Thus, when we say that the coefficient of variation is a relative measure of dispersion, we mean that the value of the standard deviation is considered relative to the size (value) of the _____ of the distribution.

mean

70 Thus, if the arithmetic mean of a distribution is 100 and the standard deviation is 15, the value of the coefficient of variation is

$\dfrac{15}{100} = 0.15$ $V = \dfrac{s}{\bar{X}} =$

71 Being rather simple, the formula for the coefficient of variation is one that is rather easily memorized, particularly if we keep in mind the basis used for making it a relative measure. Thus

$\dfrac{s}{\bar{X}}$ $V =$

72 Using the coefficient of variation, we can compare the dispersion of two distributions that would otherwise be noncomparable. For example, suppose that during a particular month stock issue A had a mean price of $150 with a standard deviation of $12 and stock issue B had a mean daily market price of $5 with a standard deviation of $1. In dollar terms, which stock experienced more variability in its daily market price? (A/B)

A

73 Stock A certainly fluctuated more in terms of actual dollar changes, but your immediate reaction is probably that this is not the proper basis for comparison and that the dollar fluctuations relative to the average price are more relevant. Of course, this is the basis for the coefficient of variation. Accordingly, compute the following values, using the data from Frame 72:

$$\frac{s}{\bar{X}} = \frac{12}{150} = 0.08$$

$$\frac{s}{\bar{X}} = \frac{1}{5} = 0.20$$

V (stock A) =

V(stock B) = *answer*

$$\frac{0.20}{0.08} = 2.5$$

74   In regard to the respective average prices of stocks A and B, therefore, more variability in market price has been experienced by stock B. This stock was _____ (number) times more variable than stock A.

75   Whereas the range, quartile deviation, mean deviation, and standard deviation are all absolute measures of dispersion, the

relative

coefficient of variation is a(n) _____ measure of dispersion.

4.f ▪ measuring skewness and kurtosis

When we introduced the concepts of skewness and kurtosis in Unit 2, it was on the basis of the visual appearance of the frequency curve that we described a distribution of measurements as being negatively skewed, symmetrical, or positively skewed on the one hand, or platykurtic, mesokurtic, or leptokurtic on the other hand. See Frames 59 to 69 in Unit 2 to review these concepts. In this section we shall first define the moments about the arithmetic mean and then illustrate their use in measuring the skewness and kurtosis of a distribution of measurements.

76   As used in a statistical context, the word ‘moment’ refers to the sum of the deviations from the mean in respect to sample size. Thus the *first moment* is defined as $m_1 = \Sigma x/n \, (= \Sigma fx/\Sigma f$ for grouped data). According to our discussion in Sec. 4.c, what numerical value does the first moment *always* have?

0 (because Σx always equals zero; see Frames 25 and 26)

$$m_1 = \frac{\Sigma x}{n} = \underline{\hspace{1cm}} \text{ (number)}$$

77   As we observed before, the sum of the deviations about the mean always equals zero, and thus the value of the first moment about the mean m_1 is also always equal to zero. The second moment about the mean is defined as $m_2 = \Sigma x^2/n$. We have previously referred to this formula in this unit. By what other symbol can it be represented, for sample data? _____

s^2 (*not* s, which would be the square root of this value)

78   Following sequentially from the formulas for the first and second moments about the mean presented in Frames 76 and 77, what must be the formula for the third moment?

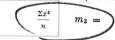

$$m_3 = \frac{\Sigma x^3}{n}$$

a₃ = skewness (handwritten annotation)

79 The third moment is used as the measure of skewness for a distribution of measurements. In order to make this measure relative rather than absolute, it is necessary to divide the third moment by s^3 for sample data, and the result is represented by the symbol a_3 (read: "a-three"). Thus the formula

$$a_3 = \frac{m_3}{s^3}$$

is used for the purpose of measuring the _____ of a distribution of measurements.

(answer box: skewness)

80 When $a_3 = 0$, the distribution is *symmetrical*; when $a_3 > 0$ (read: "is greater than zero"), the distribution is *positively skewed*; and when $a_3 < 0$ ("is less than zero"), the distribution is *negatively skewed*. Thus, as we have used the terms "positively" and "negatively" skewed, we have been in effect referring to the arithmetic sign of _____.

(answer box: a_3)

81 In interpreting the value of a_3, exact symmetry of the distribution of measurements is indicated by a value of _____ (number).

(answer box: 0)

82 Similarly, the fourth moment about the mean and the related value of a_4 (read: "a-four") provide the basis for evaluating the kurtosis of a distribution of measurements. Given that

$$a_3 = \frac{m_3}{s^3} \quad \text{with } m_3 = \frac{\Sigma x^3}{n}$$

$a_4 = $ KURTOSIS. (handwritten annotation)

then

$$a_4 = \underline{\quad} \quad \text{with } m_4 = \underline{\quad}$$

(answer box: $\frac{m_4}{s^4}, \frac{\Sigma x^4}{n}$)

83 The numerical basis for interpreting a_4 is different from a_3. When $a_4 = 3$, the distribution is *mesokurtic*; when $a_4 > 3$, it is *leptokurtic*; and when $a_4 < 3$, the distribution is *platykurtic*. Thus, instead of the balancing point being zero, as for a_3, the balancing point in interpreting a_4 has a value of _____ (number).

(answer box: 3)

84 The computation of the third and fourth moments and the associated divisions by s^3 and s^4 to determine the values of a_3 and a_4 are quite laborious, and we shall not carry out the actual calculations at this point. However, you should be able to interpret the various possible values of a_3 and a_4, which are indicative of the extent of _____ and _____ of a distribution of measurements, respectively.

(answer box: skewness and kurtosis)

85 A distribution of measurements for which $a_3 < 0$ and $a_4 < 3$ would be described as being _____ and _____.

(answer box: negatively skewed / platykurtic)

negatively skewed	**86** A distribution of measurements for which $a_3 < 0$ and $a_4 > 3$ would be described as being _____ and
leptokurtic	_____.

0; < 3	**87** For a distribution that is symmetrical and platykurtic, the value of a_3 is _____ and the value of a_4 is _____.

88 During our discussion of the standard deviation, we singled out the *normal distribution* as being particularly useful in statistical analysis and described its characteristics. For a collection of measurements whose distribution approximates the normal curve, the

0 3	value of a_3 is _____ and the value of a_4 is _____.

review

highest observed value minus lowest observed value	**89** (Sec. 4.a, Introduction; Frames 1-8) For ungrouped data the range is equal to _____
boundary	_____. For grouped data the range is equal to the upper _____ of the highest class with tabulated frequencies
boundary	minus the lower _____ of the lowest class with tabulated frequencies.

50	**90** (Frames 9-10, 15-17) The value of the quartile deviation represents half of the interval containing the middle _____ percent of the measurements, arranged in an array.

range	**91** (Frames 3-5, 7, 20) Of the measures of dispersion, which one is most unstable in terms of its value? _____ Which one
quartile deviation	can be used even with open-end distributions? _____ _____.

QD	**92** (Frames 11-14, 18-19) For a symmetrical distribution of measurements, med $\pm$ _____ contains 50 percent of the measurements.

93 (Frames 21-25) The symbol x represents the amount of devia-

mean	tion from the _____. For sample data the value of x is
$X - \bar{X}$ (*not vice versa*)	obtained by solving the formula $x =$ _____.

absolute values (of the deviations)	**94** (Frames 26-32) In the formula for MD, whether for ungrouped or grouped data, it is not the values of the deviations that are averaged but the _____ that are averaged.

95 (Sec. 4.d, Introduction; Frame 41) The standard deviation of

s	a sample is represented by the symbol _____, and the standard
σ	deviation of a population is represented by the symbol _____.

96 (Frames 33-40) The basic formula for the standard deviation involves taking the square root of the mean of the _____

squared deviations	_____.

97 (Frames 42–56) Other than the value of n (or Σf), the *computational formulas* for the standard deviation require determination of the sum of the measurements and the sum of the squared measurements, whereas the *deviation formulas* require just the sum of the squared deviations. Why, then, does the deviation formula usually involve greater arithmetic difficulty?_____

> The deviations, which have to be squared, are usually fractional values.

98 (Frames 57–61) For a set of measurements that is normally distributed, the interval defined by $\mu \pm$ _____ includes 68 percent of the measurements.

> σ (or $\bar{X} \pm s$)

99 (Frames 62–68) The *variance* of a sample of measurements, used in advanced methods of statistical inference, is equal to _____.

> s^2 (or $\dfrac{\Sigma x^2}{n}$)

100 (Sec. 4.e, Introduction; Frames 69–75) The measure of variation that is relative rather than absolute is V, the coefficient of _____. Its computation involves determining the ratio of the standard deviation to the _____ of the distribution of measurements.

> variation
>
> mean

101 (Frames 76–88) For a distribution of measurements that is positively skewed and leptokurtic, the value of a_3 is _____ and the value of a_4 is _____.

> >0
>
> >3

employee absence during a three-month period

Employee identification number	*Number of days absent*
001	5
002	0
003	1
004	7
005	1
006	2
007	9
008	5
009	1
010	3

problems (solutions given on page 350)

1 For the data above, for which you computed the values of the three principal averages and the quartiles at the end of Unit 3, compute the following measures of dispersion:

(a) the range
(b) the quartile deviation
(c) the mean deviation

(d) the standard deviation, using the formula that requires the least computational effort

(e) the coefficient of variation

Grade-point average	Number of students
1.0–1.4	0
1.5–1.9	2
2.0–2.4	10
2.5–2.9	9
3.0–3.4	6
3.5–3.9	3

2 For the academic grade averages above, again repeated from Unit 3, compute the values of:

(a) the range

(b) the quartile deviation

(c) the mean deviation

(d) the standard deviation, using the formula that requires the least computational effort

(e) the coefficient of variation

3 For the following very simple array of measurements, for which both the mean and the standard deviation are integers, determine the values of a_3 and a_4 and interpret your results.

X
___

2
2
4
6
6
8
10
10
___

additional problems   **4** Given the sample of test scores following, compute:

(a) the range

(b) the quartile deviation

(c) the mean deviation

(d) the standard deviation, using the deviation-score formula

(e) the variance

(f) the coefficient of variation

ten randomly selected scores on a short examination

8	5	10	10	10
8	7	10	8	12

5 The following frequency distribution is a partial report of the number of student errors in the responses written in a self-instructional unit:

Errors	f
15–19	6
20–24	3
25–29	2

(a) Determine the value of the range for these grouped data.

(b) Compute the quartile deviation.

(c) Compute the value of the standard deviation, using the computational formula.

6 Can the value of the standard deviation computed in Prob. 5c be used to define the boundaries within which the middle 68 percent of the measurements is located? Why or why not?

unit 5 • probability

The theory of probability owes its early development to the interest of European mathematicians in games of chance during the latter part of the seventeenth century. Since then probability theory has become the basis for the development of the techniques of statistical inference that are used in all fields of basic and applied research, including economic analysis and managerial decision making. Many of the examples in this unit refer to games of chance simply because such examples are less complex and hence serve to illustrate basic principles more clearly. In later units we shall cover specific techniques of inference and decision making as they apply to business and economic data. In this unit we shall consider two approaches to the computation of probabilities, the range of values that a probability figure can have and some of its characteristics, rules of combining probabilities, and alternative interpretations of probability values.

5.a • the meaning of probability

In terms of the method by which probability values are calculated, the *classical* and *relative-frequency* definitions represent two distinctly different approaches to the field of probability. The two methods do not necessarily lead to the calculation of substantially different probability values for a given situation, but they differ in *when* the probability figure is calculated. The *classical approach* to probability involves an a priori determination of probability values; that is, the values are calculated before any events are observed. In the *relative-frequency approach*, on the other hand, probabilities are calculated after the outcomes of a number of events have been observed.

⅕

1 If we place five tokens, numbered 1 through 5, in a box and then plan to withdraw one token at random from the box, the probability of the token numbered 3 being drawn is ($\frac{1}{2}$ / $\frac{1}{3}$ / $\frac{1}{5}$ / $\frac{3}{5}$).

only one

2 In concluding that the probability of drawing token 3 is $\frac{1}{5}$, you made the assumptions and did the calculations that conform to the classical approach to probability. One assumption that you made, which we shall discuss in greater detail in a later section of this unit, is that the five possible outcomes are *mutually exclusive,* that is, that on any one drawing of a token, (only one / several) outcome(s) can occur.

impossible

3 Thus, by the assumption that the possible outcomes are *mutually exclusive,* we expect that getting both tokens 3 and 4 on one selection of tokens is (possible / impossible).

exclusive

no

4 In addition to assuming that the possible outcomes are mutually _____, you assumed also that the alternatives are *equally likely* to occur. For example, would you still believe that the probability of selecting token 3 is $\frac{1}{5}$ if you learned that it is half the size of the other tokens? (yes / no)

denominator numerator	**5** Finally, you computed a fraction to represent the probability value in which the total number of possible outcomes became the value of the (numerator / denominator) and the number of desired outcomes became the value of the (numerator / denominator).
$\frac{2}{5}$	**6** For example, suppose that the five tokens were numbered 1, 1, 1, 3, and 3. In this case, the probability of a 3 being selected is ($\frac{1}{2}$ / $\frac{1}{5}$ / $\frac{2}{5}$).
exclusive likely	**7** The two assumptions that we made in arriving at the probability value of $\frac{2}{5}$ are that the choice of any one of the five tokens is mutually _____ and equally _____.
classical	**8** Thus one approach to the computation of a probability value states: "If an event can occur in n mutually exclusive and equally likely ways, then the probability of an outcome involving x is the value of the fraction fx/n, where fx is the frequency with which x is contained in ." This is a statement of the _____ approach to probability.
$\frac{1}{2}$	**9** When a "fair" coin is tossed, there are two mutually exclusive and equally likely outcomes: that the face of the coin will show a head or a tail. The probability of a head is represented by the fraction $fx/n = $ _____.
$\frac{1}{52}$	**10** In a deck of 52 cards, the probability of obtaining an ace of spades on a particular drawing of one card is $fx/n = $ _____.
$\frac{13}{52} = \frac{1}{4}$	**11** The probability of drawing any spade on a particular draw of the cards is _____.
a priori	**12** The classical approach to probability assumes a basic symmetry in the possible outcomes of an event. Thus a coin must be fair, or counterbalanced. It is only on the basis of this assumption that an (a priori / a posteriori) calculation of probabilities is possible.
classical	**13** In many decision-making situations involving business and economic data, however, the alternative outcomes are not equally likely, nor are their respective probabilities known beforehand. This fact limits the usefulness of the _____ approach to probability in such circumstances.
circular	**14** In addition, there is a related and more basic criticism of the classical approach to calculating probability. In the formula fx/n, n is defined as "the total number of mutually exclusive and *equally likely* outcomes." Since the term "equally likely" itself presumes a prior understanding of probability, this definition is essentially (circular / operational) in nature.

15 Thus the classical approach to probability has been criticized because (**a** / **b** / both **a** and **b**):

(a) It involves a circular definition.

(b) It is not useful when the "equally likely" assumption cannot be made.

both **a** and **b**

16 In the classical approach to probability, the assumptions are made that the alternative outcomes are _____ _____ and _____, and the calculation of probability values is typically done (before / after) any events and their outcomes are actually observed.

mutually exclusive
equally likely
before

17 An alternative approach to probability relies on the *relative frequency* of an observed outcome. This definition states that the probability of an outcome is the observed relative _____ of that outcome in a very large number of events.

frequency

18 As contrasted to the classical approach to probability, the actual observation of a repeated event and its associated outcomes is necessary in the _____ approach to probability.

relative-frequency

19 In using the relative-frequency approach to probability, as the number of observations of events and their outcomes is increased, the accuracy of the probability figure based on these observations is (increased / decreased).

increased

20 As the number of observations increases, the observed relative frequency of an outcome tends to become stable. In Fig. 5.1, for example, we have a graphic portrayal of the observed relative frequency of heads in 300 tosses of a coin. As the number of tosses of the coin increases, the relative frequency of heads appears to stabilize at about a value of _____.

0.5

figure 5.1 ▪ relative frequency of heads in 300 tosses of a coin.

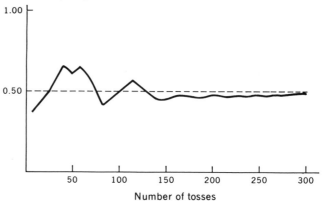

Relative frequency

1.00

0.50

50   100   150   200   250   300

Number of tosses

21 Notice that we stated that the relative frequency stabilized "at about" 0.5. One difficulty with the relative-frequency definition of probability is that a probability value calculated on the basis of any finite number of observations can always be improved by making more observations. Thus probability figures based on observed relative frequency are invariably (exact / estimated).

22 On the other hand, unless we are willing to assume that all possible outcomes are equally likely, the principal method available to compute the probability value is the _____ _____ approach.

5.b ▪ expressing probability

In this section we shall present the standard symbol system used in elementary consideration of the topic of probability and consider the range of values that a probability figure can have. In addition, we shall introduce the use of Venn diagrams for portraying the possible outcomes of a single event.

23 The symbol that we shall use to denote the probability of an outcome is P. Thus $P(A)$ denotes the probability that outcome _____ will occur.

24 Some authors prefer to use other symbols for probability instead. Thus $Pr(B)$, $p(B)$, and $pr(B)$ all refer to the probability of outcome B. In terms of the notation system being used in this unit, the probability of B is represented by _____.

25 Whether the classical or the relative-frequency definition of probability is followed, what is the smallest value that a probability figure can have? (Consider the lowest possible value of the expected or observed relative frequency.) _____

26 A probability of 0 signifies that there is (no / some / a high) chance that the outcome in question will occur.

Note: Since the value of the probability figure derived from the relative-frequency approach is an estimate rather than an exact figure, a probability of 0 might also indicate that the occurrence of the outcome is very rare, but not necessarily impossible.

27 Can the numeric value of a probability ever be negative? (yes / no)

28 On the other hand, what is the maximum possible value of P (or what is the maximum possible value of the fraction representing the expected or observed relative frequency)? _____

Note: Again, if the relative-frequency approach has been used in calculating the value of P, a probability of 1 might indicate that a rare exception is possible, so that the outcome in question is virtually, but not completely, certain.

29 Therefore the lowest possible value of P, indicating very little or no chance of the outcome in question occurring, is _____; certainty or virtual certainty of an outcome is indicated by a probability value of _____.

0
1

30 Particularly in games of chance, probabilities are often expressed as odds rather than in terms of the probability values we have been discussing in the last few frames. Thus 3:2 (read: "3 to 2") odds regarding the occurrence of an outcome suggests that for every three possible outcomes of an event that are favorable there are _____ that are unfavorable.

two

31 Therefore, when odds are used to designate probability, the number or proportion of possible outcomes are compared in the order of (favorable:unfavorable / unfavorable:favorable).

favorable: unfavorable

32 For example, the odds of obtaining a 6 on one throw of a six-sided die would be expressed as _____:_____.

1:5

33 Similarly, the odds of obtaining a head on one toss of a fair coin, ignoring the possible on-edge outcome, would be expressed as _____.

1:1

34 Since odds involve a comparison of favorable to unfavorable possible outcomes whereas the fraction representing probability compares the number of favorable outcomes to the total possible outcomes, given the odds, we can readily stipulate probability values and vice versa. If the odds are 1:5, for example, the probability of a favorable outcome is _____ (fraction), and the probability of an unfavorable outcome is _____.

$\frac{1}{6}$ (one favorable outcome of the total number of six)
$\frac{5}{6}$

35 Similarly, odds of 3:2 indicate that the probability of the favorable outcome is _____ and the probability of the unfavorable outcome is _____.

$\frac{3}{5}$
$\frac{2}{5}$

36 On the other hand, if the probability of a favorable outcome is $\frac{1}{3}$, the odds of its occurrence would be expressed as _____: _____.

1:2 (Of the total of three types of outcomes, one is favorable and two are unfavorable.)

37 Similarly, for a probability of $\frac{5}{6}$, the odds for the favorable outcome would be expressed as _____.

5:1

38 In addition to expressing the probability of favorable and unfavorable outcomes, odds are used to express payoff in betting

4

down (Thus there is less of a payoff for an outcome whose probability of occurrence is high.)

Venn

Venn

sample
outcomes

$P(A)$

situations. Thus 4:1 odds in this case means that for each $1 bet the payoff is $_____ in the event of a successful outcome.

39   It is not our intention to go into an analysis of what constitutes a fair bet in this unit. In general, of course, as the odds expressing the probability of a successful outcome go up, the related payoff odds go (up / down).

40   Probability situations can be visually portrayed by means of Venn diagrams. A diagram that is understood to enclose all of the possible outcomes of an event, with one or more outcomes specifically identified, is called a _____ diagram.

41   The set of all possible outcomes is termed a *sample space*, and any one outcome is identified as a *point* in that space. Thus an enclosed sample space, with one or more types of points identified, is called a _____ diagram.

42   Or, turning the description about, a Venn diagram involves an enclosed _____ space with one or more points, or types of _____, identified.

43   A Venn diagram is used to portray all of the possible outcomes of an event, and the relative area given to a possible outcome in the diagram need not be indicative of its probability. Figure 5.2, for example, is a Venn diagram which represents $P(\underline{\hspace{1cm}})$ in a sample space.

figure 5.2 ▪ Venn diagram illustrating $P(A)$.

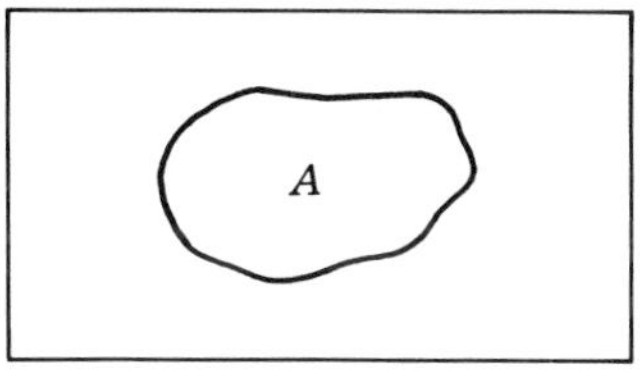

$P(\sim H)$

44   If $P(A)$ is the probability of outcome A occurring, then $P(\sim A)$ (read: "probability of not A") is the symbol which indicates the probability of outcome A not occurring. Similarly, if $P(H)$ indicates the probability of obtaining a head on a single toss of a coin, then the probability of *not* obtaining a head on a single toss of a coin is indicated by _____.

45   By the very nature of the two outcomes involved, the probability of a successful outcome plus the probability of a nonsuccessful outcome must be equal to 1. Or, symbolically,

$P(\sim H)$

$$P(H) + \underline{\hspace{2cm}} = 1$$

46 Figure 5.3 is a Venn diagram illustrating the principle we have just discussed. Note that $P(H) + P(\sim H)$ occupies (all / most / none) of the sample space within the diagram.

figure 5.3 ▪ **Venn diagram illustrating that** $P(H) + P(\sim H) = 1.$

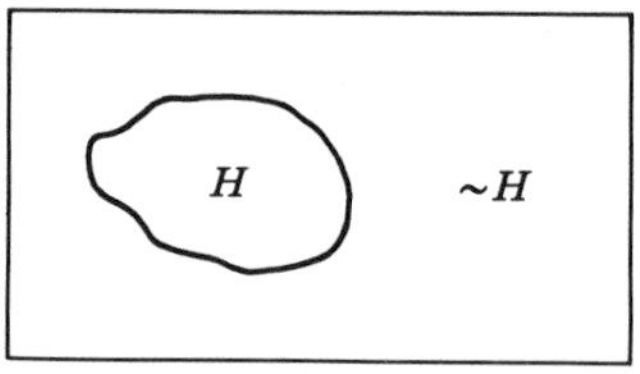

47 Another principle connected with the numeric value of probabilities is that the sum of the probabilities of all mutually exclusive outcomes must be equal to 1. This implies that one of the outcomes must occur. Symbolically, we can represent this by the equation

1

$\Sigma P_i = $ _____ (value).

48 Thus we can represent the total probability of outcome A either occurring or not occurring by the equation _____ _____, and we can represent the sum of the probabilities of all mutually exclusive outcomes by the equation _____.

$P(A) + P(\sim A) = 1$

$\Sigma P_i = 1$

49 Given a student's average grade "going into the final exam," suppose that the probability that he will earn an A in a particular course is 0.20, the probability of a B is 0.50, and the probability of a C is 0.30. Complete the Venn diagram below to represent this situation.

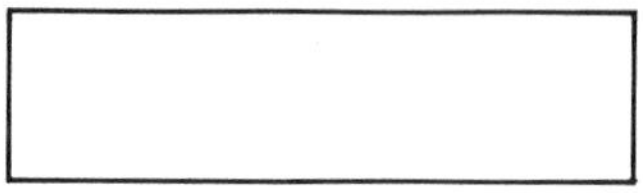

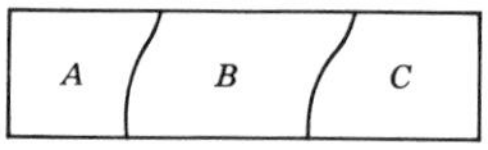

(any division of the space, as long as $A + B + C$ = entire sample space)

summary

50 The probability of an outcome called X is represented by _____. Its lowest possible numeric value is _____, and its highest possible numeric value is _____.

$P(X)$ 0
1

51 When odds are used to express the probability of a favorable outcome, odds of 4:5 indicate a probability value of _____ (fraction).

$\frac{4}{9}$

52 The sum of the probability of X, represented by $P(X)$, and the probability that X does not occur, represented by _____, is equal to _____; the sum of all mutually exclusive outcomes of an event, represented by _____, is also equal to 1.

$P(\sim X)$
1
ΣP_i

5.c ▪ mutually exclusive and nonexclusive outcomes of an event

In a single event, such as the drawing of a card from a deck of cards, various outcomes are possible, some being mutually exclusive and some not. Two or more outcomes are mutually exclusive if the occurrence of one automatically precludes the occurrence of the other. In this section we shall consider the rules of addition that apply in determining the probability that *either* of two or more outcomes will occur, both when these outcomes are mutually exclusive and when they are not.

---

exclusive

53 In a single toss of a coin, the occurrence of a head and the occurrence of a tail are mutually _____ outcomes.

---

mutually exclusive

54 Similarly, since a sales quota either will or will not be achieved, the two possible outcomes are _____.

---

no

mutually exclusive

55 In a single drawing of a card from a deck of cards, can both an ace and a king be drawn? (yes / no) Therefore these two possible outcomes are _____.

---

yes

are not

56 In a single drawing of a card from a deck of cards, can both an ace and a spade be drawn? (yes / no) Therefore these two possible outcomes (are / are not) mutually exclusive.

---

57 If A and B are mutually exclusive outcomes of a chance event, the probability that either A *or* B will occur is the sum of their respective probabilities. Symbolically,

$P(A)+P(B)$

$$P(A \text{ or } B) = P(A + B) = P(\underline{\quad}) + P(\underline{\quad})$$

---

58 According to this rule of addition, the probability of obtaining either a head or a tail on one toss of a coin (falling on edge being eliminated from consideration) is $P(H) + P(T) = \frac{1}{2} + \frac{1}{2} = 1$. The probability of drawing either an ace or a king on one draw of a card from a deck of 52 cards is _____.

$\frac{4}{52} + \frac{4}{52} = \frac{8}{52} = \frac{2}{13}$

---

59 Of course, the rule of addition can be extended to the situation in which there are more than two mutually exclusive outcomes. Refer to the proportions given in Table 5.1. To begin with, what is the probability that a family chosen at random from this group has five or more children? _____

0.15 (The proportion is directly indicative of the probability of occurrence.)

table 5.1 ▪ proportions of families with various numbers of children in a particular community

Number of children	0	1	2	3	4	5 or more
Proportion	0.10	0.10	0.20	0.25	0.20	0.15

60 Further, what is the probability that a family chosen at random from this group has three or more children (i.e., either "3" or "4" or "5 or more")? _____

$0.25 + 0.20 + 0.15 = 0.60$

61 If outcomes A and B are *not* mutually exclusive, then the probability of A *or* B occurring is the probability that A will occur plus the probability that B will occur minus the probability that both A and B will occur. Symbolically,

$P(A$ or $B) = $ _____ $+$ _____ $- P(A,B)$

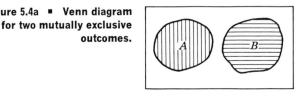

$P(A) + P(B) - P(A,B)$

62 The rationale of subtracting the probability of the joint occurrence of A and B is best illustrated by the use of a Venn diagram. In which figure, 5.4a or 5.4b, are the two outcomes represented as being mutually exclusive? (5.4a / 5.4b)

5.4a

figure 5.4a ▪ Venn diagram for two mutually exclusive outcomes.

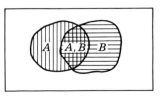

figure 5.4b ▪ Venn diagram for two nonexclusive outcomes.

63 Now consider Fig. 5.4b. If we were to add the probability of A to the probability of B in order to obtain the probability of either outcome A or outcome B occurring, what area in the Venn diagram would be added in twice, in effect? (A / B / A,B)

A,B (read: "A and B")

64 Therefore the effect of subtracting the probability of the joint occurrence is to correct for the overlap in A and B when the two outcomes are not mutually exclusive. For nonexclusive outcomes, then, $P(A$ or $B) = $ _____.

$P(A) + P(B) - P(A,B)$

65 The rule of addition for mutually exclusive outcomes can be considered a special case of the rule for nonexclusive outcomes. This is so since the value of $P(A,B)$ for mutually exclusive outcomes is always equal to _____.

0 (Note that there is no area A,B in Fig. 5.4a.)

66 According to the rule of addition for nonexclusive outcomes, what is the probability of drawing either an ace *or* a spade from a deck of 52 cards? _____

$\frac{4}{52} + \frac{13}{52} - \frac{1}{52} = \frac{16}{52} = \frac{4}{13}$

summary

67 The rule of addition applies when there are several possible outcomes of a *single* event. Thus we gave examples involving the

one   one

toss of _____ (number) coin(s) and the drawing of _____ (number) card(s) from a deck.

68 When two possible outcomes of an event are mutually exclusive, the formula used to calculate the probability that either outcome will occur is _____. When two possible outcomes are *not* mutually exclusive, the formula used to compute the probability that either outcome will occur is _____ _____.

$P(A) + P(B)$

$P(A) + P(B) - P(A,B)$

5.d ▪ independent events, dependent events, and conditional probability

When two or more events are separated in time or space, such as the tossing of two coins or the tossing of the same coin twice in succession, the outcomes of the events may be independent of one another or they may be dependent. If events are independent, then the probability of a particular outcome in a second event is unaffected by the outcome of the preceding event. If the events are dependent, then the probability is affected by the nature of previous outcomes. In this section we shall consider the rules of multiplication for computing the probability of joint occurrences of certain outcomes in two or more separate events.

69 Suppose that a coin is tossed twice in succession. Is the probability of obtaining a head on the second toss of the coin affected by whether or not a head was obtained on the first toss? (yes / no)

no

70 Therefore two tosses of a coin represent events whose outcomes are (dependent / independent).

independent

71 The rule of multiplication states that if A and B are independent outcomes of two events, the probability of their joint occurrence is the product of their probabilities. The algebraic equation representing this rule is $P(A,B) = P(\_\_\_\_\_)P(\_\_\_\_\_)$.

$P(A)P(B)$

72 Thus the probability of obtaining tails on two consecutive tosses of a coin is _____.

$(\tfrac{1}{2})(\tfrac{1}{2}) = \tfrac{1}{4}$

73 Just as Venn diagrams are useful for portraying the possible outcomes in a single occurrence of an event, *tree diagrams* are particularly useful for portraying the possible outcomes of successive, or multiple, events. Therefore a tree diagram is useful in applying the rule of (addition / multiplication) in computing probabilities.

multiplication

74 Figure 5.5 presents the tree diagram for two successive tosses of a coin. The probability of any particular joint outcome is determined by multiplying the probability of the first outcome by the probability of the second outcome, which is to follow it. With reference to Fig. 5.5, what is the probability of obtaining a tail and then a head, in this order? _____

$(\frac{1}{2})(\frac{1}{2}) = \frac{1}{4}$

**figure 5.5 ■ tree diagram
for two consecutive tosses
of a coin.**

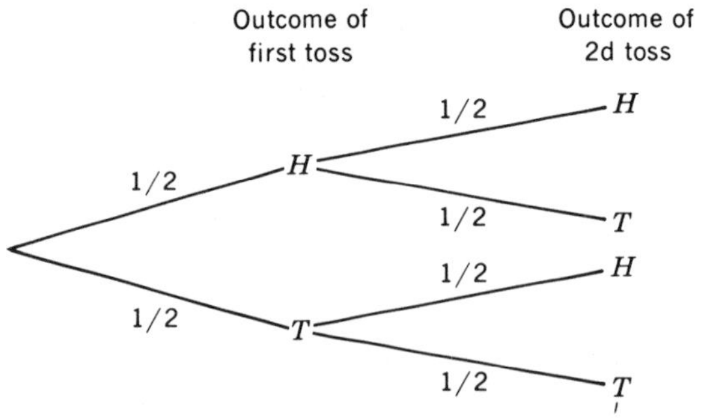

Outcome of first toss	Outcome of 2d toss

75 With reference to Fig. 5.5, what is the probability of obtaining a head and then a tail, in this order? _____

$(\frac{1}{2})(\frac{1}{2}) = \frac{1}{4}$

76 With reference to Frames 74 and 75, therefore what is the probability of obtaining a head and a tail in *any* order on two tosses of a coin (i.e., tail and head *or* head and tail)?

$\frac{1}{2}$ (Both the HT and TH pairs of outcomes qualify, and so their probabilities are summed.)

77 Unlike the outcomes in games of chance, events and their related outcomes in the field of business and economics are seldom independent. Suppose that the probability of a corporate-tax cut within a year has been assessed as 0.50 and that the probability of our major competitor's making no major product changes is 0.30, with these two events considered to be independent of one another. In this case the probability of *both* outcomes occurring is

_____ .

$(0.50)(0.30) = 0.15$

78 If two events are not independent, then the concept of *conditional probability* has to be used to determine the probability of a particular sequence of outcomes. The symbol $P(B|A)$ means the probability of B occurring, given that outcome _____ has occurred in a previous event.

A ($B|A$ is read as "B given A." It is *not* the fraction B/A.)

79 Whenever two (or more) events are dependent, the probability value which takes into account the previous occurrence of a particular outcome is called _____ probability.

conditional

80 If A and B are the outcomes of two dependent events, the probability of their joint occurrence is the probability of A multiplied by the conditional probability of B, given that A has occurred. Symbolically, $P(A,B) = P(A)P(\underline{\quad})$.

$P(A)P(B|A)$

81 For example, suppose that we have an urn with three red balls and two black balls. Using R to represent the drawing of a red

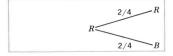

ball and B the drawing of a black ball, $P(R) = \underline{\quad}$ and $P(B) = \underline{\quad}$

82 Now, if we draw one ball from the urn and do *not* replace it, the probabilities associated with a second drawing of a ball from the urn are dependent on the outcome of the first drawing, thus exemplifying a conditional-probability situation. In the tree diagram below enter the missing probability values for the second drawing when the first ball drawn and not replaced is red (R).

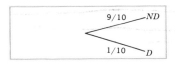

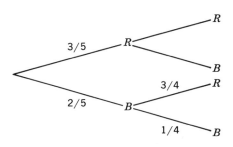

83 In the diagram of Frame 82, the conditional probability of choosing a black ball at random, given that a red ball has been withdrawn, would be represented by the symbol $P(\underline{\quad}|\underline{\quad})$ and has a probability value in this case of $\underline{\quad}$.

84 Assume that a shipment of ten motors includes one motor that is defective. Enter the probabilities associated with obtaining a nondefective (ND) and a defective (D) motor in the inspection of the first motor in this shipment on the tree diagram below.

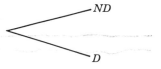

85 If we plan to inspect two motors out of the shipment, we would of course sample without replacement, since we would not want to check the same motor twice. Accordingly, enter below all the probability values for the second motor inspected, under the conditions both that the first motor inspected is nondefective and that it is defective.

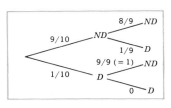

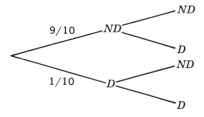

86 With reference to the tree diagram of Frame 85, what is the probability that neither of the two motors chosen at random, and without replacement, will be defective? _____

$(\%_0)(\%) = {}^7\!\%_0 = \%$

summary

$P(A,B) = P(A)P(B)$
$P(A,B) = P(A)P(B|A)$

87 Algebraically, the rule of multiplication for joint outcomes in two events that are independent is $P(A,B) = $ _____ _____ ; for dependent events it is stated as $P(A,B) = $ _____ _____.

88 The rule of multiplication for independent events can be considered as a special case of the rule for dependent events, because when the two events and their respective outcomes are independent, then the value of $P(B|A)$ is equal to the value of $P($_____$)$.

$P(B)$

89 A probability statement of the form $P(B|A)$ is called a _____ probability.

conditional

90 The diagram which is particularly useful for illustrating the possible outcomes of two or more sequential events, whether independent or dependent, is called a _____.

tree diagram

5.e ▪ subjective probability

There are two points of view regarding the interpretation of numerical probabilities. The first, called the *objective* approach, interprets a probability value as being indicative of the expected frequency of a particular outcome in a set of events. In this unit we have implicitly used the objective approach for interpreting the probabilities determined by both the classical and relative-frequency methods of computing these values. The second approach to interpreting a probability value is based on the strength of the belief that a reasonable person holds concerning the occurrence of an outcome and is thus called the *subjective* approach. In this section we shall merely introduce and illustrate the concept of subjective probability, which has recently grown in importance in advanced applications of statistical methods.

91 When we interpret the probability value of $\frac{1}{2}$ as indicating that a particular outcome will occur about half the time in a series of repetitions of an event, such as tossing a coin, we are implicitly following the _____ approach to interpreting probability.

objective

92 Suppose it is reported that the probability is 0.70 that a labor-contract settlement will be made in the auto industry. Can this particular event be repeated a number of times, so that a series of outcomes can be tallied? (yes / no)

no

93 Thus, when there is a single or unique event and the opportunity for only a single outcome, the interpretation of probability in

inappropriate	terms of the expected frequency of that outcome, as is done in the objective approach, seems (appropriate / inappropriate).
subjective	**94** On the other hand, the approach to interpreting probability which considers this value to be indicative of the strength of a belief, and which is particularly suited to considering the outcome of a unique event, is the _____ approach.
belief	**95** Even when an event is not unique by its nature, if we are concerned about the outcome of only a particular occurrence of the event, the probability figure may be more indicative of a strength of _____ than it is of expected frequency.
objective	**96** For example, if we have information which indicates that the probability of business failure in the auto-wash industry is 0.20, this could be interpreted in terms of an expected frequency of business failure, thus utilizing the _____ approach to interpreting probability.
subjective	**97** However, if we apply the probability value of 0.20 to a single firm in the industry, a strength-of-belief interpretation may be more meaningful, thus illustrating the _____ approach to interpreting the same probability figure.
subjective	**98** Since managerial decisions are often directed toward specific situations, rather than a series of identical events, economic-decision theory makes important use of the _____ approach to interpreting probability.
review	**99** (Sec. 5.a, Introduction; Frames 1–16) The classical, or a priori, approach to the computation of probabilities assumes that all possible outcomes of an event are _____
mutually exclusive equally likely	and _____.
relative-frequency	**100** (Frames 17–22) The computation of probabilities on the basis of empirical evidence, that is, by observing the outcomes of a repeated event, is termed the _____ approach.
0 1	**101** (Frames 23–29) The minimum numeric value that a probability figure can have is _____, and its maximum possible value is _____.
relative-frequency	**102** (Frame 28, Note) If a probability of 1 is interpreted to mean that an outcome is virtually, but not absolutely, certain, then the _____ approach to computing the value of the probability figure must have been used.

¾	**103** (Frames 30–39) If the odds expressing the probability of a favorable outcome are 3:1, the probability value for the favorable outcome is _____ (fraction). If the probability of an outcome is ⅛, the odds regarding its occurrence would be stated as _____ : _____.
1:7	

Venn	**104** (Frames 40–43) By enclosing a sample space and identifying points within that space, any or all of the possible outcomes in a particular situation or event may be portrayed by the resulting _____ diagram.

1	**105** (Frames 44–46) For any event the probability of a successful outcome plus the probability of a nonsuccessful outcome must be equal to a value of _____.

1	**106** (Frames 47–52) The sum of the probabilities of all mutually exclusive outcomes of an event must be equal to a value of _____.

mutually exclusive	**107** (Sec. 5.c, Introduction; Frames 53–56) When the occurrence of one outcome in an event automatically precludes the possibility of another outcome, the two outcomes are said to be _____ _____.

$P(A) + P(B)$	**108** (Frames 57–60) If A and B are mutually exclusive outcomes of a chance event, the probability that either A or B will occur is given by the equation $P(A \text{ or } B) =$ _____.

$P(A) + P(B) - P(A,B)$	**109** (Frames 61–68) If A and B are not mutually exclusive outcomes of an event, then the probability that either A or B will occur is given by the equation $P(A \text{ or } B) =$ _____.

$P(A)P(B)$	**110** (Sec. 5.d, Introduction; Frames 69–77) The probability of both A and B occurring, where A and B are outcomes of two independent events, is represented by the equation $P(A,B) =$ _____ _____.

$P(A)P(B|A)$	**111** (Frames 78–90) The probability of both A and B occurring, where A and B are the outcomes of two dependent events, is represented by the equation $P(A,B) =$ _____.

tree	**112** (Frames 73–76, 82–85) The diagram which is especially useful for portraying the possible outcomes of two or more sequential events, whether they are dependent or independent, is the _____ diagram.

conditional	**113** (Frames 78–80) If two events are dependent, the concept of _____ probability has to be used to determine the probability of a particular sequence of outcomes.

114 (Sec. 5.e, Introduction; Frames 91–98) The interpretation of a probability value in terms of the expected frequency of an outcome is consistent with the _____ approach to probability; considering it to be indicative of the strength of belief in regard to a particular outcome is consistent with the _____ approach to probability.

objective

subjective

**problems
(solutions given
on page 352)**

1 Given the following probabilities concerning the number of additional engineering personnel that will be needed in a company during the next two years:

Number of engineers	<100	100–199	200–299	300–399	400–499	≥500
Probability	0.10	0.15	0.30	0.30	0.10	0.05

(a) What is the probability that the company will need 400 or more additional engineers during the next two years?

(b) What is the probability that the company will need at least 200 but not more than 399 additional engineers?

2 If the probability is 0.30 that an engineering-job applicant has a graduate degree, 0.70 that he has had some work experience as an engineer, and 0.20 that he has both, of 300 applicants approximately what number would have either a graduate degree *or* some professional work experience?

3 Construct a Venn diagram for the situation described in Prob. 2, using G for graduate degree and W for work experience.

4 Given a time period during which two-thirds of the common stock issues have advanced in market price or remained unchanged while one-third have declined in price, suppose the market performance of three randomly selected shares of stock is analyzed.

(a) Using A to signify that the price of the stock has advanced or remained unchanged and D to signify a price decline, construct the tree diagram illustrating the probabilities of price advances and declines for the sample of three stocks. (*Hint:* This should be a three-step diagram, left to right.)

(b) Referring to the diagram, what is the probability that all three of the stock issues have experienced a decline?

(c) What is the probability that at least one of the stock issues has declined in price? (*Hint:* Only one path in the tree diagram does not satisfy this requirement, and hence the probability of the three sequential outcomes in this path can be subtracted from 1.0.)

5 The probability of a rise in consumer demand in our product field next year is estimated to be 0.70. If this increase in demand materializes, the probability is 0.80 that our company sales volume will increase. If it does not materialize, the probability is 0.50 that our sales volume will increase.

(a) Construct a tree diagram illustrating the various possible outcomes and the probabilities related thereto, using R and NR for a rise and no rise in consumer demand, and I and NI for an increase and no increase in company sales, respectively.

(b) What is the probability that there will be a rise in consumer demand *and* an increase in our company sales volume?

(c) What is the probability that there will be both no rise in consumer demand and an increase in our company sales volume?

additional problems **6** Of 1,000 assembled components, ten have a wiring defect and five have a structural defect. There is good reason to believe that no component has both defects.

(a) Construct a Venn diagram to illustrate the various possible outcomes, using WD for wiring defect, SD for structural defect, and ND for no defect. $\frac{10}{1000}$

(b) What is the probability that a randomly chosen component will have a wiring defect? $\frac{15}{1000}$

(c) What is the probability that a randomly chosen component will have a wiring defect *or* a structural defect?

7 Of 100 people in a structured consumer sample, 60 are over 30 years of age and 80 are classified as urban rather than rural residents. Of the 80 urban residents, 48 are over 30 years old.

(a) Construct a Venn diagram to illustrate the sample composition, using the symbols >30 and ≤30 for over 30 years of age and 30 or under, and U and R for urban and rural, respectively.

(b) What is the probability that a randomly chosen person from this sample will be over 30 years old?

(c) What is the probability that a randomly chosen person will be over 30 years old *or* an urban resident? $= .92$

8 One percent of a large number of packages of cookies is underweight in contents. If two packages of cookies are sampled:

(a) Construct the tree diagram for this problem, using C for correct weight and U for underweight.

(b) What is the probability that both packages will be underweight?

(c) What is the probability that one but not both will be underweight?

9 Three out of 15 bank teller's account reports contain procedural errors. An auditor samples two of these accounts without replacement.

(a) Construct the tree diagram illustrating the possible outcomes and probabilities, using E for an account with an error and NE for no error.

(b) What is the probability that neither of the accounts he samples will include an error?

(c) What is the probability that he will find both to be in error?

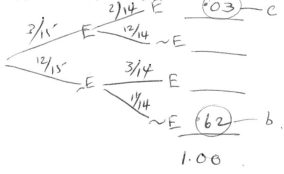

6.

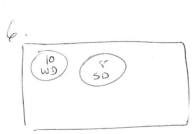

7.

8.

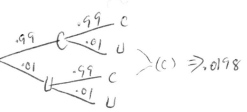

unit 6 · probability distributions

In this unit we shall define the nature of probability distributions in general, and then we shall describe the specific characteristics of two probability distributions that are used extensively in the procedures of statistical inference: the binomial and normal probability distributions. We had a brief preview to interpreting areas under the normal probability curve in Unit 4, in conjunction with discussing the use of the standard deviation as a measure of dispersion. Our discussion of tree diagrams in Unit 5 will be extended in this unit and will serve as the basis for introducing the binomial probability distribution and its characteristics.

6.a · the nature of probability distributions

Probability distributions are closely related to frequency distributions. As introduced in Unit 2, a frequency distribution is a listing of all possible outcomes, or classes of measurements, with an indication of the observed frequency of each outcome. Similarly, a probability distribution also lists all possible outcomes, or classes of measurements, but instead of observed frequencies, the probability associated with each outcome is indicated.

1 If three coins are tossed simultaneously, the possible number of heads that can occur as an outcome of this sequence of events

| 0; 1; 2; 3 |

is _____, _____, _____, or _____.

2 Though there are four possible outcomes to this sequence of events, how many can actually occur on a single toss of three coins?

| one |

_____ (number)

3 Suppose that the group of three coins is tossed ten times, and the number of times that 0, 1, 2, and 3 heads is observed is posted in a table, as illustrated below. This tally of the observed frequency

| frequency |

of occurrence of each possible outcome is called a _____ distribution.

Number of heads	Observed frequency
0	2
1	4
2	4
3	0

4 If we were to repeat the procedure and once again toss the three coins ten times, would we be likely to obtain exactly the same dis-

| no |

tribution of frequencies as those reported in Frame 3? (yes / no)

5 Instead of tabulating the actual frequency of occurrence of each possible outcome, we can determine and indicate the probability of each outcome. If we assume that the three coins are fair, would the probability of obtaining two heads, for example, change from time to time? (yes / no)

6 Whereas a listing of the *observed frequencies* of all possible outcomes of classes of measurements is called a frequency distribution, a listing of the *probabilities* of all possible outcomes is called a _____ distribution.

probability

7 In terms of the definitions given in Frame 6, the following table is a (frequency / probability) distribution.

frequency

Weekly sales volume	Observed number of salesmen
Under $900	2
$900–$1,199	8
$1,200–$1,499	3
$1,500+	1

8 In terms of this discussion the following table is a (frequency / probability) distribution.

probability

Number of heads	Probability
0	$\frac{1}{8}$
1	$\frac{3}{8}$
2	$\frac{3}{8}$
3	$\frac{1}{8}$

9 Thus a probability distribution includes a listing of all possible _____ of an event or sequence of events along with the _____ associated with each outcome.

outcomes

probability

10 Given a probability distribution, we can also develop a distribution of expected frequencies by multiplying each probability value by the total number of repetitions of the event or sequence of events. On this basis, and by referring to Frame 8 for the probability values, complete the table below.

Number of heads	Expected frequency on 24 tosses of three coins
0	_____
1	_____
2	_____
3	_____

3 ($= 24 \times \frac{1}{8}$)
9 ($= 24 \times \frac{3}{8}$)
9 ($= 24 \times \frac{3}{8}$)
3 ($= 24 \times \frac{1}{8}$)

11 Though there are many possible bases for "generating" a distribution of expected frequencies, two are extensively used in statistical inference and hence serve as the subject matter for the remainder of this unit. These are the binomial and normal probability distributions. Of course, no matter what basis is used to develop a distribution of expected frequencies, the observed frequencies in any particular instance (seldom / often) exactly correspond to the expected pattern.

seldom

12 Thus the expected frequencies of obtaining 0, 1, 2, and 3 heads on 24 tosses of three coins, which we determined in Frame 10, seldom exactly correspond to the observed frequency distribution of outcomes. In what way, then, is a probability distribution, or expected frequencies derived therefrom, of any use? _____

Actual results tend to be close to this; in the long run this is the best estimate.

_____

6.b ▪ the binomial distribution

The binomial distribution is actually a family of distributions all of which have certain characteristics in common. A key characteristic of binomial distributions is that they are distributions of discrete data rather than continuous data. Thus a frequency distribution describing the measured voltage of a number of batteries does not lend itself to being represented by a binomial distribution, whereas a frequency distribution indicating the number of times that 0, 1, 2, and 3 batteries have been found to be defective in batches of three that are tested does lend itself to being represented by a binomial distribution. Measurement of voltage is of course on the continuous scale of measurement, as discussed in Unit 1, whereas "number of defective batteries" represents counting rather than measuring and is thus discrete. In this section we shall discuss the use of tree diagrams in generating binomial distributions and then illustrate how the expansion of the binomial $q + p$ achieves the same result.

13 Illustrated below is a distribution of observed frequencies of heads on twelve tosses of three coins. If we wish to determine the probability of each outcome based on the assumption that all coins are fair, would the probability distribution that we construct be a binomial distribution? (yes / no)

yes

Number of heads	Observed frequency
0	2
1	5
2	4
3	1

14 Binomial distributions are so named because they can be generated by expansion of the binomial $q + p$ to various powers.

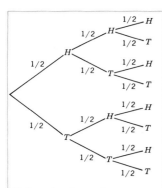

(A three-step diagram is necessary, since there is a sequence of three events.)

Before we discuss this procedure, we shall first illustrate how the values of the probabilities that are entered in a binomial probability distribution can be determined by the use of the familiar tree diagram. For the example in which three fair coins are tossed, complete the tree diagram below.

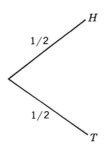

15 Now, using the tree diagram, compute the probability of each possible sequence of outcomes and post each probability value in the appropriate space below. If you are experiencing any difficulty at this point, review Frames 73 to 86 of Unit 5.

Probability of each sequence of outcomes

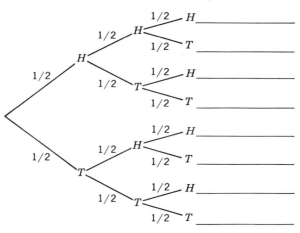

16 The diagram in Frame 15 indicates that there are eight unique sequences of outcomes that are possible and that each has a probability of occurrence of ⅛. However, if we are not concerned about maintaining the separate identity of each coin, then some of the probabilities may be combined. For instance, if we are simply interested in the probability of obtaining one head when three coins are tossed. then it does not matter which of the three coins has fallen heads so long as it is one of them. Referring to the same tree

the binomial distribution ▪ 103

diagram and combining probabilities where appropriate, complete the following probability distribution.

Number of heads	Probability
0	____
1	____
2	____
3	____

⅛
⅜
⅜
⅛

17 The probabilities posted in the distribution in Frame 16 indicate that though there is just one sequence by which no heads or three heads can be obtained as an outcome, the outcome of one head or two heads can each be obtained in _____ (number) different ways.

three

18 Thus a probability distribution always lists all possible _____ _____ of an event or sequence of events and the value of the _____ associated with each.

outcomes (or classes of measurements)

probability

19 In the space below, construct the tree diagram and the probability distribution for the number of heads when one coin is tossed.

tree diagram

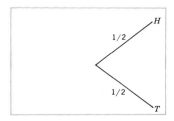

probability distribution

Number of heads	Probability
____	____
____	____

0 ½
1 ½

20 What distinguishes the probability distribution in Frame 19 from a frequency distribution? _____

Probabilities instead of observed frequencies are reported.

21 In using tree diagrams to generate binomial probability distributions, there are two essential requirements. One is that there be two mutually exclusive outcomes associated with each event in the diagram, and the other is that the events represented by the separate steps in the diagram be independent of one another. The latter stipulation indicates that the probability of obtaining a head, for example, (can / cannot) be different in different steps of the same tree diagram.

cannot (because changes in the values of probabilities in a tree diagram indicate dependent events)

22 Thus the essential characteristics of a binomial distribution, from the standpoint of tree diagrams, is that at each choice point in the tree diagram there be _____ (number) branches and that the probabilities in each step be (dependent on / independent of) previous outcomes.

23 The requirement that there be only two branches at each choice point is not necessarily so restrictive as it sounds, for problems can often be restated to conform to this requirement. For example, suppose that we are interested in the probability distribution of obtaining 0, 1, or 2 sixes when two six-sided dice are tossed. In constructing a tree diagram for this problem, how can we reduce the six branches to two branches at each choice point in the tree diagram? _____

24 The tree diagrams for all binomial distributions contain two branches at each choice point and independent probability values that do not change from step to step in the tree diagram. Can the values of the probabilities differ for different tree diagrams? (yes / no) Can the number of steps in the tree diagrams representing two different binomial probability distributions be different? (yes / no)

25 In tossing coins, we can simultaneously toss 1 coin, 2 coins, or n coins, and each situation will be represented by a different tree diagram. Similarly, the probability value of the successful outcome at each step in the tree diagram might be $\frac{1}{2}$, as for a fair coin, or it might have any other value, such as a probability value of $\frac{1}{6}$ associated with a 6 being obtained on a fair die. These facts are the basis for our introductory remark that the binomial distribution (is / is not) a single distribution of probabilities and (is / is not) an entire family of related distributions.

26 In terms of the tree diagrams that can be used to determine the probability values to be entered in a binomial probability distribution, what two attributes do all such tree diagrams have in common?

_____

_____

27 The two ways in which tree diagrams representing binomial distributions can vary are _____

_____.

28 When a tree diagram is used, the number of independent events (such as number of coins tossed, or number of manufactured components being sampled for inspection) is represented by the number of _____ in the diagram.

29 If there are three events in a sequence of events, for example, three coins being repeatedly tossed, then there are four possible types of outcomes in terms of the observed number of heads (or tails): 0, 1, 2, and 3 heads. Thus we can state the general rule that when there are n events in a sequence of events, there are $n +$ _____ (number) possible types of outcomes for the overall sequence.

> 1

30 If five motors are sampled for the purpose of detailed inspection, the number in which some defect is found can vary from _____ (number) motors to _____ (number) motors. In this case, then, there are _____ (number) possible types of outcomes.

> 0; 5
> 6 (0 through 5 possible defectives)

31 Put another way, the number of possible types of outcomes is _____ (number) greater than the number of independent events or steps represented in the tree diagram.

> 1

32 As another example of the use of a tree diagram to generate a binomial distribution, suppose that 10 percent of the components produced in a given manufacturing department have a particular defect. If two components are sampled, construct the tree diagram that can be used to determine the probabilities of 0, 1, or 2 components being defective and present the associated probability distribution in tabular form.

tree diagram

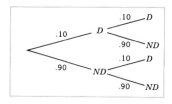

binomial probability distribution for number of defective motors

Number defective	Probability
0	0.81
1	0.18
2	0.01

33 Using the data in Frame 32, construct the distribution of expected frequencies for the number of defective components when

100 batches of two components each are sampled and 10 percent of the components have a defect.

Number defective	Expected frequencies in 100 samples of two each
0	——
1	——
2	——

<table>
<tr><td>81</td></tr>
<tr><td>18</td></tr>
<tr><td>1</td></tr>
</table>

34 Or, using the probability distribution for a somewhat different purpose, suppose that we sample one batch of two components and find that both components are defective. Given the assumption that 10 percent of the components are defective, is this outcome possible? (yes / no) Is this kind of outcome likely to occur very often? (yes / no) Given this observed outcome, might it be useful to consider the possibility that the overall percentage of defective components is actually greater than 10 percent? (yes / no)

yes

no (probability of only 0.01)

yes (since then the probability of obtaining two defective components would be greater)

35 We could continue with other examples that would require the construction of tree diagrams with different numbers of steps and different probability values. Each change along either of these lines (would / would not) change the probability distribution thereby generated. All of the distributions generated, however, could be described as being _____ probability distributions.

would

binomial

36 We have used the tree diagram to introduce the nature of the binomial distribution because of your familiarity with tree diagrams from Unit 5. Most authors discuss binomial distributions only from the algebraic point of view, for this is the basis for the term "binomial distribution." In the binomial $q + p$, p stands for the probability of success on a single event. If we toss a single coin, and obtaining a head is defined as success, then $q =$ _____ (number) and $p =$ _____ (number).

½ (or 0.5)

½ (or 0.5)

37 Of course, the specific values of p and q can vary from problem to problem, but their sum is always 1.0, as is true also of the branches coming from one point in a tree diagram. The number of events in the sequence is indicated by the exponent of the binomial. Thus $(q + p)^1$, or simply $q + p$, is the binomial expansion for generating a probability distribution when one coin is tossed. When three coins are tossed, the binomial term to be expanded is $(q + p)$ _____ (write in the exponent of the binomial).

$(q + p)^3$

38 Now, for the relatively simple example involving the tossing of three coins, let us expand the binomial in terms of the appropriate power, arithmetically solve for the value of each term in the expansion, and see what this gives us. We shall present a technique for expanding binomial terms in Frames 47 to 55, but as you may recall from your studies of algebra,

$$(q + p)^3 = q^3 + 3q^2p + 3qp^2 + p^3$$

Now, if we substitute the values $\frac{1}{2}$ for q and $\frac{1}{2}$ for p, we get

$$(\tfrac{1}{2})^3 + 3(\tfrac{1}{2})^2(\tfrac{1}{2}) + 3(\tfrac{1}{2})(\tfrac{1}{2})^2 + (\tfrac{1}{2})^3 = \underline{\qquad} + \underline{\qquad}$$
$$+ \underline{\qquad} + \underline{\qquad}$$

$\frac{1}{8} + \frac{3}{8} + \frac{3}{8} + \frac{1}{8}$

---

39 Refer to Frame 16, where we used a tree diagram to generate the binomial probability distribution for the number of heads when three coins are tossed. To what do the values in Frame 38 correspond? _____

---

to the probability of obtaining 0, 1, 2, and 3 heads, respectively

---

40 Similarly, let us use the method of binomial expansion to determine the probability distribution for the number of defective components obtained when batches of two components are sampled and historical data indicate that 10 percent of the components have some defect. If p is defined as the probability of obtaining a defective component in a single inspection, then $q = $ _____ (number) and $p = $ _____ (number).

0.90 (or $\frac{9}{10}$); 0.10 (or $\frac{1}{10}$)

$(q + p)^2$

events

41 For the sampling of two components $(q + p)^n = (q + p)$_____ (fill in the exponent). Thus the n stands for the number of _____ in the sequence of events being described.

---

42 Given that $q = 0.90$ and $p = 0.10$, and that

$$(q + p)^2 = q^2 + 2qp + p^2$$

the values of the three terms of this expansion, corresponding to the probability of obtaining 0, 1, and 2 defective components, are _____ (number), _____ (number), and _____ (number).

0.81; 0.18; 0.01

---

43 But when we obtain the three probability values in Frame 42, how do we know that the 0.81 is the probability of no defective components being obtained rather than the probability of both components being defective, for example? The *exponents* in the binomial expansion indicate this. Thus the first term in the binomial expansion, q^2, can be interpreted as indicating the probability of no defective components and two nondefective components; $2qp$ indicates the probability of obtaining one nondefective and one defective component, and p^2 indicates the probability of obtaining _____ (number) nondefective components and _____ (number) defective components.

0; 2 (Since there is no q in this term, its exponent is understood to be 0.)

---

44 For the problem in which we tossed three coins (Frame 38), the appropriate binomial expansion is $q^3 + 3q^2p + 3qp^2 + p^3$. On the basis we have just introduced, and given that $p = $ probability

	0
	3
	1; 2

of heads and q = probability of tails, the first term of this expansion indicates the probability of obtaining _____ (number) head(s) and _____ (number) tail(s), and the second term indicates the probability of obtaining _____ (number) head(s) and _____ (number) tail(s).

45 Thus the exponents included in each term of the binomial expansion are useful in interpreting the meaning of the term. Now, what about the coefficient of each term (e.g., the 3 in $3q^2p$)? Compare the tree diagram below with the related binomial expansion. Given that the arithmetic solution of the term $3q^2p$ indicates the probability of obtaining one head and two tails, what additional information does the coefficient 3 provide about this outcome?

that there are three ways of obtaining one head and two tails (H, T, T; T, H, T; and T, T, H)

$$q^3 + 3q^2p + 3qp^2 + p^3$$

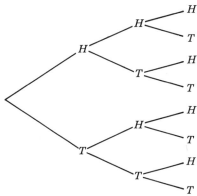

46 Thus binomial probability distributions can be generated algebraically by binomial expansions or diagrammatically by tree diagrams, and given one type of solution, we can construct the other. For example, given the binomial expansion $q^4 + 4q^3p + 6q^2p^2 + 4qp^3 + p^4$, by noting the sum of the exponents in any one term, we can directly tell that the related tree diagram has _____ (number) steps.

	four

47 The question that we have not yet discussed is: "How do you determine the exponents and coefficients for each term of a binomial expansion?" To begin with, for $(q + p)^n$ we can observe that there are always ($n - 1$ / n / $n + 1$) terms in the expansion (refer to the expansion to the fourth power in Frame 46 if necessary).

	$n + 1$

48 Let us first address ourselves to determining the values of the *exponents* for each term of the binomial expansion. In the expansion of $(q + p)^n$ you may have observed that the first term of the expansion is always q^n (it can also be thought of as $q^n p^0$, which equals q^n, since any value raised to the zero power equals 1). Then in the succeeding terms of the expansion the exponent of q is progressively (increased / decreased) by 1 and the exponent of p is progressively (increased / decreased) by 1 until the final term of any binomial expansion is p^n.

decreased

increased

49 Omitting all coefficients, indicate the appropriate exponents of q and p in each term of the following expansion.

$$(q + p)^5 = \underline{\hspace{0.8cm}} + \underline{\hspace{0.8cm}} + \underline{\hspace{0.8cm}} + \underline{\hspace{0.8cm}}$$
$$+ \underline{\hspace{0.8cm}} + \underline{\hspace{0.8cm}}$$

$q^5 + q^4p + q^3p^2 + q^2p^3 + qp^4 + p^5$

50 Referring to the expansion in Frame 49 if necessary, we can also observe that for the expansion of $(q + p)^n$ the sum of the exponents of q and p in any one term of the expansion always equals $(n - 1 \ / \ n \ / \ n + 1)$.

n

51 There are also procedural rules for determining the coefficient of each term, but since these rules are rather involved, we shall use a table of coefficients instead. Refer to Table A.2. For the general binomial term $(q + p)^n$, this table can be used to determine the coefficients for $n = 1$ through $n = \underline{\hspace{0.8cm}}$ (number).

10

52 Each line of the table corresponds to a given value of n in $(q + p)^n$, and each column corresponds to one term of the expansion. Instead of being identified as "first term," "second term," etc., the terms are more specifically identified according to the values of the exponents of $\underline{\hspace{0.8cm}}$.

p

53 Using Table A.2, enter the values of the coefficients in the following expansion.

$$(q + p)^5 = \underline{\hspace{0.8cm}}q^5 + \underline{\hspace{0.8cm}}q^4p + \underline{\hspace{0.8cm}}q^3p^2$$
$$+ \underline{\hspace{0.8cm}}q^2p^3 + \underline{\hspace{0.8cm}}qp^4 + \underline{\hspace{0.8cm}}p^5$$

1; 5; 10; 10; 5; 1

54 Similarly, expand the binomial $(q + p)^4$, using both the rules for exponents that we have presented and Table A.2 to determine the value of the coefficient for each term.

$q^4 + 4q^3p + 6q^2p^2 + 4qp^3 + p^4$

$$(q + p)^4 = \underline{\hspace{6cm}}$$

$q^3 + 3q^2p + 3qp^2 + p^3$

55 $(q + p)^3 = \underline{\hspace{6cm}}$

56 Using the expansion in Frame 55, if batches of three motors are being inspected and the assumption is made that 10 percent of the motors being received have some defect, construct the

probability distribution for the number of defective motors that
are obtained.

Number of
defective
motors   *Probability*

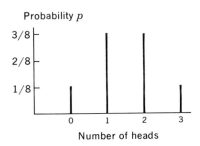

0	0.729
1	0.243
2	0.027
3	0.001

$$> = q^3 = (.9)^3$$
$$\rightarrow 3q^2 p$$

57 Since a probability distribution includes an exhaustive listing
of all possible outcomes, along with related probability values, we
would expect the sum of the probabilities to equal 1.0. Is this true
for the data of Frame 56? (yes / no)

yes

58 A binomial probability distribution, or a distribution of expected
frequencies based on a binomial expansion, can be presented
graphically as well as in tabular form. For example, the following
histogram illustrates the probability of obtaining 0, 1, 2 and 3 heads
on the repeated tossing of three fair coins. In contrast to the
histograms discussed in Unit 2, however, there is no width, or
thickness, to each bar in the figure. Why would it be inappropriate
to have the second bar in the figure extend from 0.5 to 1.5 as
boundaries, for example? _____
_____

because discrete data are being represented, allowing for no fractional
values

Probability p

3/8

2/8

1/8

    0   1   2   3
     Number of heads

59 In this section we have illustrated the fact that for certain
kinds of events the probability of each possible outcome, and
hence the expected frequency of that outcome, can be anticipated
by the expansion of the _____ equation.

binomial

60 The binomial expansion applies to situations in which the
probability distribution is for (continuous / discrete) data, and the
several events that are included in a sequence (such as batches
of four items being inspected) have individual probability values
that are (dependent / independent).

discrete

independent

61 The calculation of probabilities that is accomplished by appropriate binomial expansion can be accomplished also by the construction and use of a _____ diagram. In either case there are two ways in which binomial distributions can differ from one another. One is in the number of _____ in the sequence of events being investigated, and the other way is in the value of the _____ associated with each successful outcome.

62 At this stage in our discussion of statistical inference and probability theory, we cannot yet fully illustrate the practical applications of binomial probability distributions. As a brief indication of one type of use, suppose that the quality standard in a production process allows a maximum of 1 percent defective items, and for batches of five items that are inspected the actual frequency distribution has significantly more defective items than the expected distribution of frequencies which is based on a binomial distribution. What would we be likely to conclude? _____

6.c ▪ the normal distribution

Another type of probability distribution that can be used to generate a distribution of expected frequencies is the normal distribution. Whereas the binomial distribution is applicable to frequency distributions of discrete data, the normal distribution is applicable to data measured on the continuous scale. Hence any and all fractional values are possible when measuring, as contrasted to counting. Since it is not possible to list all possible fractional values in a table for the purpose of indicating probabilities, the probability distribution is presented in the form of a relative-frequency curve. Thus the normal probability curve is the general graphic representation of the normal probability distribution. Just as was true for the binomial distribution, the normal distribution is actually a family of distributions with certain common characteristics. In this section we shall define the common characteristics of normal probability distributions and illustrate how our knowledge regarding the characteristics of the normal curve can be applied for the purpose of specifying the probability of obtaining various measured outcomes.

63 You may recall that in Unit 4, while discussing dispersion, we had a brief introduction to the characteristics of the normal distribution. At that point we said that a normal distribution is one that is both symmetrical and mesokurtic. This means that the frequency curve for a normally distributed set of measurements (is / is not) skewed, (is / is not) peaked, and (is / is not) flat.

64 Though we shall not go through such a statistical determination of normality in this unit, in Unit 4 we demonstrated that the extent of skewness can be statistically determined by calculating a_3 and

a_4 (See Unit 4, Frames 79–88.)

the extent of kurtosis can be determined by calculating _____.

65 Binomial distributions vary from one another in terms of the values of n and p in the binomial $(q + p)^n$. Normal distributions vary from one another in terms of their values of the mean and standard deviation. Thus (many / few / only one) distribution(s) of measurements can be correctly described as being normally distributed.

many

66 The frequency curves for all distributions of measurements that approximate the normal distribution are similar in appearance; they are often described as bell-shaped, as illustrated in the diagram below. In terms of skewness and kurtosis, all frequency curves that approximate the normal probability distribution can be described as being _____ and _____.

symmetrical; mesokurtic

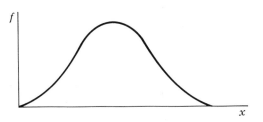

67 But you might legitimately ask: "Why should we expect obtained measurements to conform to the normal probability distribution at all? What is its special importance?" There are two distinct answers to these questions, and the one that is more significant statistically cannot be adequately explained until after we discuss sampling in Unit 7. The first reason is that many measured outcomes in nature, particularly those that are affected by a great number of causative variables, actually do yield distributions of measurements that approximate normal distributions. In the area of personal characteristics, examples are measurements of height, weight, and IQ. The general observation is that near the arithmetic mean of such distributions of measurements there are relatively (few / many) observed measurements, whereas for values that are increasingly smaller or larger than the mean the observed number of measurements tends to be relatively (low / high).

many

low

68 For example, given that the mean IQ, or intelligence quotient, on a certain intelligence test is 100 with a standard deviation of 15, we would expect (fewer / more) IQ scores between 115 and 130 than between 100 and 115.

fewer

69 The second reason why the normal probability distribution is useful is that collections of sample statistics, such as sample means, tend to be normally distributed *even though the population* from which the samples were taken is not itself normally distributed. Thus, if the amount of personal debt is not normally distributed, a distribution of the average amounts of personal debt reported by groups of 30 respondents (will / will not) tend to be normally distributed.

70 Since variables that are continuous can take on any fractional value, it is not meaningful to try to specify the probability that one particular value, representing an infinitely small point along the horizontal axis of a frequency curve, will occur. Rather, we specify the probability that an observed measurement will fall between two defined boundaries. To determine this probability, we begin with the assumption that the entire area under the normal probability curve is equal to a value of 1.0. Given the fact that a normal curve is symmetrical, what is the probability that a measurement chosen at random from a normally distributed set of measurements will be greater than the mean in value? $p =$ _____

71 You may wonder why the probability value for Frame 70 is not just under 0.5, since the mean itself is not included in the interval. But in the continuous probability distribution we are using, *any* infinitesimally small point, including the point at which the mean itself is located, is assumed to take up *none* of the area under the normal curve. Thus the two problems—viz., the probability that a score will be larger than the mean and the probability that a score will be equal to the mean or larger—(are / are not) considered to be identical problems for practical purposes.

72 Similarly, if we are given the information that a proportion of 0.34 of the measurements in a normal distribution is included in the interval from the mean to the value that is one standard deviation beyond the mean (for IQ, from 100 to 115), what proportion of measurements is included in the interval from one standard deviation below the mean (IQ of 85) to one standard deviation above the mean (IQ of 115)? _____

73 The illustration below summarizes the information which we have just presented. On the basis of the illustration, what is the probability that a measurement chosen at random will be larger than $\mu + 1.0\sigma$ (larger than an IQ of 115)? $p =$ _____

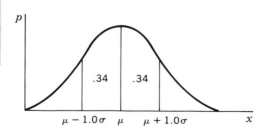

74 The examples in Frames 72 and 73 are virtually identical to those used in introducing the concept of the normal curve in Unit 4. The difference, an important one, is that we are now working with proportions of area under the curve and with probability, instead of with percentages of measurements. Put another way, instead of using the normal distribution with a particular observed distribution of frequencies, we are in addition using it as a _____ distribution.

> probability

75 The examples in Frames 72 and 73 have all been based on the given information that the proportion of measurements included between μ and $\mu + 1.0\sigma$ for a normal distribution is .34. But what about other intervals under the normal curve? The standard format of the table of areas under the normal curve gives proportions for various intervals that begin at the mean and extend to some point specified in terms of units of the standard deviation. Thus, given a mean of 100 and a standard deviation of 15 for adult IQ, if we want to determine the probability of a randomly chosen measurement being between 100 and 130, we would want to use the table to find the proportion of area included between the point μ and the point $\mu +$ _____ σ.

> 2.0 (since 130 is two standard deviations from the mean in the positive direction)

76 Since we have to work with deviations in terms of standard deviation units in order to use the table we are about to introduce, it is convenient to use a standard formula to accomplish this transformation of measurements and to give this transformed measurement a special name. A measurement that expresses the deviation from the mean in terms of the standard deviation is the Z, and its formula is $Z = (X - \mu)/\sigma$. Use this formula to determine the value of Z for the score of 130 in the problem in Frame 75.

> $$\frac{130 - 100}{15} = +2.0 \qquad Z = \frac{X - \mu}{\sigma} =$$

77 Refer to Table A.1, "Table of Areas under the Normal Curve." This table reports the proportions of the normal-curve area included between μ and various values of _____.

> Z (This table is considered the most important table in the Appendix.)

78 Given a mean of 50 and a standard deviation of 10 for a set of measurements that is normally distributed, suppose we wish to determine the probability that a randomly chosen measurement will be between 50 and 55. Since $\mu = 50$, that value corresponds to the lower limit represented in Table A.1. Then the first computational step is to transform 55 into units of Z.

> $$\frac{55 - 50}{10} = +0.5 \qquad Z = \frac{X - \mu}{\sigma} =$$

79 The next step is to utilize Table A.1 to determine the proportion of the area under the normal curve included between μ and a Z

0.1915	value of $+0.50$. Referring to the table, we find that the proportion equals _____.

80 Therefore, given a normal distribution with a mean of 50 and a standard deviation of 10, the probability that a measurement between the values of 50 and 55 will occur is _____. The probability that a value larger than 55 will occur is _____. The probability that a value smaller than 50 will occur is _____.

0.1915
$0.5000 - 0.1915 = 0.3085$
0.5000 (the entire lower half of the probability curve)

81 Consider the elements of the formula $Z = (X - \mu)/\sigma$. A negative value of Z signifies that the interval for which a proportion (or probability) is desired is located (below / above) the mean.

below

82 Table A.1, however, reports areas only for positive deviations from the mean. In Frame 80 we found that the probability of obtaining a measurement between 50 and 55, when the mean is 50 and the standard deviation is 10, is 0.1915. What would you expect to be the probability of obtaining a measurement between 45 and 50, in this case? $p =$ _____

0.1915

83 Since the normal curve is symmetrical, the proportions included on one side of the mean are equivalent to those on the other side. Therefore, when measuring areas between μ and values of Z, whether the Z value is positive or negative (does / does not) directly affect the use of the table of areas under the normal curve.

does not

84 If a transformed measurement yields a positive Z value, it is (smaller / larger) than the mean of the distribution. If a transformed measurement yields a negative Z value, it is (smaller / larger) than the mean of the distribution.

larger
smaller

85 Given a normal distribution with a mean of 50 and a standard deviation of 10, what is the probability that a value between 50 and 70 will occur by chance?

$\dfrac{70 - 50}{10} = +2.0$
0.4772 (from Table A.1)

$$Z = \frac{X - \mu}{\sigma} =$$

$$p =$$

86 For the same distribution, what is the probability that a measurement with a value between 35 and 50 will be obtained by chance?

$\dfrac{35 - 50}{10} = -1.5$
0.4332

$$Z = \frac{X - \mu}{\sigma} =$$

$$p =$$

87 So far we have always had the interval begin at the mean. Since this is the basis upon which Table A.1 is constructed, beginning the interval at the mean makes for the easiest type of problem. If the interval does not begin at the mean, then we have to do some subtracting or adding of areas in order to arrive at the appropriate probability value. For the example we have been discussing, in which the mean is 50, suppose we want to determine the probability that a measurement falls between 60 and 70. Indicate the area of the curve in which we are interested by shading it in on the curve below.

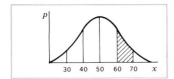

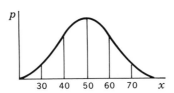

88 The area we want to indicate in the curve of Frame 87 cannot be directly determined by using Table A.1 because all intervals in this table begin with the mean as the lower limit (or the mean as the upper limit, if the Z value for the other limit is negative). However, suppose we determine the proportion between μ and 60 and the proportion between μ and 70. We can then determine the proportion of area included between 60 and 70 by subtracting the proportion included between μ and _____ from the proportion included between μ and _____.

60
70

89 Refer to Table A.1 and complete the following, given that $\mu = 50$, $\sigma = 10$, and $Z = (X - \mu)/\sigma$.

2.0	0.4772	
1.0	−0.3413	
	0.1359	

Area μ to 70 = area μ to _____ σ = _____
Area μ to 60 = area μ to _____ σ = − _____   (subtract)
Area 60 to 70 =   _____ (remainder)

90 For a distribution of measurements whose mean is 50 and standard deviation is 10, what is the probability that a randomly chosen measurement will be between 55 and 60? To aid you in setting up the problem, shade in the area under consideration on the diagram below and then determine the area by reference to Table A.1.

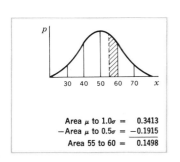

Area μ to 1.0σ =	0.3413
− Area μ to 0.5σ =	−0.1915
Area 55 to 60 =	0.1498

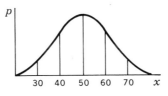

91 For a distribution whose mean is 50 and standard deviation is 10, what is the probability that a measurement chosen at random will be larger than 65?

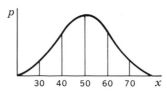

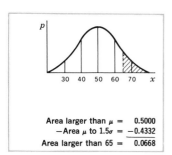

Area larger than μ =	0.5000
$-$Area μ to 1.5σ =	-0.4332
Area larger than 65 =	0.0668

92 For a distribution of measurements whose mean is 50 and standard deviation is 10, what is the probability that a measurement chosen at random will be between the values of 35 and 45?

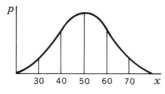

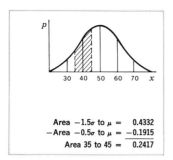

Area -1.5σ to μ =	0.4332
$-$Area -0.5σ to μ =	-0.1915
Area 35 to 45 =	0.2417

93 Now let us introduce a problem requiring addition, instead of subtraction, of areas taken from Table A.1. For the same distribution for which $\mu = 50$ and $\sigma = 10$, what is the probability that a measurement chosen at random will be between 35 and 65?

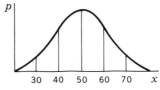

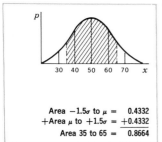

Area -1.5σ to μ =	0.4332
$+$Area μ to $+1.5\sigma$ =	$+0.4332$
Area 35 to 65 =	0.8664

94 With $\mu = 50$ and $\sigma = 10$, what is the probability that a measurement chosen at random will be between 40 and 70?

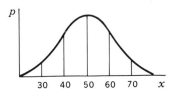

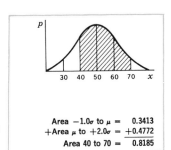

Area -1.0σ to μ =	0.3413
+Area μ to $+2.0\sigma$ =	+0.4772
Area 40 to 70 =	0.8185

95 When the normal probability distribution is used in hypothesis testing, we are typically interested in the probability associated with a randomly chosen measurement having an extremely high or extremely low value relative to the assumed mean of the distribution. Graphically, this means that we are interested in the proportions of area included in the tails of the distribution. For example, if we are interested in the probability that a randomly chosen measurement will be smaller than 30 or larger than 70, shade in the areas on the curve below for which we need to determine proportions of area.

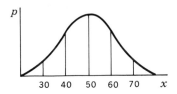

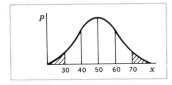

96 In using Table A.1 for the problem in Frame 95, we determine the proportion in each of the tails by subtraction, as we have been doing in Frames 88 to 92, and then we sum the two proportions in order to determine the probability of an extremely high *or* low value. Carry out these calculations below, using the data from Frame 95, and given that $\mu = 50$ and $\sigma = 10$.

Proportion less than 30 =

_____ − _____ = _____

+Proportion greater than 70 =

_____ − _____ = _____

0.5000 − 0.4772 =	0.0228
+0.5000 − 0.4772 =	+0.0228
	0.0456

Probability of a measurement <30 or >70 =
("less than 30 or greater than 70")

_____

97 Just as for the binomial probability distribution, the practical applications of the normal probability distribution can only be appreciated after we discuss statistical inference in some detail. As indicated in Frame 96, however, one fact of some importance is that by using the normal distribution, we can often specify the _____ that an outcome will be extremely low or high in value relative to the value of the mean.

probability

98 Aside from its more important uses in statistical inference, the normal distribution is widely used in interpreting the relative meanings of measurements or scores that are normally distributed, and, as it happens, most aptitude test scores are so distributed. Thus, in interpreting the meaning of any measurement taken from a set of measurements that is normally distributed, we need just two statistical values: the _____ of the distribution and the _____ of the distribution.

mean

standard deviation

review

99 (Sec. 6.a, Introduction; Frames 1–12) A probability distribution involves a listing of all possible _____ associated with an event along with related _____ values.

outcomes (or classes of outcomes)

probability

100 (Sec. 6.b, Introduction; Frame 13) Binomial probability distributions can be used only in conjunction with data that are (discrete / continuous).

discrete

101 (Frames 14–15) Given that 20 percent of the prospective customers that are contacted actually make a purchase, construct the tree diagram illustrating the probability values involved when a group of three prospects are contacted, using S for sale and NS for no sale.

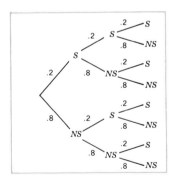

102 (Frames 16–20) Using the tree diagram of Frame 101, construct the probability distribution for the possible number of sales that can be completed when three prospects are contacted.

Number of sales   *Probability*

0	0.512
1	0.384
2	0.096
3	0.008

103 (Frames 21–27)   In which of the following ways can the tree diagrams for different binomial distributions differ?

yes   **(a)** number of steps (yes / no)

no (There are always two.)   **(b)** number of branches at each choice point (yes / no)

(c) change in the value of p (or q) within a given tree diagram

no   (yes / no)

yes   **(d)** different values of p in different tree diagrams (yes / no)

104 (Frames 28–35)   The number of events n in a sequence of

steps   events is indicated by the number of _____ in the tree diagram, and the number of possible types of outcomes for the

$n + 1$ entire sequence is equal to ($n - 1$ / n / $n + 1$).

105 (Frames 36–42, 46–53)   We can generate a binomial distribution algebraically by expanding the binomial $q + p$ to various powers. For the example in which three sales prospects are contacted (Frames 101 and 102), indicate the terms of the binomial expansion.

$(q + p)^3 = q^3 + 3q^2p + 3qp^2 + p^3$ $(q + p)^n =$

106 (Frames 43–45)   The exponents of the terms of the binomial expansion are useful for indicating the meaning of the probability value that each term represents. For the data of Frame 105, if $p = 0.2$, indicate the probability that two out of the three sales prospects make purchases and one does not.

$3qp^2 = 3(0.8)(0.2)^2 = 0.096$

107 (Frames 54–62)   Construct the probability distribution for the data of Frames 105 and 106 and portray the results graphically by means of a histogram.

Number of sales   *Probability*

0	0.512
1	0.384
2	0.096
3	0.008

(These figures are of course identical to those of Frame 102.)

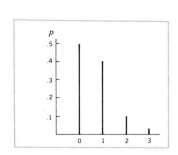

Probability, p

Number of sales

108 (Sec. 6.c, Introduction; Frames 63–69) The characteristics of the normal probability distribution, which is used in conjunction with (discrete / continuous) data, are such that its probability curve is _____ and _____.

continuous

symmetrical; mesokurtic

109 (Frames 70–74) A normally distributed set of measurements can be portrayed by using the normal probability curve or by organizing the data into classes and indicating the probability associated with each class. Why are not all of the possible outcomes, and the related probabilities, listed instead? _____
_____

Since a distribution of measurements is continuous, listing of all possible fractional outcomes is impossible.

110 (Frames 75–78) In Table A.1 the areas reported are for intervals whose lower limit is _____ and whose upper limit is expressed in terms of _____. The latter symbol represents the deviation of measurement from the mean of a distribution expressed in units of the _____ deviation.

μ

z

standard

111 (Frames 79–86) Given that the mean of a distribution of measurements is at 75 with a standard deviation of 5.0, what is the probability that a measurement will be between 75 and 85?

$+2.0$; 0.4772

Area 75 to 85 = area μ to _____ σ = _____

112 (Frames 87–91) For the same distribution, what is the probability that a measurement will be between 85 and 90 in value?

Area μ to $+3.0\sigma$ =	0.4986
− Area μ to $+2.0\sigma$ =	−0.4772
Area 85 to 90 =	0.0214

113 (Frame 92) For the same distribution, what is the probability that a measurement will be between 65 and 70 in value?

Area -2.0σ to μ =	0.4772
− Area -1.0σ to μ =	−0.3413
Area 65 to 70 =	0.1359

114 (Frames 93–97)   For the same distribution, what is the probability that a measurement will be between 65 and 90 in value?

Area −2.0σ to μ =	0.4772
+Area μ to +3.0σ =	+0.4986
Area 65 to 90 =	0.9758

115 (Frame 98)   If a set of measurements is normally distributed, then we can specify the probability of various categories of outcomes provided that we know the values of the _____ of

mean

standard deviation

the distribution and the _____ of the distribution.

problems
(solutions given on page 353)

1   Given that 70 percent of the television viewers tuned in to a certain program also watch the sponsor's commercial, suppose that samples of three independently chosen viewers are interviewed regarding the commercial.

(a) Develop the probability distribution for the number in each sample who actually saw the commercial by the use of a tree diagram, designating those who watched the commercial by W and those who did not watch it by NW.

(b) Develop the same probability distribution algebraically.

(c) Construct a histogram for this distribution.

(d) What is the probability that none of the three chosen viewers watched the commercial? Suppose that the probability values were reversed, so that only 30 percent of the viewers watched the associated commercial. What would then be the probability of all three viewers not having watched the commercial?

2   An aptitude test for graduate study in a certain professional field yields test results that approximate the normal distribution with a mean of 500 and a standard deviation of 100.

(a) About what percentage of test scores would be located between 300 and 700?

(b) Of 10,000 test scores, how many would we expect to be 225 or lower in value? 675 or larger?

(c) Suppose the top 10 percent of the scores are to be regarded as distinctly superior. What is the lowest score that belongs in this category? (*Hint:* In this kind of problem you have to use Table A.1 in the reverse of the usual direction. That is, the proportion to be included in the upper tail of the distribution is known, and the unknown Z value needs to be determined from the table and then used to calculate the relevant test score.)

additional problems

3   Given an automatic threading machine that is out of adjustment, resulting in 20 percent of the bolts being defective, for samples of three bolts each:

(a) Develop the probability distribution for the number of defective bolts by the use of a tree diagram, designating defective bolts by D and nondefective bolts by ND.

(b) Develop the same probability distribution by expansion of the binomial $q + p$.

(c) Construct a histogram for the distribution.

(d) What if only 2 percent of the bolts being produced are defective? What is the probability that a randomly selected batch of three bolts will contain at least one defective bolt?

4 The average (mean) selling price of a selected large sample of stock issues is $110 with a standard deviation of $25. Assuming a normal distribution of prices:

(a) What proportion of the stock is priced at $80 or less per share?

(b) What is the probability that a randomly chosen issue of stock from this sample will have a per-share selling price between $100 and $125?

(c) What proportion of the stock is priced at more than $150 per share?

(d) Below what selling price does the lowest-priced 20 percent of the stock sell?

$$Z_1 = \frac{100 - 110}{25} = -.4 \rightarrow .1554$$

$$Z_2 = \frac{125 - 110}{25} = .6 \rightarrow \begin{array}{c} .2257 \\ \hline .3811 \end{array}$$

* can't combine $-.4 + .6$ before we look at the table.

unit 7 · sampling and sampling distributions

In Units 5 and 6 we have studied some of the major principles of probability and the nature of probability distributions. The topics of sampling and sampling distributions, covered in this unit, will complete our coverage of the material that you need to know before proceeding into the area of statistical inference. From the standpoint of the sampling process itself, we shall consider the role of sampling in statistical inference, some general sampling problems, and the principal methods of sampling. In Sec. 7.c we shall introduce and define the nature of sampling distributions, which provide the essential basis for estimating population values and testing the significance of differences between observed and expected sample values.

7.a · the role of sampling

Whenever it is impossible, inconvenient, or expensive to measure the characteristics of every element that is included in a population, we are obliged to estimate these values on the basis of the known characteristics of one or more samples taken from that population. Thus through the process of statistical inference population values, or *parameters,* can be estimated from sample values, or *statistics.* The relationship between a census and a sample was considered in Unit 1. In computing the values of sample statistics, such as the mean and the standard deviation, it is important that we identify the population about which we are concerned and follow a sampling procedure that will permit us to generalize about that population.

1 Such measurements as the mean, median, and standard deviation can be either parameters or statistics, depending on whether a _____ or a _____ is being described.

population; sample

2 The procedure of collecting information about a population is called a _____; collecting information about a sample is referred to as the process of _____.

census

sampling

3 The procedure by which the characteristics of a population are described on the basis of known sample values is called statistical _____.

inference

4 Of course, not all decisions about a population need to be made on the basis of inference. For example, in the assembly of transistor radios, a final inspection to ascertain that every radio is operative (does / does not) involve statistical inference, whereas the selection of a few radios to test their endurance when subjected to physical abuse (does / does not) involve statistical inference.

does not

does

5 For any finite population, that is, a population that is made up of a known and limited number of elements, a census, or 100 percent sample, is always a possibility. However, if it is expensive or inconvenient to measure every element in a population, or if the measuring process itself destroys or affects the elements, then the process of _____ needs to be used.

6 An infinite population is one in which the number of elements is boundless. For example, there is no limit as to the number of times a coin could be tossed to ascertain the "true" probability of the occurrence of a head. Therefore a census of an infinite population is (always / never) possible.

never

7 For the following areas of information about specified populations, indicate an *s* for those best determined by sampling and statistical inference and indicate a *c* for those best determined by a census:

s (since this is presumably destructive testing)

c (since we are concerned about every individual patient's welfare)

c

s

____ **(a)** resistance of light bulbs to high voltage
____ **(b)** extent of patient recovery following operative procedure
____ **(c)** determining the "age" of the accounts receivable in a small company
____ **(d)** the preference of voters in a gubernatorial election one month before the election

8 The procedures of statistical inference that we shall study in the following units will be of three general types:

(a) point estimation
(b) interval estimation
(c) hypothesis testing

Consider the two types of estimation listed above, using the arithmetic mean as an example. The estimation of the specific value of a population mean based on the value of a sample mean involves _____ estimation.

point

9 Refer to the three types of statistical inference listed in Frame 8. Whereas *point estimation* is involved whenever the specific value of a population mean is being estimated, specifying the range of values within which the mean is located at a known level of probability involves _____.

interval estimation

10 Do not refer to the frames above. Two kinds of estimation of a parameter can be made through statistical inference: _____ and _____ estimation.

point

interval

11 If the mean operating life of all television tubes, based on a sample, is estimated as 8,000 hours, _____ estimation is involved. If we are able to conclude that the probability is 0.95 that the mean operating life is between 7,500 and 8,500 hours, _____ estimation is involved in our application of statistical inference.

point

interval

12 On the other hand, *hypothesis testing* is concerned with testing the likelihood that an assumed population value is correct, based on sample evidence. As was true for point and interval estimation, hypothesis testing also concerns the application of the techniques of _____.

statistical inference

13 For our television-tube example, if we begin with the assumption that the average tube life is 8,500 hours (based, perhaps, on a quality-control standard), determining the probability that this assumption is correct considering the value of an obtained sample mean involves _____ testing.

hypothesis

14 Thus there are three major types of uses for the methods of statistical inference as aids in decision making: _____ _____, _____, and _____ _____.

point estimation; interval estimation
hypothesis testing

15 In any use of sampling and statistical inference, it is particularly important that the *sampled population* be the same as the *target population,* which is the one about which we wish to make generalizations. For the following sampling situations, indicate an s when the sampled population is the same as the target population and indicate a d when the two populations appear to differ:

d

____ **(a)** a sample of Motorola television tubes tested for the purpose of determining the operating life of television tubes in general

s

____ **(b)** a sample of Motorola television tubes tested to determine the operating life of Motorola television tubes in general

d

____ **(c)** a sample of Motorola television tubes tested to determine the quality of Motorola products in general

d

____ **(d)** a sample of college students polled to determine the general popularity of a political candidate

d (Not all voters are listed in the telephone directory!)

____ **(e)** a sample of people chosen from a telephone directory polled to determine the general popularity of a political candidate

16 Thus the accuracy of any inferences made on the basis of a sample is dependent on whether or not the sampled population is the same as the _____ population.

target

17 In addition to being chosen from the appropriate population, the sample must be chosen in a specified way in order to permit the valid use of the methods of statistical inference. On this basis there are three types of samples: *convenience samples, judgment samples,* and *probability samples.* Taking those elements which happen to be most readily available for the sample would result in obtaining a _____ sample.

convenience

18 Of the three types of samples given in Frame 17, the one in which the selection of sampled elements is based on the experience and judgment of the selector is the _____ sample.

judgment

19 Finally, in contrast to the choice of items for the sample on the basis of convenience or personal choice, if the procedure followed results in every element in the population having a known, and usually equal, chance of being chosen for inclusion in the sample, the result is a _____ sample.

probability

20 Indicate the types of samples described below by posting a c for a convenience sample, a j for a judgment sample, and a p for a probability sample.

j

c

c

p

____ **(a)** A public-opinion pollster stops at several locations in a town and talks to people who appear to be representative of the town's residents.

____ **(b)** A pollster stations himself at a busy intersection in town to obtain interviews with a sample of the town's residents.

____ **(c)** Noticing a large manufacturing plant, the pollster gets the permission of the management to have a questionnaire distributed, thus getting at the views of a cross section of the town's residents rather rapidly.

____ **(d)** Using a listing of all residents in the town, he places each name on a slip of paper, places all slips in a bowl and chooses a 10 percent sample by alternatively picking a name and mixing the slips until the desired sample size is achieved.

21 Of the three types of samples described in Frame 20, the one which allows the maximum amount of selector bias in determining which items are typical of those in the population is the _____ sample.

judgment

22 Though a judgment sample may be a good one in terms of representativeness, the difficulty with this type is that the errors due to sampling cannot be measured or predicted. Are the errors associated with a convenience sample measurable and predictable? (yes / no)

no

23 Only when the selection of individual elements for sample inclusion is left to some form of chance, or random, procedure can the probability of various types of sampling errors be specified. Therefore the methods of statistical inference can legitimately be used only when the sample taken from the target population is a _____ sample.

probability

24 We can be certain about the parameters of a population only if we conduct a census and avoid measurement errors. However, population parameters can be estimated with a *known degree of confidence* if the sample collected is a _____ sample, but this cannot be done if the sample is a _____ or _____ sample.

probability

convenience; judgment

summary

parameter

statistical inference

25 A measurement of a sample, called a sample statistic, is often used to estimate a population characteristic, or _____, by the application of the methods of _____.

point estimation

interval estimation; hypothesis testing

26 Three major types of applications of statistical inference, which we shall cover in later units, are _____, _____, and _____.

27 In order to use the methods of statistical inference appropriately, it is essential that the sampled population be the same as the _____ population. Of the three types of samples that can be taken, there is no way of knowing the degree of accuracy of a _____ or _____ sample, whereas the degree of accuracy of a _____ sample can be statistically specified.

target

convenience; judgment

probability

7.b ▪ methods of probability sampling

A number of methods have been devised to ensure the attainment of a probability sample and thereby make it possible to use the methods of statistical inference. The first of these—simple random sampling—is the most important because it illustrates the basic requirements to be satisfied in probability sampling in general and is itself often used as part of a more elaborate sampling method. In addition to simple random sampling, we shall discuss systematic sampling, stratified sampling, and cluster sampling in this section.

known

28 The essential requirement of probability sampling, which permits the valid use of the methods of statistical inference, is that every element in the population has a(n) (known / unknown) probability of being included in the sample.

29 *Simple random sampling* is the most direct approach to the objective of obtaining a probability sample. In its most elementary form, assigning a number to each element in the population, posting these on individual slips of paper and placing them in a bowl, and drawing some slips out of the bowl while thoroughly mixing them is an example of _____.

simple random sampling

30 For a simple random sample, not only each element but also each combination of elements has the same chance of being included in the sample. Put another way, a random sample is one chosen in such a way that all samples of the given size, representing all possible combinations of elements, have an (equal / unequal) chance of being selected.

equal

31 The procedure in simple random sampling is such as to ensure that the personal judgment of the person collecting the sample (does / does not) enter into the choice of the elements.

> does not

32 For a survey being supported by the merchants of a particular shopping center, a poll taker stops 100 people along the sidewalk to get their opinions about the center. Can this be considered a simple random sample? (yes / no) Why or why not? _____
_____
_____

> no
> His selection of individuals is not likely to be random, but based on their appearance.

33 Because the method of blind choice is often difficult to put into practice, *tables of random numbers* have been constructed for use in selecting the specific elements to be included in a _____
_____ sample.

> simple random

34 Table A.7 is an example of a table of random numbers. Such tables often run to many pages and differ in the number of digits listed in each column. But the feature that all such tables have in common is that the numbers are listed in a (sequential / random) order.

> random

35 As an example of the use of such a table, assume that there are 897 elements, numbered 001 to 897, in a population, and that we wish to take a sample of 50 elements. We would enter the table at any arbitrary point and read the digits in groups of three, reading either to the right, left, downward, or upward, and choose the elements represented by those code numbers. What would we have to do about three-digit numbers greater than 897 in value? _____
_____
_____

> Ignore them, since there are no elements numbered beyond 897.

36 Just as we generally ignore values that do not represent any code numbers, we ignore also any code numbers that occur a second time by chance, since it is not usually considered desirable to have an element represented more than once in a sample. For the example in which we have elements numbered from 001 to 897, enter Table A.7 and list the first five elements that would be included in your sample: _____, _____, _____, _____, _____.

> Any choice, but remember that you usually begin arbitrarily within the table, not at the first value from the top.

37 In order to be used with a table of random numbers, every element in the target population being sampled must be identified by a _____.

> number

38 In the two situations a number that is obtained from a table of random numbers is ignored: when _____
_____ and when _____
_____

> no element in the population is represented by that number
>
> the element has already been selected for the sample

39 Thus in *simple random sampling* a blind choice or an automatic randomization procedure is followed to obtain a random sample. In *systematic sampling,* on the other hand, elements are selected from the population at a uniform interval of a listed order, time, or space. For example, if we take a 10 percent sample of telephone subscribers by starting at an arbitrary point in a telephone directory and choosing every tenth name in both directions of the listing, a _____ sampling procedure is involved.

systematic

40 Systematic sampling differs from simple random sampling in that each combination of elements does not have an equal chance of being selected. For example, if every fifth sequentially numbered element is being chosen for a systematic sample, the elements numbered 233 and 235 (could / could not) both be included in the sample.

could not

41 Through the use of a systematic sample, as contrasted to the simple random sample, there is also the possibility of introducing a systematic error. For example, if every fifth house is a corner house, then a survey of households directed at adequacy of street lighting will introduce a _____ bias when every fifth house is chosen for the sample.

systematic (Either all of the sampled houses would be corner houses or none of them would be corner houses.)

42 Therefore, whenever there is some kind of sequential pattern to the elements being sampled, systematic sampling (would / would not) be an appropriate method by which to obtain a probability sample.

would not

43 On the other hand, as compared with simple random sampling, systematic sampling usually requires (more / less) time for the choice of elements to be included in the sample and thus results in a (higher / lower) sampling cost.

less

lower

44 Contacting every tenth purchaser of a new car from a dealership and obtaining his evaluation of the post-sale service that he obtained is an example of _____ sampling as applied in customer relations

systematic

45 A third sampling method, which is based on having some knowledge about the characteristics of the population and their relationship to the variables being measured, is called *stratified sampling.* For example, in a study of student attitude toward having a college football team, if we suspect that there are important differences between undergraduate and graduate students in this regard, then the use of _____ sampling would be appropriate.

stratified

46 In a study of consumer attitudes toward a new product design, classifying individuals in the target population by sex and age groups and then taking a 10 percent sample (either simple random or systematic) from each population group in order to assure proportional representation in the sample is another example of _____ sampling.

47 Though the example just cited involved a proportionate sampling from each population group, or stratum, this is not a requirement of stratified sampling. More important, the sample from each stratum should be large enough in number to be representative of that stratum. For example, given 5,500 undergraduate and 800 graduate students, the *relative* sample size (i.e., proportion sampled) might be smaller for the (undergraduate / graduate) group than for the other stratum.

48 Whether the sampling is proportionate or nonproportionate, the assurance of appropriate representation of various population groups in the sample and a reduction in the required size of a sample are advantages of _____ sampling.

49 Finally, *cluster sampling* involves the random selection of elements *in groups,* rather than as individual elements. For example, if we wanted to investigate the wage rates in manufacturing firms of a given size category in a certain state, the random selection of a number of firms and the collection of wage rates for *all* employees in those *selected* firms would exemplify _____ sampling.

50 Cluster sampling is often used as a matter of necessity rather than choice. In the preceding example, obtaining a simple or systematic random sample of all employees working in the manufacturing firms included in the target population would probably be relatively (easy / difficult).

51 The example we gave would also be referred to as *single-stage sampling,* since all of the elements in the selected clusters are included in the sample. When there are two or more stages in the sampling process, the cluster sampling is called *multistage sampling.* For example, including only the employees from randomly selected departments of the randomly selected firms would be an example of _____ sampling.

52 Thus the selection of elements in groups rather than as individual elements is referred to as _____ sampling. When all of the elements in the primary groups are included in the sample, this is called _____ sampling. When the sampling process involves the selection of subgroups from within the primary sample groups, this is called _____ sampling.

53 When the primary groups being sampled are geographical in nature, the term *area sampling* is applied to the cluster-sampling method. Because political polls often involve choices of samples within counties, then election districts, then blocks, then particular homes, such sampling can be referred to as (single- / multi-) stage _____ sampling.

summary

54 The four principal sampling methods for obtaining a probability sample which we have discussed are _____, _____, _____, and _____ sampling.

55 Using a manufacturing process as an example, subjecting every twentieth generator produced to an intensive quality inspection involves the use of _____ sampling.

56 In the same situation, choosing groups of generators, such as a half hour's output, and subjecting every generator in the group to an intensive inspection exemplifies _____ sampling.

57 When an inspector attempts to choose generators for intensive inspection on some impartial basis, or when the quality-control department specifies the serial numbers of the generators to be inspected by the use of a table of random numbers, _____ _____ sampling is involved.

58 When generators of several different types are being manufactured, sampling according to the type of generator in order to assure appropriate representation of each type in the sample involves _____ sampling.

59 In terms of the number of steps in the sampling procedure, cluster sampling can be referred to as being either _____ or _____ sampling. When the groups being sampled in cluster sampling are geographic in nature, the method is often called _____ sampling.

60 No matter what sampling method is used in the attempt to obtain a probability sample and minimize sampling cost, it is particularly important that every element chosen for the sample actually be included in the sample. In a consumer survey involving the use of mailed questionnaires, if 30 percent of a randomly selected sample return the questionnaires and 70 percent do not, can the 30 percent respondent group be considered a random sample of the target population? (yes / no)

61 Therefore, in studies in which people are the elements of the sample, and they can choose either to participate or not to participate, repeated followup to get as high a participation by those in the sample as possible is (unnecessary / desirable / essential).

essential

7.c ▪ sampling distributions

In Unit 6 the normal probability curve was used to interpret the meaning of a measurement when the mean and standard deviation of a group of measurements are known. Similarly, we could interpret the meaning of a particular sample statistic, such as the sample mean, if we knew the mean and standard deviation of the actual or expected frequency distribution for that statistic. As contrasted to a distribution of individual measurements, such a frequency distribution for a statistic is called a *sampling distribution,* and it is the basis for most of the methods of statistical inference that we shall cover in later units. A frequency distribution representing the means taken from a great many samples of the same size, for example, would be called the *sampling distribution of the mean.* In this section we shall focus on the sampling distribution of the mean as a specific case in point and illustrate how the characteristics of this distribution can be determined without actual recourse to collecting a large number of samples and determining their respective arithmetic means.

62 If we were to take two, three, four, or more random samples of the same size from a population, would we expect that the numerical values of the sample statistics, such as the means, would be identical from sample to sample? (yes / no)

no

63 Therefore it is possible to construct a frequency distribution for any collection of sample statistics, such as the sample mean; this is referred to as a _____ distribution.

sampling

64 Any frequency distribution, including a sampling distribution, can be described by identifying the mean and the standard deviation of the distribution. Thus a sampling distribution of means can be described by identifying the _____ of the means and the _____ of the _____.

mean; standard deviation

means

65 A distribution of medians would be called the _____ _____ of the _____ and could be described by identifying the _____ and _____ for this distribution.

sampling distribution

median

mean; standard deviation

66 Like any standard deviation, the standard deviation of a sample statistic measures the amount of variability of a distribution of values. However, unlike measurements, variability in the value of a sample statistic, such as the sample mean, represents *sampling error* in estimating the associated population parameter. Thus the standard deviation of the mean is called the *standard error of the mean,* and it indicates the amount of sampling error in estimating the population _____ on the basis of a known sample _____.

mean

mean

67 Similarly, for the sampling distribution of medians it is more appropriate to say that this distribution can be described by identifying the mean of the medians and the _____ _____ of the medians.

standard error

68 The sampling distribution of a collection of standard deviations can be described by identifying the _____ and _____ _____ of the standard deviations.

mean

standard error

69 When a population of measurements is normally distributed, the sampling distributions of statistics for samples taken from that population also approach normality. If we wish to use a sample statistic, such as a sample mean, in estimation or hypothesis testing, why would we be interested in the normality of the sampling distribution? _____

_____

because this permits us to use the normal probability distribution for the purpose of statistical inference

70 Furthermore, if the sample size is sufficiently large, such as greater than 30, then *any* population of measurements, regardless of its form, will generate sampling distributions that are normally distributed. This is called the *central-limit theorem,* and it is particularly important because it permits the use of the _____ _____ curve in interpreting sampling distributions taken from nonnormally distributed populations.

normal probability

71 The theorem which states that a distribution of sample statistics, such as the sample mean, will tend to follow a normal distribution as sample size is increased, regardless of the characteristics of the parent population, is called the _____ _____ theorem.

central-limit

**figure 7.1 ▪ a population
with a rectangular distribution
of values and associated
sampling distributions of the
mean for $n = 2$, $n = 5$, and
$n = 30$.**

**figure 7.2 ▪ a normally
distributed population of
values and associated
sampling distributions of the
mean for $n = 2$, $n = 5$, and
$n = 30$.**

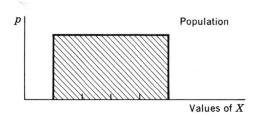

p Population

Values of X

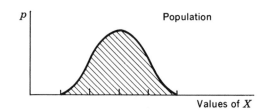

p Population

Values of X

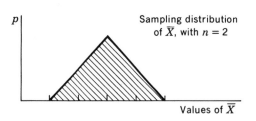

p Sampling distribution
of $\overline{X}$, with $n = 2$

Values of $\overline{X}$

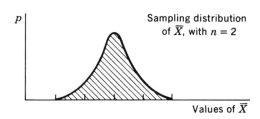

p Sampling distribution
of $\overline{X}$, with $n = 2$

Values of $\overline{X}$

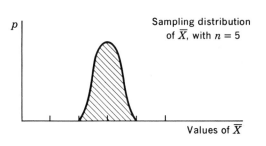

p Sampling distribution
of $\overline{X}$, with $n = 5$

Values of $\overline{X}$

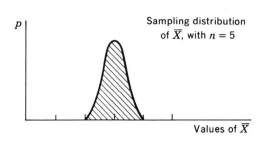

p Sampling distribution
of $\overline{X}$, with $n = 5$

Values of $\overline{X}$

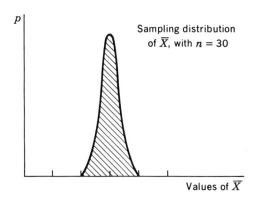

p Sampling distribution
of $\overline{X}$, with $n = 30$

Values of $\overline{X}$

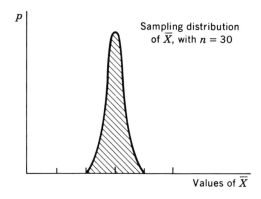

p Sampling distribution
of $\overline{X}$, with $n = 30$

Values of $\overline{X}$

72 For example, compare the populations represented at the top of Figs. 7.1 and 7.2. The population in Fig. 7.1 follows a (normal / rectangular) distribution, and the population of Fig. 7.2 follows a _____ distribution.

73 The three additional diagrams in each figure portray the distribution of sample means for each population under three conditions: when sample size n is equal to _____ (number), _____ (number), and _____ (number).

74 As indicated by the sequence of diagrams in Figs. 7.1 and 7.2, as sample size is increased, the distribution of a sample statistic becomes _____.

75 Of course, if we had to select a number of samples from a population in order to generate a sampling distribution, such as that for the mean, we would still face a formidable task. Fortunately, formulas for determining or estimating the characteristics of sampling distributions have been developed, making the collection of a large number of samples (necessary / unnecessary).

figure 7.3a ▪ frequency distribution of aptitude test scores ($N = 1,000$).

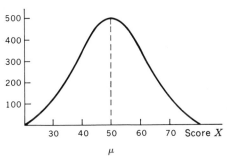

figure 7.3b ▪ expected sampling distribution of aptitude test means for 100 samples ($n = 25$).

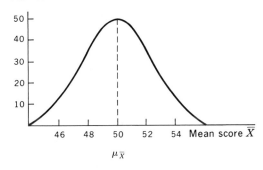

76 Refer to Figs. 7.3a and 7.3b, which portray the frequency distribution of a population of test scores and the expected sampling distribution of the mean for 100 samples of 25 each (sampling with replacement of elements in the population). Comparison of these distributions indicates that the mean of a large number of sample means (does / does not) tend to be equal to the mean of the parent population.

does

77 In the case of Figs. 7.3a and 7.3b, $\mu_{\bar{X}} = \mu = $ ———— (number).

50

78 With reference to these figures, does it appear that the standard error of the means $\sigma_{\bar{X}}$ equals the standard deviation of the population of measurements σ? (yes / no)

no (Notice the values posted along the two horizontal axes.)

79 Given a continuous process producing steel wire with a mean breaking strength μ of 300 pounds and a standard deviation of 15 pounds, the expected mean breaking strength of a large number of sample means of $n = 25$ is ———— pounds.

300

80 When sampling from a population that is infinite, or when sampling with replacement, the formula for determining the standard error of the mean $\sigma_{\bar{X}}$, when the population standard deviation σ is known, is $\sigma_{\bar{X}} = \sigma/\sqrt{n}$. Therefore, for the data of Frame 79

$$\frac{15}{\sqrt{25}} = \frac{15}{5} = 3 \text{ pounds}$$

$$\sigma_{\bar{X}} = \frac{\sigma}{\sqrt{n}} =$$

standard error of the mean.

81 Thus, whereas the mean of a sampling distribution of means is equal to the population mean, the standard error of the mean is always (larger / smaller) than the standard deviation of the population.

smaller (except when $n = 1$, in which case each sample is actually an individual measurement)

82 The formula $\sigma_{\bar{X}} = \sigma/\sqrt{n}$ also suggests that as the sample size n becomes larger, the standard error of the mean $\sigma_{\bar{X}}$ becomes (larger / smaller).

smaller

figure 7.4 ▪ distribution of a normal population and the sampling distributions of the arithmetic means for samples of size $n = 4$ and $n = 25$.

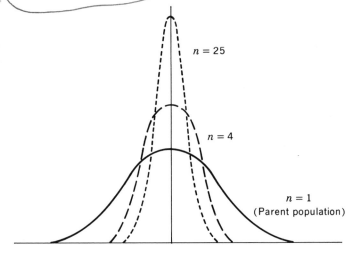

$n = 25$

$n = 4$

$n = 1$
(Parent population)

83 For example, refer to the overlapping sampling distributions presented in Fig. 7.4. Again, this figure indicates that as sample size is increased, the variability among sample means (increases / decreases).

84 When sampling from a population that is finite, and when sampling without replacement, a *finite correction factor* has to be included in the formula for the standard error of the mean, which then becomes

$$\sigma_{\bar{X}} = \frac{\sigma}{\sqrt{n}} \sqrt{\frac{N - n}{N - 1}}$$

where N is the number of elements in the population and n is the number of elements in the sample. Given 65 accounts receivable with a mean age of 30 days and a standard deviation of 10 days, compute the standard error of the mean for a sample size of 16.

$$\frac{10}{\sqrt{16}} \sqrt{\frac{65 - 16}{65 - 1}} = \frac{10}{4} \sqrt{\frac{49}{64}}$$
$$= \frac{10}{4} \frac{7}{8} = \frac{70}{32} = 2.2$$

$$\sigma_{\bar{X}} = \frac{\sigma}{\sqrt{n}} \sqrt{\frac{N - n}{N - 1}} =$$

85 With reference to the formula in Frame 84, the effect of the finite correction factor is to (increase / decrease) the value of the standard error of the mean.

86 As a rule of thumb, the finite correction factor need not be used when the sample size n is less than 5 percent of the population size N. Thus, if 16 accounts are sampled from a total of 65 accounts receivable, the finite correction factor (should / need not) be used. If 16 accounts are sampled from a total of 650 accounts, the finite correction factor (should / need not) be used.

87 In Frames 76 to 86 we have determined the mean of a large number of sample means and the standard error of this sampling distribution on the basis of knowing the mean and standard deviation of (a sample / the population).

88 In many situations, however, we do not know the population parameters. Rather, we are likely to know the value of the mean and standard deviation of a single _____.

Summary!

89 When we have knowledge of a *sample* mean and standard deviation, the first step is that of estimating the population mean and standard deviation on the basis of the sample statistics, and the second step is that of estimating the mean and standard error of the sampling distribution of the _____ based on the estimated population parameters.

90 In the case of estimating the population mean μ when only one sample has been collected, the best unbiased estimate is the sample mean itself, assuming of course that the requirements of random sampling have been satisfied. Thus the expected value of the population mean $E(\mu) =$ _____ (symbol).

$\bar{x}$

91   Since $\mu_{\bar{x}} = \mu$, and since $E(\mu) = \bar{X}$, the value of the sample mean can directly be taken as the best estimate of the mean of the sampling distribution of means itself, thus reducing the two steps to the one step $E(\mu_{\bar{x}}) =$ _____ (symbol).

$\bar{x}$

92   For estimating the standard error of the sampling distribution of means, we similarly first estimate the standard deviation of the population on the basis of knowing the standard deviation of a single sample of measurements. The formula $E(\sigma) = s\sqrt{n/(n-1)}$ is used for this purpose. The formula indicates that as an estimator of the population parameter, the value of the sample standard deviation is usually a bit too (high / low).

low (The fraction within the radical is always greater than 1.0.)

93   If $\sigma_{\bar{x}} = \sigma/\sqrt{n}$ for an infinite population and

$$E(\sigma) = s\sqrt{\frac{n}{(n-1)}}$$

then the two steps can once again be reduced to one, resulting in

$\dfrac{s}{\sqrt{n-1}}$

$$(E)\sigma_{\bar{x}} = \frac{s(\sqrt{n}/\sqrt{n-1})}{\sqrt{n}} = \frac{s\sqrt{n}}{\sqrt{n}\sqrt{n-1}} =$$

94   Whenever the value of the standard error of the mean is estimated on the basis of a *sample* standard deviation, rather than computed on the basis of a known *population* standard deviation, it is designated by the symbol $s_{\bar{x}}$ rather than by the symbol _____.

$\sigma_{\bar{x}}$

95   Therefore we can determine or estimate the value of the standard error of the mean by the formula

$$\sigma_{\bar{x}} = \frac{\sigma}{\sqrt{n}} \quad \text{or} \quad s_{\bar{x}} = \frac{s}{\sqrt{n-1}}$$

> standard of error of the mean.

In addition, each of these formulas may include the use of the finite correction factor. In total, therefore, there are _____ (number) possible formulas for computing the standard error of the mean.

four

96   Of the four possible formulas for computing the standard error of the mean that are listed below, which one is appropriate when sampling without replacement from a *finite population* and the

value of the *sample* standard deviation is known? **(a / b / c / d)**

(a) $\sigma_{\bar{x}} = \dfrac{\sigma}{\sqrt{n}}$

(c) $s_{\bar{x}} = \dfrac{s}{\sqrt{n-1}}$

(b) $\sigma_{\bar{x}} = \dfrac{\sigma}{\sqrt{n}} \sqrt{\dfrac{N-n}{N-1}}$

(d) $s_{\bar{x}} = \dfrac{s}{\sqrt{n-1}} \sqrt{\dfrac{N-n}{N-1}}$

d

97 In Frame 96 which formula for the standard error of the mean would be used when sampling from an *infinite population* and the *sample* standard deviation is known? **(a / b / c / d)**

c

98 In Frame 96 which formula for the standard error of the mean would be used when sampling from an *infinite population* and the *population* standard deviation is known? **(a / b / c / d)**

a

99 In Frame 96 which formula for the standard error of the mean would be used when sampling from a *finite population* without replacement and the *population* standard deviation is known? **(a / b / c / d)**

b

statistical inference (or estimation; hypothesis testing)

100 Beginning with Unit 8, we shall use the standard error of the mean in problems involving the use of statistical methods for the purpose of ——————————————.

review

parameters
statistics
statistical inference

101 (Sec. 7.a, Introduction; Frames 1–7) Population character-istics, or ————————, can be estimated on the basis of knowing sample values, or ————————, by applying the methods of ——————————————.

point estimation

102 (Frames 8, 10) Of the three types of statistical inference to be discussed further in later units, estimating the specific value of a population standard deviation on the basis of a sample standard deviation is an example of ——————————————.

hypothesis testing

103 (Frames 12–14) Testing the assumption that an assumed population value is correct and that the difference between it and an obtained sample value is within the realm of expected chance variation involves the use of ——————————————.

interval estimation

104 (Frames 9–11) Specifying a range of values within which the standard deviation of the population is located at a known level of probability is an example of ——————————————.

target

105 (Frames 15–16) Because we can make valid statistical infer-ences only about a population that has actually been sampled, it is important that the sample population be the same as the ———————— population.

106 (Frames 17–27) In addition, of the three types of samples that can be obtained from a target population there is no way of anticipating the degree of accuracy of a _____ or _____ sample, whereas the degree of accuracy of a _____ sample can be statistically specified.

convenience; judgment

probability

107 (Frames 39–44, 54–55) Of the four principal sampling methods that we discussed, all of which are aimed at obtaining a probability sample, the method by which every nth (fifth, tenth, etc.) element in space or time is chosen for inclusion in the sample is called _____ sampling.

systematic

108 (Frames 45–48, 58) The sampling method in which specific groups are identified within the population being sampled so that appropriate representation in the sample is assured is _____ sampling.

stratified

109 (Frames 28–38, 57) Use of a table of random numbers or some other systematic procedure to attain a blind choice of elements to be included in the sample is included in _____ _____ sampling.

simple random

110 (Frames 49–53, 56, 59–61) As the first step in the sampling process, when the procedure is such that groups of elements rather than individual elements are considered for inclusion in the sample, _____ sampling is involved. When all the elements in the selected groups are included in the sample, the procedure is called _____ sampling; when there is a further selection within the selected groups, it is called _____ sampling. When the groups and subgroups represent geographic locations, the sampling procedure is often called _____ sampling.

cluster

single-stage

multistage

area

111 (Sec. 7.c, Introduction; Frames 62–68) A distribution of medians taken from many samples of the same size would be called the _____ distribution of the medians, and it could be described by identifying the _____ and the _____ _____ of this distribution.

sampling

mean; standard error

112 (Frames 69–74) When sample size is greater than 30, any sampling distribution tends toward the normal distribution, even if the population of measurements from which it was generated was not normally distributed. This fact is important because it permits us to use the _____ distribution for the purpose of _____.

normal probability

statistical inference

113 (Frames 75–79, 87–91) When the population mean μ is known, the mean of the sampling distribution of means $\mu_{\bar{x}}$ can be specified as being equal to _____. When a single sample mean $\bar{X}$ is known, $\mu_{\bar{X}}$ is estimated as being equal to _____.

114 (Frames 80–86, 92–100) For each of the following formulas used for computing the standard error of the mean, indicate the characteristics of the situation in which it would be used in terms of **(a)** whether σ or s is known; and **(b)** whether the population is infinite or finite in size.

(a) (σ / s) is known
(b) (infinite / finite) population

$$s_{\bar{X}} = \frac{s}{\sqrt{n-1}} \sqrt{\frac{N-n}{N-1}}$$

(a) (σ / s) is known
(b) (infinite / finite) population

$$\sigma_{\bar{X}} = \frac{\sigma}{\sqrt{n}}$$

(a) (σ / s) is known
(b) (infinite / finite) population

$$s_{\bar{X}} = \frac{s}{\sqrt{n-1}}$$

(a) (σ / s) is known
(b) (infinite / finite) population

$$\sigma_{\bar{X}} = \frac{\sigma}{\sqrt{n}} \sqrt{\frac{N-n}{N-1}}$$

problems
(solutions given
on page 354)

1 An oil company desires to ascertain the factors affecting consumer choice of gasoline service stations in a test area; it has accordingly obtained the names and addresses of all registered car owners in that area. Describe how this list could be used in choosing each of the four major types of probabilty samples discussed in this unit.

2 A population consists of the four values: 3, 6, 9, and 10.

(a) Compute the population mean μ.
(b) Compute the population standard deviation σ.
(c) Suppose that samples of size two each are taken from this population, sampling without replacement. List all of the possible pairs of values that can constitute a sample.
(d) For each of the pairs identified in Prob. 2c, compute the sample mean $\bar{X}$ and demonstrate that the mean of all possible sample means $\mu_{\bar{X}}$ is equal to the mean of the population μ from which the samples were taken.
(e) Compute the standard error of the mean by determining the standard deviation of the means identified above in respect to $\mu_{\bar{X}}$.
(f) Compute the standard error of the mean by using the appropriate formula given in the unit, and verify that the value thus computed is the same as that determined in Prob. 2e.

3 In the production of television picture tubes, the quality-control standard requires a mean operating life of 10,000 hours with an expected standard deviation of 500 hours. For samples of 25 television tubes each, what is the expected sample mean and standard error of the sampling distribution of the mean?

4 For Prob. 3 suppose that we have no information other than that the mean operating life for a sample of 10 tubes is 9,800 hours with a standard deviation of 400 hours. Estimate the value of the standard error of the mean.

5 For a random selection of 26 stock issues taken from a listing of 257 issues, the market price has advanced by an average (mean) of $3 per share during a fiscal quarter, with a standard deviation of 50 cents.

(a) What is the best estimate for the mean price rise for all 257 stock issues?
(b) For samples of 26 each, what is the estimated standard error of the mean?

additional problems **6** Distinguish among convenience, judgment, and probability samples by indicating how an auditor might use each type in investigating the accuracy of a large number of spare-parts inventory figures.

7 Differentiate the meanings of σ, s, $\sigma_{\bar{X}}$, and $s_{\bar{X}}$.

8 A population consists of just the three values 1, 3, and 8.

(a) Compute μ.
(b) Compute σ.
(c) Suppose that samples of size two each are taken from this population, sampling without replacement. List all of the possible pairs of values that can constitute a sample.
(d) For each of the pairs identified in Prob. 8c, compute the mean $\bar{X}$ and demonstrate that $\mu_{\bar{X}} = \mu$.
(e) Compute the standard error of the mean by using the values of the sample means identified in Prob. 8d.
(f) Compute the standard error of the mean by using the formula which does not rely on any sample data being known.

9 A sample of 50 ball bearings taken from a large number being manufactured has a mean weight per bearing of 1.5 ounces with a standard deviation of 0.1 ounce.

(a) What is the best estimate for the average per-bearing weight of all bearings being manufactured?
(b) Estimate the value of the standard error of the mean.

10 Suppose that the 50 sampled bearings of Prob. 9 are taken from a particular production run that includes just 150 bearings in the total population.

(a) What is the best estimate for the average per-bearing weight for the 150 bearings?
(b) What is the estimated standard error of the mean in this case?

unit 8 · estimating population values

As we indicated in Unit 7, the three principal applications of statistical inference are directed toward the purposes of point estimation, interval estimation, and hypothesis testing. The first two of these procedures, which comprise the contents of this unit, are both concerned with the estimation of population parameters based on known sample statistics. Throughout our discussion of these methods, the assumption will be made that the sample whose values are being used for the purpose of estimation has been selected by one of the sampling methods aimed at obtaining a probability sample. Point estimates are given in the form of one number, or a particular point, whereas interval estimates identify the range of points within which a population parameter is likely to be located. Since probability values can be specified for interval estimates but not for point estimates, interval estimation is the more important of the two as a method of inference and is consequently given most of the attention in this unit. After a brief discussion of point estimation, we shall discuss the procedures of interval estimation as applied to the population mean, the difference between the means of two populations, and population proportions.

8.a · point estimation

The basic objective in choosing a point estimator of a population parameter is to use the one whose distribution of values taken from several samples would be concentrated near the true parameter being estimated. Throughout this book we shall differentiate estimated parameters from actual measured parameters by inserting a "cap" over the usual parameter symbol. For example, $\hat{\mu}$ (read: "mu-cap") is the symbol for the estimated mean of a population. In this section we shall discuss several criteria used by statisticians to identify a good estimator and then present the point estimates used for the most frequently estimated population parameters: the mean, total quantity, difference between the means of two populations, standard deviation, proportion, total number in a category, and the difference between the proportions of two populations.

1 Where $\bar{X}$ and μ are the symbols used to designate the sample and population means, respectively, and p and π are used to designate the sample and population proportions, the estimated population mean is designated by the symbol _____, and the estimated population proportion is designated by the symbol _____.

2 Throughout our discussion of the criteria of a good estimator, we shall use estimation of the population mean as the example. In Unit 7 we suggested that the mean of a randomly chosen sample $\bar{X}$ is an unbiased estimator of the population mean. This factor of _unbiasedness_ suggests that if we were to take a large number of random samples from a given population, the means of these samples would (all be equal to μ / be larger than μ about as often

be larger than μ about as often as they are smaller than μ

as they are smaller than μ / have no systematic relationship to the value of μ).

3 Thus the criterion of *unbiasedness* for a good estimator also suggests that the mean of an infinitely large number of sample means taken from the same population $\mu_{\bar{X}}$, illustrated on the frequency curve below, is equal to the mean of the _____ from which the samples were taken.

population

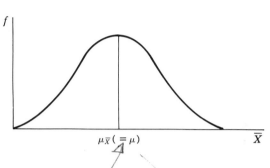

$\mu_{\bar{X}}\,(=\mu)$ $\overline{X}$

4 Since the sample means $\bar{X}_i$ cluster symmetrically about the population mean μ, and since the most likely value of a randomly chosen sample mean is the value of μ itself, then $E(\bar{X})$ (read: "expected value of the sample mean") $= \mu$. The expression $E(\bar{X}) = \mu$ is often used to represent the criterion which we have been discussing, that of _____.

unbiasedness

5 In addition to unbiasedness, the criteria of *consistency, efficiency,* and *sufficiency* are used in identifying a good estimator. The criterion of consistency can be represented symbolically by $\bar{X} \rightarrow \mu$ as $n \rightarrow N$ (read "$\rightarrow$" as "approaches"). This suggests that for a *consistent* point estimator, as sample size is increased, the value of the estimator generally (remains unaffected / continues to vary by the same amount / comes closer and closer to the population value being estimated).

comes closer and closer to the population value being estimated

6 The criterion of *unbiasedness* can be symbolized by

$\hat{X}$

$E(\underline{\hspace{1cm}}) = \mu$

The criterion of *consistency* indicates that as $n \rightarrow N$, _____ $\rightarrow$ _____.

$\hat{X} \rightarrow \mu$

7 The two criteria for point estimation which we have discussed thus far are those of _____ and _____. The criterion of *efficiency* suggests that the good estimator is one whose sampling distribution is most closely concentrated around the parameter being estimated. Put another way, that sample statistic is to be preferred as an estimator whose standard error is the (smallest / largest) in value.

unbiasedness   consistency

smallest

8 The criterion of a good estimator that takes into consideration the relative sizes of the standard errors of alternative estimators is that of _____.

9 For a *symmetrically* distributed population of values, would the sample median X_{med} be an *unbiased* estimator of the population mean μ? (yes / no) Would X_{med} be a *consistent* estimator of μ? (yes / no)

10 Thus, for a symmetrically distributed population of values a sample median is both an unbiased and a consistent estimator of the population mean. For large samples it can be shown that $\sigma_{med} = 1.2533\sigma_{\bar{X}}$ (i.e., $\sigma_{med} > \sigma_{\bar{X}}$). Therefore, as compared to the sample mean, is the sample median an *efficient* estimator of the population mean? (yes / no) Why or why not? _____

_____

11 The final criterion of a good estimator, in addition to unbiasedness, consistency, and efficiency, is that of *sufficiency*. An estimator is sufficient if it makes such use of all the available sample information that no other estimator would add any information about the (statistic / parameter) being estimated.

12 If an estimator does not make use of all available and relevant sample information, then it does not satisfy the criterion of _____

_____.

13 Of the four criteria for a good estimator, the criterion which indicates that the expected value of the estimator should be most likely equal to the value of the parameter, and that in the long run just as many values of the estimator should be larger than the parameter as smaller, is that of _____. The stipulation that the value of the estimator should approach the value of the parameter as sample size is increased concerns the criterion of _____.

14 That the standard error of an estimator should be smaller than that of other possible estimators concerns the criterion of _____; the requirement that an estimator should use all of the information available in a sample concerns the criterion of _____.

15 Match the list of criteria with the summary descriptions listed on the right by entering the appropriate letters:

____ unbiasedness **(a)** $\bar{X} \to \mu$ as $n \to N$
____ consistency **(b)** use of all available sample data
____ efficiency **(c)** lowest value of standard error
____ sufficiency **(d)** $E(\bar{X}) = \mu$

16 Thus the four criteria used by statisticians to define the characteristics of a good estimator are those of _____, _____ _____, _____, _____.

17 The criteria have not been presented with the objective that you will actually apply them in conjunction with problems presented in this book, but for the purpose of making you aware of the factors that statisticians consider in identifying good estimators. For estimating the population mean, for example, it can be shown that the sample statistic which satisfies all of the criteria discussed, and is thus the best estimator of the population mean, is the sample _____.

mean

18 Now, it may be your reaction that statisticians are making much mathematical ado about nothing. After all, is it not obvious that the equivalent sample statistic is always the best estimator of the same population parameter (sample mean as estimator of population mean, for example)? But let us turn an earlier example around. For a symmetrically distributed population, in which the values of the mean and median coincide, would a sample mean be an *unbiased* estimator of the population *median*? (yes / no) Would the sample mean be a *consistent* estimator of the population median? (yes / no)

yes

yes

19 Continuing from Frame 18, given that $\sigma_{\text{med}} = 1.2533\sigma_{\bar{X}}$, which sample statistic, the mean or the median, is a more *efficient* estimator of the population median for symmetrical populations? (mean / median)

mean

med for med.   mean for mean

20 Thus the equivalent sample statistic is not necessarily the best estimator of a population parameter. In addition to their use in selecting an estimator, the criteria which we have been discussing are applied for the purpose of improving estimators. For example, it has been found that the standard deviations of samples taken from a population tend to be systematically smaller than the standard deviation of the population itself, the amount of discrepancy being dependent on sample size. Given this knowledge, multiplying the value of a sample standard deviation by a correction factor results in a (better / poorer) estimator of the population standard deviation.

better

21 Table 8.1 presents the most frequently used point estimators of population values. In this table the statistic which is multiplied by a factor in order to correct for its bias as an estimator is the sample standard deviation. The factor by which this statistic is multiplied is _____, indicating that as an estimator the value of the sample standard deviation s tends to be too (low / high).

table 8.1 ■ **frequently used point estimates**

Population parameter	Estimator
Mean, μ	$\bar{X}$
Total quantity in a population of values	$N\bar{X}$
Difference between the means of two populations	$\bar{X}_1 - \bar{X}_2$
Standard deviation, σ	$s\sqrt{\dfrac{n}{n-1}}$
Proportion, π	p
Total number included in a category of the population	Np
Difference between the proportions included in two populations	$p_1 - p_2$

22 The two parameters in Table 8.1 whose meaning may not be entirely clear to you are "total quantity in a population" and "total number included in a category of the population." Suppose that out of a population of 100 drugstores a sample of 25 stores chosen at random has an average inventory investment of $150 in a particular product (at cost). What would be the estimated average per-store inventory value for the population of 100 stores? _____

$150 ($\mu = \bar{X}$)

23 For the example in Frame 22, what is the *total* dollar inventory carried by the 25 sample stores? _____.
What is the estimated total dollar inventory carried by all 100 stores? _____

$n\bar{X} = 25(\$150) = \$3,750$

$N\bar{X} = 100(\$150) = \$15,000$

Proportion ↰

24 Suppose that instead of being able to obtain dollar inventory figures, we can determine only whether or not each of the stores in the sample of 25 stores carries the particular product in question. If 20 of the 25 stores carry the product, the sample proportion p equals _____ (number). The estimated population proportion $\hat{\pi}$ equals _____ (number).

0.80 ($^{20}/_{25} = 0.80$)
0.80 ($\hat{\pi} = p$)

25 According to the data in Frame 24, the estimated number of stores in the population of 100 stores that carry the product in question is _____ (number).

$Np = 100(0.80) = 80$

26 In conjunction with the criterion of consistency, we would have more confidence in the accuracy of any point estimate as sample size is (decreased / increased). The effect of sample size on the accuracy of estimates is not easily illustrated when point estimates are involved, but its effect is readily apparent in interval estimation, discussed in Sec. 8.b.

increased

8.b ▪ confidence intervals for the estimation of the population mean

In terms of the sequence of topics in this book, we have now arrived at the first really important application of the methods of inference to problems of decision making. Specifically, we shall make use of the standard error of the mean and the characteristics of the normal probability distribution in order to estimate the interval of values within which a population mean or a population total is located with a known level of probability. Such an interval is called a *confidence interval* and the *degree of confidence* associated with it indicates the percentage of such intervals that would include the population mean, if many such intervals based on independent sample means were computed.

27   As we have seen in Units 6 and 7, the proportion of the normal distribution which lies within various distances of the mean, expressed in units of the standard deviation, can be determined by reference to Table A.1, the table of areas under the normal curve. In using this table, the direction and amount of deviation of a value from the mean of a distribution are determined by using the formula $(X - \mu)/\sigma$, which is represented by the symbol _____.

Z

28   There are three particular values of Z that are so frequently used in problems of inference that they are worth listing separately. As indicated in Table 8.2, these are the values that serve as the boundaries for the "middle" 90, 95, and 99 percent of the distribution of measurements. Thus, just as we have previously observed that the limits defined by $\mu \pm 1.0\sigma$ include 68 percent of the measurements of a normally distributed variable, so also the limits $\mu \pm$ _____ σ include 90 percent of the measurements, $\mu \pm$ _____ σ include 95 percent of the measurements, and $\mu \pm$ _____ σ include the middle 99 percent of the measurements.

1.64; 1.96

2.58

table 8.2 ▪ areas under the normal curve

Z, number of standard deviation units from the mean	Area lying between $\mu - Z\sigma$ and $\mu + Z\sigma$
1.64	0.90
1.96	0.95
2.58	0.99

29   You should be able to verify the accuracy of the Z values given in Table 8.2 by reference to Table A.1. For example, if we look up the area associated with a Z value of 1.96, the proportion given in the table is _____ (number). Since this is the proportion of area included between μ and $+1.96\sigma$, the proportion included between -1.96σ and $+1.96\sigma$ can be determined by multiplying the above proportion by _____ (number), resulting in a total proportion or area of _____ (number).

0.4750

2

0.9500

30 Using the information given in Table 8.2, and given a population of values for which $\mu = 100$ and $\sigma = 15$, we can conclude that 68 percent of the measurements are included between the limits 85 and 115, which correspond to the range from $\mu - 1\sigma$ to $\mu + 1\sigma$. Similarly, 90 percent of the measurements in a normally distributed variable are included between the limits _____ (number) and _____ (number), which correspond to $\mu - $ _____ σ and $\mu + $ _____ σ.

31 Continuing from Frame 30, we could also conclude that 95 percent of the measurements are included between 70.6 and 129.4, which corresponds to $\mu - 1.96\sigma$ and $\mu + 1.96\sigma$, and that 99 percent of the measurements are included between _____ (number) and _____ (number), which corresponds to $\mu - $ _____ σ and $\mu + $ _____ σ on the normal probability distribution.

32 However, in this unit we are concerned not with individual measurements but with sample means. Therefore we are also not concerned with the standard deviation of a population as such, but rather with the standard error of a hypothetical collection of means taken from a population. Therefore the distinction between a distribution of measurements, on the one hand, and a sampling distribution of means, on the other, is critical to an understanding of all of the remaining material in this unit. *If you are not certain of this distinction, review the last part of Unit 7 on sampling distributions right now!* Suppose that the sample mean of 50 randomly chosen measurements is 99 with a sample standard deviation of 14. Assuming an infinite population, indicate the appropriate formula for computing the standard error for the expected distribution of sample means around the population mean.

(a) $\sigma_{\bar{X}} = \dfrac{\sigma}{\sqrt{n}}$ **(c)** $s_{\bar{X}} = \dfrac{s}{\sqrt{n-1}}$

(b) $\sigma_{\bar{X}} = \dfrac{\sigma}{\sqrt{n}} \sqrt{\dfrac{N-n}{N-1}}$ **(d)** $s_{\bar{X}} = \dfrac{s}{\sqrt{n-1}} \sqrt{\dfrac{N-n}{N-1}}$

33 Thus the particular formula that is used to determine the value of the standard error of the mean depends on whether the population or sample standard deviation is known and whether or not the size of the population is infinite. Using the formula chosen in Frame 32, compute the standard error of the mean when $\bar{X} = 99$, $s = 14$, and $n = 50$.

$s_{\bar{X}} = \dfrac{s}{\sqrt{n-1}} =$

34 Now, we actually do not know the value of μ, for this is the parameter whose value we wish to estimate. However, suppose the value of μ is actually 100. As a point estimate, is the mean of the

no ($\mu = 99$, whereas $\mu = 100$)

sample data just reported a correct estimate of μ? (yes / no)

35 Rarely would a sample mean be exactly equal to μ, but the values of several sample means would tend to cluster around the value of μ, as illustrated in Fig. 8.1. In the long run, what percentage of the sample means would be included within the limits designated by the dotted lines in Fig. 8.1? _____ percent

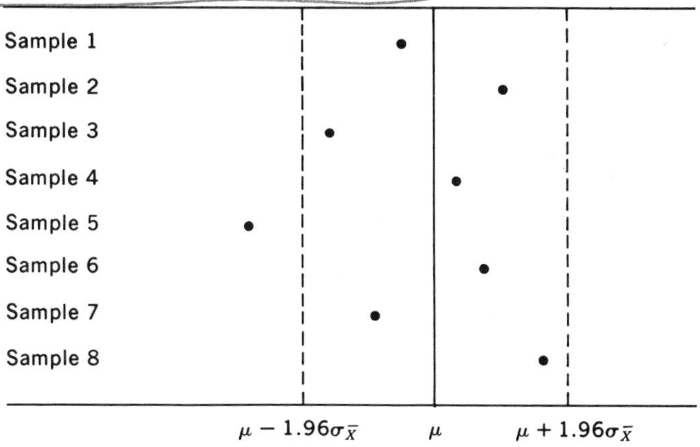

95

figure 8.1 ▪ values of several sample means in relation to the population mean.

$$\mu - 1.96\sigma_{\bar{X}} \qquad \mu \qquad \mu + 1.96\sigma_{\bar{X}}$$

36 Given that $\mu = 100$ and $s_{\bar{X}} = 2.0$ (refer to Fig. 8.1 if necessary), 95 percent of a large number of sample means would lie between the values _____ (number) and _____ (number).

$\mu \pm 1.96s_{\bar{X}} = 96.08$ and 103.92

37 Compare the limits identified in Frame 36 with the limits identified in the first part of Frame 31. Why do they not correspond in value? _____

The limits in Frame 31 designate the range within which 95 percent of the *measurements* would be located, whereas the limits of Frame 36 designate the range within which 95 percent of the *means* would be located.

38 But of course in problems of estimation we do not know the value of the parameter, for that is what we are estimating. Furthermore we have the value of just one estimator available, that is, one sample mean. Given that $\bar{X} = 99$, $s = 14$, $n = 50$, and $s_{\bar{X}} = 2.0$, if we were to construct an interval as an estimate of the location of the population mean, the value that would be at the center of this interval estimate, based on our available knowledge, is (99 / 14 / 2.0 / 100).

99

39 The value of $\bar{X}$ would be at the center of the confidence interval because this is the best estimate of μ that we have. Further, suppose that the interval is constructed by using the formula $\bar{X} \pm 1.96s_{\bar{X}}$. For the data of Frame 38 the two limits of the confidence interval are _____ (number) and _____ (number).

$99 \pm 1.96(2.0) = 99 \pm 3.92 = 95.08$ and 102.92

40 The location of this confidence interval relative to the population mean is portrayed as "sample 1" in Fig. 8.2. Does this interval estimate include the point at which the population mean is located? (yes / no)

| yes |

figure 8.2 ■ ninety-five percent confidence intervals computed about several sample means.

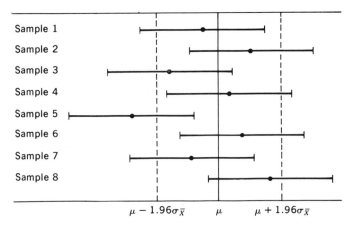

$$\mu - 1.96\sigma_{\bar{X}} \qquad \mu \qquad \mu + 1.96\sigma_{\bar{X}}$$

41 Of the confidence intervals portrayed in Fig. 8.2, how many do not include within their limits the point at which the parameter μ is actually located? _____ (number)

| 1 (for sample 5) |

42 Still with reference to Fig. 8.2, when using the formula $\bar{X} \pm 1.96s_{\bar{X}}$ (or $\bar{X} \pm 1.96\sigma_{\bar{X}}$) to construct the confidence interval within which the population mean is assumed to be located, what percentage of time will such intervals actually include the population mean? _____ percent. Of all such intervals which could be constructed, for what percentage of them will the value of the population mean be larger than the upper limit of the interval? _____ percent. For what percentage would the true mean be lower in value than the lower limit of the interval? _____ percent

| 95 (Of all possible sample means, 95 percent of them are within 1.96 Z units of μ.) |
| $2\frac{1}{2}$ |
| $2\frac{1}{2}$ |

43 If we had used a Z value of 1.64 in constructing the interval estimates for Fig. 8.2, then the population mean would in the long run be included within _____ percent of these intervals; the use of 2.58 would result in the mean being included within _____ percent of the intervals.

| 90 |
| 99 |

44 Because the construction of interval estimates using appropriate standard error values and the normal probability curve permits us to know how often such intervals will include the parameter being estimated, they are called *confidence intervals,* and the limits of a confidence interval are called *confidence limits.* Using the estimation formula $\bar{X} \pm Zs_{\bar{X}}$, compute the 90 percent confidence interval for estimating the population mean given that $\bar{X} = 99$, $s = 14$, $n = 50$, and $s_{\bar{X}} = 2.0$.

Confidence limits = _____ and _____

| $99 \pm 1.64(2.0) = 99 \pm 3.28 = 95.72$ and 102.28 |

45 Given that $\bar{X} = 99$, $s = 14$, $n = 50$, and $s_{\bar{X}} = 2.0$, determine the 99 percent confidence interval for estimating μ.

Confidence interval = _____ to _____

99 ± 2.58(2.0) = 99 ± 5.16 = 93.84 to 104.16

46 Which confidence interval, that of Frame 44 or that of Frame 45, is more likely to include the parameter being estimated? Frame (44 / 45). Why then would the other interval ever be used; that is, what is the price paid for maximizing the probability that the interval will include the parameter being estimated? _____

_____

45

The 99 percent confidence interval is wider, and thus may be less useful for decision-making purposes, than the 90 or 95 percent confidence intervals.

47 Along these lines, to say that a population value, such as μ, is located between $-\infty$ (read: "minus infinity") and $+\infty$ ("plus infinity") would define the 100 percent confidence interval, but an interval this wide would have no practical value in decision making. The confidence limits that are most often used are the 95 percent limits. If a decision maker consistently uses 95 percent confidence limits in estimating population values, his interval estimates will be correct _____ percent of the time.

95

48 As an example of a decision-making situation in which interval estimation of the population mean would be useful, suppose that a random sample of 50 employees taken from a total of 626 employees of a firm has an average weekly wage of $110 with a standard deviation of $10.50. Circle the appropriate formula below for computing the standard error of the mean:

(a) $\sigma_{\bar{X}} = \dfrac{\sigma}{\sqrt{n}}$ **(c)** $s_{\bar{X}} = \dfrac{s}{\sqrt{n-1}}$

(b) $\sigma_{\bar{X}} = \dfrac{\sigma}{\sqrt{n}} \sqrt{\dfrac{N-n}{N-1}}$ **(d)** $s_{\bar{X}} = \dfrac{s}{\sqrt{n-1}} \sqrt{\dfrac{N-n}{N-1}}$

d (s rather than σ known, finite population, and $n > 5\%N$; see Unit 7, Frames 96–99.)

49 Using formula **d** and the data in Frame 48, compute the standard error of the mean for samples of $n = 50$.

$$s_{\bar{X}} = \frac{10.5}{\sqrt{49}} \sqrt{\frac{626-50}{625}}$$
$$= \frac{10.5}{7} \left(\frac{24}{25}\right) = 1.5 \left(\frac{24}{25}\right) = \$1.44$$

50 Given that $\bar{X} = \$110$, $s = \$10.50$, $n = 50$, $N = 626$, and $s_{\bar{X}} = \$1.44$, estimate the average weekly wage paid in the firm, using 95 percent confidence limits and carrying your answer to the second decimal place.

Limits $= \bar{X} \pm 1.96s_{\bar{X}}$
$= 110 \pm 1.96(1.44)$
$= \$107.18$ and $\$112.82$

51 In Frame 50, if we had computed the 90 percent confidence limits instead of the 95 percent limits, the resulting interval would have

narrower

wider

been (narrower / wider) than the one which we obtained, whereas if we had computed the 99 percent confidence limits, the confidence interval would have been (narrower / wider).

52 In problems of the kind we have just presented, the decision maker often is as interested in estimating the total quantity, in this case the total amount of wages paid in the firm, as he is in estimating the average wage. With reference to the data in Frame 50, what is the one best (point) estimate for the total wages paid in the firm during the survey week?

$$N\mu = N\bar{X} = 626(\$110) = \$68,860$$

53 The general formula used to determine the confidence limits for estimating a total quantity in a population is $N\bar{X} \pm NZs_{\bar{x}}$. The only way in which this estimation formula differs from the one used for determining confidence limits for the mean is that both terms in the formula are multiplied by _____.

N (number of elements in the population)

54 Accordingly, for the example in which $\bar{X} = \$110$, $s = \$10.50$, $n = 50$, $N = 626$, and $s_{\bar{x}} = \$1.44$, determine the 95 percent confidence limits for estimating the total wages paid in the company carrying your answer to the nearest cent.

$626(110 \pm 626(1.96)(1.44)$
$= 68,860 \pm 1,766.82 = \$67,093.18$
and $\$70,626.82$

55 In this section we have presented the procedures for determining the confidence intervals for the population mean and the total quantity in a population. In order to make such estimates, we need to know the value of the sample mean and we need to estimate the value of the standard _____ of the mean. Finally, the confidence limits are set by utilizing the known characteristics of the _____ probability distribution.

error

normal

8.c ▪ confidence intervals for the difference between two population means

Up to now we have discussed only the standard error of the mean and its use in estimation. However, every sample statistic has an associated standard error, and this standard error would be used in conjunction with estimating the parameter corresponding to the known statistic. Whereas we have used the estimation formula $\bar{X} \pm Zs_{\bar{x}}$ (or $\bar{X} \pm Z\sigma_{\bar{x}}$) for estimating the population mean, the more general formula used for defining confidence limits is point estimate $\pm Zs_{stat}$, where s_{stat} is read as "standard error of the statistic." Though we shall not discuss the computation of confidence limits for such parameters as the population median and population standard deviation, you should now be capable of making such estimates if given the appropriate point-estimate and standard-error formulas. In this section we shall briefly discuss one additional type of parameter estimate: estimation of the difference between the means of two populations.

56 No matter what population parameter is being estimated, the essential procedure, or formula used, is basically the same. The

point	midpoint of the confidence interval used in estimation is always the appropriate _____ estimate of the population parameter.
	57 When the appropriate point estimate for a parameter has been identified, an interval is defined with this point at its midpoint by adding to it and subtracting from it a chosen value of Z multiplied
error	by the standard _____ of the statistic being used as the basis for the estimate.
	58 Thus the general formula used for locating confidence limits
Point estimate $\pm Zs_{stat}$ (or $Z\sigma_{stat}$)	is _____ $\pm$ _____.

59 In Sec. 8.b as well as in this one, we have observed that a standard error can be represented by two different symbols. For example, either $s_{\bar{x}}$ or $\sigma_{\bar{x}}$ would be read as "standard error of the mean." What is the difference between these two symbols? _____

_____

_____

$s_{\bar{x}}$ indicates that the estimated standard error is based on the standard deviation of a sample being known, whereas $\sigma_{\bar{x}}$ indicates that the standard error value is based on the standard deviation of the population being known.

60 Suppose that a population whose mean is being estimated is not itself normally distributed. This would very likely be the case for the distribution of weekly wage rates, for which we estimated the average and total wages paid by a firm. Why is it still considered appropriate to use the normal probability curve in making these interval estimates? _____

_____

_____

Sample statistics, such as the means of several samples, tend to be normally distributed, even when the population from which the samples were taken is not itself normally distributed. (See Unit 7, Frames 70–74.)

61 In addition to estimating population means and total quantities, there is a frequent interest in estimating the amount of difference between the means of two populations. For example, we might be interested in estimating the difference in wage rates paid in two firms. In Table 8.1 (page 150) the point estimate used in estimating

$\bar{X}_1 - \bar{X}_2$

the difference between the means of two populations is _____.

62 As indicated by this formula, it is necessary to collect two samples, one from each of the populations in question, in order to estimate the difference between the means of the two populations. With the assumption that the standard error is computed on the basis of sample data only, the symbol that would be used to represent the standard error of the difference between two means is

$s_{\bar{X}_1 - \bar{X}_2}$ (or s_{diff})

_____.

63 Various computational formulas have been developed for determining the value of the standard error of the difference between means (s_{diff}). The formula that we shall use is not so simple as it might be, since it requires the prior computation of the standard error of each of the sample means. The formula has the advantage of brevity, however, and it also highlights the relationship between the standard error of the difference between means and the standard errors associated with the two sample means. Accordingly, the formula we shall use is *

$$s_{\bar{X}_1 - \bar{X}_2} = \sqrt{s_{\bar{X}_1}{}^2 + s_{\bar{X}_2}{}^2}$$

When the computation of this standard error is based on the standard deviation of each of the populations being known, rather than on the basis of sample standard deviations, the formula would be written as

$$\sigma_{\bar{X}_1 - \bar{X}_2} = \sqrt{\sigma_{\bar{X}_1}{}^2 + \sigma_{\bar{X}_2}{}^2}$$

---

64 In Frame 63 the value of the standard error of the difference between means can be described in words as being equal to the square root of the sum of _____

the squared values of the two standard errors of the mean

_____ .

---

65 In Sec. 8.b we found that a sample of 50 employees in a particular firm had a mean wage rate of $110 per week with a standard error of the mean of $1.44. If a sample of 40 employees taken from another firm has a mean weekly wage of $100 and a standard error of the mean of $1.50, estimate the most likely difference in average weekly pay level between the two firms.

$\bar{X}_1 - \bar{X}_2 = \$110 - \$100 = \$10$

Point estimate =

---

66 Using the data in Frame 65, compute the standard error of the difference between the means.

$$\sqrt{s_{\bar{X}_1}{}^2 + s_{\bar{X}_2}{}^2} = \sqrt{(1.44)^2 + (1.50)^2}$$
$$= \sqrt{2.0736 + 2.25}$$
$$= \sqrt{4.3236} = 2.08$$

$s_{\bar{X}_1 - \bar{X}_2} =$

---

67 With $\bar{X}_1 = \$110$, $\bar{X}_2 = \$100$, $\bar{X}_1 - \bar{X}_2 = \$10$, and $s_{\bar{X}_1 - \bar{X}_2} = \$2.08$

estimate the difference in average weekly wage rates between the two firms from which these samples were taken, using 95 percent confidence limits.

$(\bar{X}_1 - \bar{X}_2) \pm Z s_{\bar{X}_1 - \bar{X}_2}$
$\quad = \$10 \pm 1.96(2.08)$
$\quad = \$10 \pm 4.08$
$\quad\quad = \$5.92 \text{ and } \$14.08$

Confidence limits =

---

68 Given the data of Frame 67, construct the 99 percent confidence interval for estimating the difference in average weekly wage between the two firms.

$\$10 \pm 2.58(2.08) = \$10 \pm 5.37$
$\quad\quad\quad = \$4.63 \text{ and } \$15.37$

Confidence limits =

---

* The formulas for the standard error of the difference between means used throughout this book are approximations, in that they are based on assumptions that the two samples are large and that they have been independently chosen from populations with equal variances (i.e., $\sigma_1{}^2 = \sigma_2{}^2$). For a discussion of these assumptions and alternative computational procedures, see E. C: Bryant, *Statistical Analysis*, 2d ed., Chap. 5, McGraw-Hill, New York, 1966.

There is an important distinction between estimating a population mean and estimating a population proportion. The computation of a mean is related to the process of measurement, which generates data along a continuous scale, whereas the computation of a proportion is related to the process of counting, which generates discrete data. Since the normal probability distribution is continuous in nature, but the binomial probability distribution is discrete, it follows that the latter distribution should be the one used in constructing confidence intervals for estimating population proportions. But because the normal probability distribution is easier to work with than the binomial, as we shall explain below, it would be convenient if the normal probability distribution could be used in conjunction with estimating population proportions. As a matter of fact, a substitution of the normal probability distribution for the binomial distribution is possible under certain conditions; we shall discuss these conditions after illustrating the difficulty associated with using the binomial distribution itself in interval estimation.

69 Of a sample of ten university students, four are found to be smokers. Thus the proportion p of smokers in the sample is 0.4. What would be the one best point estimate of the value of the population proportion? (Refer to Table 8.1 if necessary.) $\hat{\pi}$ = _____

$p = 0.4$

70 In estimating the population mean, we used the sample mean as the basis for the point estimate and we constructed the interval around this point by using the _____ probability distribution. Though we would likewise begin the construction of an interval estimate for a proportion by using the sample proportion as the point estimate, the interval itself would be based on the characteristics of the _____ probability distribution.

normal

binomial

71 In using the table of coefficients for the binomial distribution (Table A.2) for the data of Frame 69, p = _____, q = _____, and n = _____.

0.4; 0.6

10

72 With these values for p, q, and n, the coefficient of the binomial term which indicates the probability that four of ten randomly selected students will be smokers is _____ (number); the exponents of p and q in this term are _____ and _____ respectively. Therefore the probability that four out of ten randomly selected students will be smokers, assuming that the proportion of smokers in the entire student population is 0.4, is represented by the algebraic term _____.

210

4; 6

$210p^4q^6$ (See Sec. 6.b to review the characteristics of binomial distributions.)

73 Table 8.3 presents the probabilities associated with the various possible outcomes when ten students are polled regarding whether or not they smoke, given that $\pi = 0.4$. For example, this table indicates that the probability that eight of the ten students polled will

0.0106

be smokers is _____ (number).

0.0106

table 8.3 ▪ probability distribution for obtaining various number of smokers in a sample of 10 respondents if $\pi = 0.4$

Number of smokers	Proportion	Binomial term to be solved	Probability
0	0.0	q^{10}	0.0060
1	0.1	$10pq^9$	0.0403
2	0.2	$45p^2q^8$	0.1209
3	0.3	$120p^3q^7$	0.2150
4	0.4	$210p^4q^6$	0.2508
5	0.5	$252p^5q^5$	0.2007
6	0.6	$210p^6q^4$	0.1115
7	0.7	$120p^7q^3$	0.0425
8	0.8	$45p^8q^2$	0.0106
9	0.9	$10p^9q$	0.0016
10	1.0	p^{10}	0.0001

74 When we used the normal probability distribution as the basis for constructing a confidence interval, the size of the interval on each side of the point estimate was the same because the normal probability distribution is symmetrical. Would the interval estimate for the population proportion discussed above have its point estimate at the center of the interval? (yes / no)

no (The probability distribution given in Table 8.3 is not symmetrical.)

75 Furthermore, and of even greater significance, as the true value of π changes from the presumed value of 0.4, the characteristics of the binomial distribution in terms of skewness and kurtosis also change. This suggests that any interval estimate for a proportion has to consider the characteristics of (one / more than one) binomial distribution.

more than one

76 Because of this, the use of the binomial distribution for purposes of estimation is quite complex and outside the scope of this book. Fortunately, as the sample size is increased, the binomial probability distribution approaches the normal probability distribution in its characteristics. The rule of thumb that we shall follow in determining when it is appropriate to use the normal probability distribution as a substitute for the binomial for purposes of estimation is that n be at least 50 and np and nq each be at least equal to 5. Using this rule, for the example in Frame 72, in which $n = 10$, $p = 0.4$, and $q = 0.6$, would it have been appropriate to use the normal distribution for the purpose of setting confidence limits? (yes / no)

no

77 In order to use the normal distribution in estimating a population proportion, the sample size n should be at least equal to _____ (number).

50

78 Furthermore np and nq should each be at least equal to a value of _____ (number).

5

79 For the illustration which we have been using, in which $n = 10$, $p = 0.4$, and $q = 0.6$, if we were to increase n to 64, could we then use the normal probability distribution in conjunction with defining confidence limits for the population proportion? (yes / no) Why or why not? _____

yes; because $n > 50$, $np > 5$, and $nq > 5$

80 If we use the general formula for estimation when the normal probability distribution serves as the basis, which always involves the definition of an interval to both sides of a point estimate, what is the specific formula to be used for determining the confidence limits for the population proportion?

p; Z $\hat{\pi} = \mu \pm Z s_p$

81 In the formula in Frame 80 the only symbol which we have not yet defined is s_p, which would be read as the _____ _____ of the _____.

standard error   proportion

82 The formula for the standard error of the proportion is

$$s_p = \sqrt{\frac{p(1-p)}{n}}$$

when the population from which the sample was taken is infinitely large or when the sample size is less than 5 percent of the population size. When the sample size is more than 5 percent of the population size, then the finite correction factor needs to be included in the formula, resulting in

$$s_p = \sqrt{\frac{p(1-p)}{n}} \sqrt{\frac{N-n}{N-1}}$$

For each of the formulas above, p would be replaced by π when the population proportion is known, and σ_p would then be used to represent the standard error of the proportion. Why would σ_p never be used in setting confidence limits for estimating the population proportion? _____

because we would not be estimating the value of π if its value is already known

83 Given that $p = 0.4$ and $n = 64$, compute the standard error of the proportion, using the appropriate formula taken from Frame 82 and assuming a very large population.

$$\sqrt{\frac{p(1-p)}{n}} = \sqrt{\frac{0.4(0.6)}{64}}$$
$$= \sqrt{\frac{0.24}{64}} = \frac{0.4899}{8} = 0.0612$$

$s_p =$

84 Now, referring to Table 8.2 if necessary, determine the 95 percent confidence limits for the population proportion, given that $p = 0.4$, $n = 64$, and $s_p = 0.0612$, indicating the limits to two decimal places.

$\hat{\pi} =$) *meaning of proportion*

$p \pm Zs_p = 0.4 \pm 1.96(0.0612)$
$= 0.4 \pm 0.12 = 0.28$ to 0.52

85 Thus, on the basis of the randomly selected sample of 64 university students, we would conclude that a proportion between _____ and _____ of the overall student group sampled are regular smokers, with a _____ percent degree of confidence that our estimate is correct.

0.28; 0.52

95

86 Any problem that requires estimation of a percentage can be handled as a problem requiring the estimation of a proportion for the purpose of setting confidence limits, and so we shall not bother to introduce any formulas for the standard error of a percentage as such. Thus, if a sample of 100 people taken from a group of 10,000 yields 64 percent who are in favor of a particular Federal program, we can estimate the proportion of the population sampled that is in favor of the program and then convert the confidence limits to percentages. The first step in any event, then, is to compute the standard error of the proportion. For the data in this frame

$$\sqrt{\frac{p(1-p)}{n}} = \sqrt{\frac{(0.64)(0.36)}{100}}$$
$$= \frac{(0.8)(0.6)}{10} = \frac{0.48}{10} = 0.048$$

$s_p =$

87 Now estimate the percentage of people in the group of 10,000 who are in favor of the Federal program, using 95 percent confidence limits.

$0.64 \pm 1.96(0.048) = 0.64 \pm 0.094$
0.546 and 0.734

Limits (as proportions) =

54.6% and 73.4%

Percentage limits =

88 If the limits just computed are considered too wide for the purpose of application, they can be tightened for the available sample data by _____
_____.

using a lower degree of confidence in the estimation, such as 90 percent limits

89 On the other hand, if we wish to have a narrower confidence interval but are not willing to lower the degree of confidence in the accuracy of the estimate, the narrower interval can be obtained by reducing the value of the standard error, which, in turn, can be achieved by (reducing / increasing) sample size.

increasing

90 Just as the estimation of a total quantity is simply an extension of estimating the mean of a population, the estimation of the total number included in a category is an extension of estimating the population proportion. In Frame 87 we concluded that of 10,000 people a proportion between 0.546 and 0.734 are in favor of a

Federal program. Based on this information, the confidence limits for estimating the number of people in the group of 10,000 who are in favor of the program, at the 95 percent degree of confidence, would be _____ (number) and _____ (number).

5,460; 7,340

---

91 Thus, if we have established confidence limits as proportions, then we can readily establish confidence limits for the number of people (or elements) in the category being described by multiplying the proportions by _____ (symbol).

N

---

92 Given that the estimation formula for the population proportion is $\hat{\pi} = p \pm Zs_p$, the formula for estimating the total number in a category can be written as

Number = _____ ± _____

$N_p \pm NZs_p$ [or $N(p \pm Zs_p)$]

---

93 Finally, just as we were interested in estimating the difference between the means of two populations, we might be interested in estimating the difference between the proportions of two populations. The relevant point estimate in this case is $p_1 - p_2$ and the standard error to be used is $s_{p_1-p_2}$. Therefore the formula to be used for estimating the difference between the proportions of two populations is

$\text{Diff}_{\text{prop}} = $ _____ ± _____

$p_1 - p_2 \pm Zs_{p_1-p_2}$

---

94 The formula for computing the standard error of the difference between proportions is constructed on the same basis as the formula for the standard error of the difference between means. Thus, where $s_{\bar{x}_1-\bar{x}_2} = \sqrt{s_{\bar{x}_1}^2 + s_{\bar{x}_2}^2}$,

$s_{p_1-p_2} = $

$\sqrt{s_{p_1}^2 + s_{p_2}^2}$

---

95 Given that a proportion of 0.45 of a random sample of people from one part of the country express approval of a particular Federal program with a standard error of 0.04, and that in another part of the country a proportion of 0.55 are in favor with a standard error of 0.03, estimate the difference in the proportions of people in the two sections of the country who are in favor of the program, using 95 percent confidence limits.

Limits $= (p_1 - p_2) \pm Zs_{p_1-p_2} = $

$(0.55 - 0.45) \pm 1.96$
$\qquad \sqrt{0.03^2 + 0.04^2}$
$= 0.10 \pm 1.96 \sqrt{0.0025}$
$\quad = 0.10 \pm 1.96(0.05)$
$\qquad = 0.10 \pm 0.098$
$\qquad\quad = 0.002 \text{ and } 0.198$

(In percentage terms the actual difference is estimated as being between 0.2 and 19.8 percent with the defined degree of confidence.)

---

review **96** (Introduction to Unit 8) The statistical process of estimation whereby a single, or particular, value is used to estimate a parame-

point	ter is referred to as _____ estimation; the process by which the parameter is identified as being within a defined range of values
interval	at a designated level of probability is called _____ estimation.

97 (Sec. 8.a, Introduction; Frame 1) In terms of the symbols used, a sample mean is represented by _____, a population mean is represented by _____, and an estimated population mean is represented by _____.

$\bar{X}$	
μ	
$\hat{\mu}$	

98 (Frames 2–7) We have discussed four criteria used by statisticians to define the characteristics of a good estimator. In using a sample mean as an estimator of the population mean, the criterion of unbiasedness can be represented symbolically by the relationship _____, and the criterion of consistency can be represented by _____.

$E(\bar{X}) = \mu$	
$\bar{X} \rightarrow \mu$ as $n \rightarrow N$	

99 (Frames 8–16) The criterion of efficiency indicates that the value of the estimator's _____ is at a minimum; the criterion of sufficiency indicates that _____ _____ are being used in making the estimate.

standard error	
all available data	

100 (Frames 17–21) The point estimator used to estimate the population standard deviation is $s \sqrt{n/(n-1)}$. This suggests that the sample standard deviation is a biased estimator of the population standard deviation and is generally too (low / high) in value.

low	

101 (Frames 22–26) In addition to estimating the mean and proportion of a population, we can also make use of sample data to estimate the total quantity in a population and the total number in a category of the population. For example, if a random sample of 3,000 households taken from a population of 150,000 households indicates that mean gross income per household is $7,000 and that 20 percent of the households plan to purchase a new automobile during the coming year, then we would estimate the total gross income for all 150,000 households as _____ and we would estimate that the purchase of _____ (number) automobiles is planned.

$1,050,000,000	
30,000	

102 (Frames 27–31) For a normally distributed set of measurements, 68 percent of the measurements are included in the interval represented by $\mu \pm 1.0\sigma$. Similarly, 90 percent of the measurements are included in the interval $\mu \pm \_\_\_\_\sigma$, 95 percent are included in the interval $\mu \pm \_\_\_\_\sigma$, and 99 percent are included in the interval $\mu \pm \_\_\_\_\sigma$.

1.64	
1.96	
2.58	

103 (Frames 32–37) The distinction between a standard deviation and a standard error is that a standard deviation is a measurement of the variability of individual measurements in respect to a

sample means	group mean, and the standard error of the mean, as a case in point, is a measurement of the variability of individual _____ _____ in respect to the _____.
population mean	

104 (Frames 38–41) The general estimation formula used to define the 95 percent confidence limits for the population mean is

$\bar{X} \pm 1.96 s_{\bar{x}}$ (or $\bar{X} \pm 1.96 \sigma_{\bar{x}}$)

_____.

105 (Frames 42–51) In the long run, if 90 percent confidence intervals are used to estimate a number of population values, then 10 percent of these intervals will *not* include the parameter being estimated. Using 95 percent confidence limits, as compared to 90 percent confidence limits, results in an estimation interval which

wider

is (narrower / wider).

106 (Frames 52–55) The general formula used to define the confidence limits for estimating the total quantity in a population is

$N\bar{X} \pm NZs_{\bar{x}}$ [or $N(\bar{X} \pm Zs_{\bar{x}})$; or $N\bar{X} \pm NZ\sigma_{\bar{x}}$]

_____.

107 (Frames 56–58) When based on sample data being known, the standard error of the difference between two sample means is

$s_{\bar{x}_1 - \bar{x}_2}$

usually represented by the symbol _____. Accordingly, the general formula for determining the confidence limits for estimating the difference between the means of two populations is _____

$\bar{X}_1 - \bar{X}_2 \pm Zs_{\bar{x}_1 - \bar{x}_2}$

_____.

108 (Frames 69–75) Through expansion of the binomial distribution to the appropriate power, we can determine the probability of any combination of frequencies of two types of outcomes and make use of this information in estimating the proportion of a population included in a particular category. Thus, given that a proportion of 0.20 of a randomly chosen sample of households plans the purchase of an automobile, we can estimate the proportion of

population

households in the _____ with such intentions, using a confidence interval.

109 (Frames 76–79) Because of the numerical complexity connected with using the binomial distribution in estimating a population proportion, particularly when the sample size n is large, the normal distribution is often used as a substitute for the binomial. Many statisticians believe that this substitution is legitimate when-

50

ever the sample size n is at least _____ (number) and np and nq

5

are each at least equal to a value of _____ (number).

110 (Frames 80–89) When the normal probability distribution is used as a substitute for the binomial distribution, the formula used to determine the confidence limits in estimating a population pro-

$p \pm Zs_p$

portion is $\hat{\pi} = $ _____.

111 (Frames 90–95) The formula used in estimating the total number in a category of the population, which is a variation of the formula for estimating population proportion, is _____ _____. The formula used for estimating the difference between the proportions included in two different populations is _____.

$$N_p \pm N Z s_p \text{ [or } N(p \pm Z s_p)]$$

$$p_1 - p_2 \pm Z s_{p_1 - p_2}$$

problems
(solutions given
on page 356)

1 In a department store an auditor finds that 50 randomly chosen charge accounts out of a total of 3,000 such accounts have a mean debit balance of $53 with a standard deviation of $14.

(a) Estimate the mean account balance of all charge accounts, using 90 percent confidence limits.
(b) Estimate the mean balance of all accounts using 95 percent confidence limits.
(c) Estimate the mean balance of all accounts using 99 percent confidence limits.
(d) Which one of the three estimates do you consider to be most useful? Why?

2 With the data of Prob. 1, estimate the total balance due for all 3,000 charge accounts,

(a) using 90 percent confidence limits
(b) using 95 percent confidence limits
(c) using 99 percent confidence limits

3 For two retail outlets an auditor finds that the mean charge-account balance for a random sample of 50 accounts taken at one store is $45 with an associated standard error of the mean of $2, and that at another store the mean account balance for 50 accounts is $54 with a standard error of the mean of $3. Estimate the difference between the mean account balances at the two stores, using 95 percent confidence limits.

4 In a sample of 100 graduate business students randomly selected at several major universities offering M.B.A. programs, 60 are the sons of business or professional men. Estimate the percentage of all graduate business students in the universities surveyed whose fathers are business or professional men, carrying your computation to the nearest percentage:

(a) using 90 percent confidence limits
(b) using 95 percent confidence limits
(c) using 99 percent confidence limits

5 With the data of Prob. 4, if a total of 2,000 students are enrolled in the graduate schools studied, estimate the total number whose fathers are business or professional men, using 95 percent confidence limits.

6 In attempting to assess voter sentiment regarding a state bonding proposal, a legislator has a random sample of 100 people polled in each of two districts containing a large number of voters. In the first district 60 of the 100 people interviewed expressed their approval of the proposal and in the second district 50 expressed approval. Estimate the difference between the percentage of people in the two districts supporting the bonding proposal, using 95 percent confidence limits.

additional problems *no finite correction is*

7 A random sample of 50 firms taken from an industry with 1,200 *needed* firms has an average (mean) number of employees of 77.5 with a standard deviation of 20 employees. $s \Rightarrow s_{\bar{x}} = 2.86$ $\bar{x}$

(a) Estimate the average number of employees per firm in the entire industry, using 90 percent confidence limits.

(b) Estimate the average number of employees per firm in the entire industry, using 95 percent confidence limits.

(c) Estimate the average number of employees per firm in the entire industry, using 99 percent confidence limits.

8 Using the data of Prob. 7, estimate the total number of employees working in this industry, using 95 percent confidence limits.

instead $\sqrt{\dfrac{100-50}{100-1}}$ $2.86 \Rightarrow 2.03$

9 For Prob. 7, suppose the industry includes just 100 firms rather than 1,200 firms. *Finite cor. factor* $= \sqrt{\dfrac{N-n}{N-1}}$

because $n \geq 5\% N$

(a) Estimate the average number of employees per firm in the entire industry, using 95 percent confidence limits.

(b) Estimate the total number of employees working in this industry, using 95 percent confidence limits.

10 Of the 50 firms described in Prob. 7, the operative employees of 20 of the firms belong to a national labor union.

$p = .4 \left(\dfrac{20}{50}\right)$

$q = .6$

(a) Estimate the percentage of all 1,200 firms whose employees belong to a national labor union, using a 90 percent confidence interval.

(b) Estimate the total number of firms whose employees belong to a national labor union, using a 90 percent confidence interval.

$s_p = \sqrt{\dfrac{pq}{n}}$

$= \sqrt{\dfrac{(.4)(.6)}{50}}$

$= (.07)$

11 In another industry made up of 1,200 firms, 30 of a sample of 50 firms are unionized. Estimate the difference in the proportion of firms whose employees are represented by a labor union in this industry as compared with the industry described in Prob. 10, above, using 90 percent confidence limits.

$P \pm 1.64(.07)$

see notes.

$29\% \text{ to } 51\%.$

$1.0 = 100\%$

unit 9 · hypothesis testing

Both Unit 8 and this one are concerned with statistical decision making. In Unit 8 we illustrated the use of the binomial and normal probability distributions for the purpose of estimating population values. In this unit we shall illustrate the use of the methods of statistical inference for the purpose of testing hypotheses concerning the assumed values of population parameters. Again the use of both the binomial and the normal probability distributions will be required and, in conjunction with the latter, the standard error of the appropriate statistic will be used in carrying out these tests. Thus the new material in this unit concerns the *methodology* of hypothesis testing, utilizing the probability distributions and standard-error formulas that are already familiar to you. In terms of the order of topics, we shall discuss the general nature of hypothesis testing, consider the types of errors that can be made in interpreting such tests, compare the procedure to that of estimation, and illustrate the testing of hypotheses concerning assumed values of population means and population proportions.

9.a · hypothesis testing and the null hypothesis

The assumed value of a population parameter is tested by comparing it with the value of the equivalent statistic based on a randomly selected sample from the population in question. Thus, when the value of a sample mean is "very close" to the assumed value of the population mean, we would tend to accept the assumed value as being correct. On the other hand, when a sample mean is "too different" from the assumed value of the population mean, we would tend to reject the assumed population value.

1 The processes of both estimation and hypothesis testing represent methods of decision making under conditions of uncertainty, and both exemplify the use of statistics for the purpose of (description / inference).

inference

2 In the application of these two basic varieties of statistical inference, a tentative assumption regarding the value of a parameter *prior to the collection of sample data* is made in (estimation / hypothesis testing), but no such tentative assumptions are made in (estimation / hypothesis testing).

hypothesis testing estimation

3 In hypothesis testing we begin with an assumed value for a population parameter, such as the population mean, collect sample data, and then test the likelihood that the assumed population value is in fact correct, on the basis of the sample data. Thus, as the difference between the assumed value of the population mean and the actual value of the sample mean gets larger, the probability that the assumed value is correct is (increased / decreased).

decreased

4 In any hypothesis-testing situation it is important to recognize that the accuracy of the assumed value of the population parameter, i.e., the validity of the hypothesis, cannot be tested directly. Rather, what is tested is the size of the difference between the assumed value of a population parameter and the computed value of a _____.

sample statistic

5 The ideal evidence in support of a hypothesis would be the observation that the *difference* between the assumed population value and the obtained sample value is equal to _____ (number).

0

6 Therefore, because the population hypothesis cannot be tested directly, the hypothesis of "no difference" is tested instead. This hypothesis is referred to as the *null hypothesis*. In terms of our discussion, it is clear that the null hypothesis is involved (in every application of the methods of statistical inference / in every hypothesis-testing situation / in some, though not necessarily all, hypothesis-testing situations).

in every hypothesis-testing situation

null hypothesis stated.

7 Given a manufacturing process in which the quality standard requires that the mean diameter of bearings being polished must be 0.575 inch, a sample of bearings has a mean diameter of 0.565 inch. Testing the null hypothesis in this case concerns testing the significance of the difference between the values _____ (number) and _____ (number).

0.575; 0.565 (either order)

8 In this hypothesis-testing problem, then, the question asked is: "Is the difference of 0.010 significantly different from _____ (number)?"

0

9 The significance of a difference in measurements cannot be judged on the basis of its size alone, but on the basis of its size relative to the value of the standard error for the statistic concerned. Thus the difference of 0.010 inch referred to in Frame 8 would be evaluated relative to the value of the standard error of the _____.

mean

10 Since we begin with the assumption that the assumed population value (population mean, in this case) is correct, we would expect the values of a large number of sample means to cluster symmetrically about the population value. Accordingly, on the diagram below representing the sampling distribution of means for the problem in which the production standard requires a mean bearing diameter of 0.575 inch and the sample mean is 0.565 inch, enter the appropriate values in the two blank spaces.

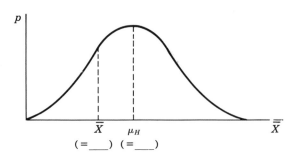

$$(= \underline{\hspace{1cm}})\ (= \underline{\hspace{1cm}})$$

11 Suppose that in Frame 10 the standard error of the mean $s_{\bar{x}}$ is equal to 0.010. What is the probability that a sample mean will have a value between 0.565 and 0.585, assuming that the population mean has been correctly identified? $p = \underline{\hspace{1cm}}$ Accordingly, what is the probability that a sample mean will differ from the hypothesized mean by 0.010 or more, in *either* direction? $p = \underline{\hspace{1cm}}$

0.68

0.32

12 For another sample from the same manufacturing process, suppose that the difference between the hypothesized population mean and the sample mean is 0.020. What is the probability that a difference this large or larger occurs by chance? Refer to Table A.1 for needed figures.

p being within these limits, in either direction, $= 2(0.4772) = 0.9544$. p being outside of these limits, $= 1 - 0.9544 = 0.0456$

13 In the process of hypothesis testing we do not question the accuracy of the observed value of the sample statistic. Rather, we question the validity of our assumption regarding the value of the population parameter. Which of the two differences discussed in Frames 11 and 12, 0.010 or 0.020, would more likely lead to a rejection of the null hypothesis? (0.010 / 0.020)

0.020

14 Rejection of the null hypothesis in the case of this example would be equivalent to saying that the assumed value of the population mean is (accepted / rejected).

rejected

9.b ▪ the level of significance and type I and type II errors

Having indicated the general basis used for accepting or rejecting a null hypothesis, our next task is to define the specific basis for this acceptance or rejection. In relation to this decision, we run the risk of making either of two types of errors: that of rejecting a hypothesis that is in fact correct or that of accepting a hypothesis that is in fact incorrect.

15   Though there is no universal standard for accepting or rejecting a null hypothesis, one specific basis that is often used is referred
to as the *5 percent level of significance.* On this basis, when the
difference between the sample statistic and the assumed population parameter is so large that a difference of that size or larger
would occur by chance with a probability of 0.05 or less when the
assumed value is in fact correct, then the null hypothesis is rejected
and the observed difference is considered to be (significant /
insignificant).

significant

16   If the 5 percent level of significance is used as the basis for
testing the hypothesis, would the null hypothesis be rejected for
the data of Frame 11? (yes / no) For the data of Frame 12? (yes / no)

no   yes

17   In published research the 1 percent level of significance also
is often used in hypothesis testing. Which of these two significance
levels, the 5 percent or the 1 percent, would lead to more frequent
rejection of the null hypothesis when a number of hypotheses are
being investigated and tested? (5 percent / 1 percent)

5 percent (since the difference required is not so large as that for the
1 percent level)

18   Figures 9.1a and b illustrate this point diagrammatically, with
hypothesis testing concerning the mean as a case in point. The
proportion of sample means included within the critical limits for
the test at the 5 percent level is 0.95, as indicated in Fig. 9.1a, and
for the test at the 1 percent level the proportion within the critical
limits is 0.99, as illustrated in Fig. 9.1b. Thus, of the two sets of
limits defined in these figures, rejection of the null hypothesis will
occur more frequently when the critical limits are set at $\mu_H \pm$ (1.96 /
2.58) $s_{\bar{x}}$.

1.96

**figure 9.1a ▪ critical limits for
testing a hypothesized mean
at the 5 percent level of
significance.**

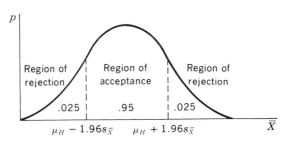

**figure 9.1b ▪ critical limits
for testing a hypothesized
mean at the 1 percent level
of significance.**

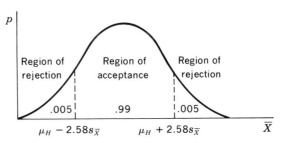

19 With reference to either Fig. 9.1a or 9.1b, all of the possible values of the sample mean that are outside of the critical limits are in the region of _____ of the null hypothesis, whereas all of the values within the defined limits are in the region of _____.

rejection
acceptance

20 In this unit we have introduced the concept of "level of significance" to identify the probability level associated with a hypothesis-testing procedure. If a hypothesis is tested using the 5 percent level of significance (or, at the 0.05 level of significance), then by definition we have indicated that we shall reject the null hypothesis if the difference between the statistic and the assumed parameter is so large that a difference of that amount or greater would occur, on the average, in _____ (number) samples out of 100 randomly chosen samples when the assumed population value is in fact correct.

five

21 In Unit 8, on statistical estimation, we used the concept of the "degree of confidence." An interval estimate defined with a 95 percent degree of confidence is such that if this basis is used consistently in defining limits for population parameters, then in the long run the defined intervals will actually include the population parameters being estimated _____ percent of the time and will fail to include the parameters being estimated _____ percent of the time.

95
5

95

22 Thus the use of the concept degree of confidence is always related to the application of the methods of statistical inference for the purpose of _____, whereas a level of significance is used in conjunction with the process of _____.

estimation
hypothesis testing

23 When the normal probability distribution is used in conjunction with *estimating* the value of a population mean, as pictured below, the value placed at the center of the distribution is ($\bar{X}$ / μ_H), but when the distribution is used in conjunction with hypothesis testing, the value placed at the center of the distribution is represented by the symbol ($\bar{X}$ / μ_H).

$\bar{X}$
μ_H

$-Zs_{\bar{X}}$ $\bar{X}$ $+Zs_{\bar{X}}$ $\bar{X}$
(or μ_H)

within	**24** With reference to the diagram in Frame 23, in the process of estimation the confidence interval is defined as being made up of those values (within / outside of) the limits $\bar{X} \pm Zs_{\bar{x}}$.

25 With reference to the same diagram, in hypothesis testing the possible values of the sample mean that would lead to a rejection of the null hypothesis (and thus to rejection of the assumed value of the population mean) are those that are (within / outside of) the limits $\mu_H \pm Zs_{\bar{x}}$.

outside of

26 When the null hypothesis is tested at the 5 percent level of significance, 5 percent of the possible values of the sample statistic are in the region of rejection when the hypothesis is in fact correct. Therefore, when the 5 percent level is used in hypothesis testing, the probability of incorrectly rejecting the null hypothesis is _____ (number).

0.05

27 Thus the probability of type I error, or rejecting a hypothesis that is in fact correct, is equal to the level of _____ being used in conjunction with the hypothesis-testing procedure.

significance

28 If we decided to test a hypothesis at the 1 percent level instead of the 5 percent level, the probability of type I error would thereby be (increased / decreased).

decreased (to 0.01)

29 However, if the probability of type I error is reduced by reducing the level of significance (and thus making it a more stringent test, in the sense that a larger difference is then needed to reject the null hypothesis), the type of error whose probability is then increased is that of accepting a null hypothesis that is in fact _____.

incorrect (or false)

30 Accepting a null hypothesis that is in fact false is referred to as a type II error. Thus, as indicated in Table 9.1, if we accept the null hypothesis, we run the risk of type _____ error, whereas if we reject the null hypothesis, we run the risk of type _____ error.

II

I

table 9.1 ▪ types of errors in hypothesis testing

	Null hypothesis true	*Null hypothesis false*
Accept hypothesis	Correctly accepted	Type II error
Reject hypothesis	Type I error	Correctly rejected

31 Type I error in hypothesis testing is the one in which we incorrectly (accept / reject) a null hypothesis that is actually (true / false).

reject

true

accept

false

32 Type II error is the one in which we incorrectly (accept / reject) a null hypothesis that is actually (true / false).

I

33 The level of significance used in testing a hypothesis directly indicates the extent of risk regarding type _____ error.

34 . Computing the probability of type II error in hypothesis testing is quite complex and beyond the scope of this unit. We can say, however, that with sample size remaining the same, when the probability of type I error is reduced by changing the level of significance being used, then the probability of type II error is (increased / also reduced).

increased

9.c ▪ hypotheses concerning population means

We shall present two ways of expressing the critical limits that are used in testing a hypothesis concerning the population mean. Though the second method, in which critical limits are identified in terms of Z values, is the commonly used procedure, our discussion of the first method is presented to enhance your understanding of the relationship between estimation and hypothesis testing. In hypothesis testing we may be interested in whether a sample mean is significantly different, in either direction, from the hypothesized value of the population mean, or we may be interested only in whether the sample mean is significantly larger (or significantly smaller) than the hypothesized value. In the former case, when no direction is specified, the test is referred to as a *two-tailed test,* whereas the test that is specifically directed toward testing differences in one direction only is called a *one-tailed test.*

35 Throughout this section we shall assume that the standard error of the mean has been computed on the basis of sample data. Therefore the appropriate formula(s) used to compute this standard error is (are) (circle letters of all correct choices):

(a) $\dfrac{\sigma}{\sqrt{n}}$

(b) $\dfrac{s}{\sqrt{n-1}}$

(c) $\dfrac{\sigma}{\sqrt{n}}\sqrt{\dfrac{N-n}{N-1}}$

(d) $\dfrac{s}{\sqrt{n-1}}\sqrt{\dfrac{N-n}{N-1}}$

b and **d** (See Unit 7, Frames 96–99, for a review.)

36 As a further review, of the two appropriate formulas **b** and **d** in Frame 35, when would formula **b** be used, as contrasted to **d**?

_____

_____

when the population is infinite in size or the sample size is less than 5 percent of the population size

37 In testing a hypothesis about the value of a population mean, first the level of significance to be used in the test is specified and then the regions of acceptance and rejection for evaluating the obtained sample mean are specified accordingly. If the 1 percent level of significance is used, indicate the percentages of sample means in each of the areas of the normal curve, below, assuming that the population hypothesis is correct.

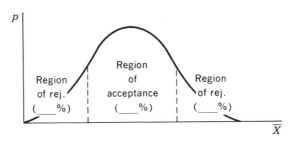

p

Region of rej. (___ %)

Region of acceptance (___ %)

Region of rej. (___ %)

X

0.5; 99; 0.5

---

38 By the first method the critical limits that separate the region of acceptance from the regions leading to rejection of the null hypothesis can be specified in a manner similar to the setting of confidence limits in the process of estimation. Thus, for testing a hypothesis at the 1 percent level, the critical limits are at $\mu_H - 2.58 s_{\bar{X}}$ and $\mu_H + 2.58 s_{\bar{X}}$. For testing a hypothesis at the 5 percent level, the appropriate critical limits are at _____ and _____ .

$\mu_H - 1.96 s_{\bar{X}}$

$\mu_H + 1.96 s_{\bar{X}}$

---

39 In contrast, the 95 percent *confidence limits* for estimating the population mean are defined by the limits _____ and _____ .

$\bar{X}$ (or μ) $- 1.96 s_{\bar{X}}$

$\bar{X}$ (or μ) $+ 1.96 s_{\bar{X}}$

---

40 Therefore the general procedure for setting confidence limits which you learned in Unit 8 can be applied also to set critical limits for the purpose of hypothesis testing. The difference is that instead of the interval being constructed about the point estimate for the population mean, it is constructed about _____ _____ .

---

the hypothesized value of the population mean (μ_H)

---

41 The sampling distribution of the mean is used as the essential vehicle for both estimating the value of the population mean and testing a hypothesis concerning its value. In estimation the degree of _____ indicates the percentage of sample means included (within / outside of) the defined limits. In hypothesis testing the level of _____ indicates the percentage of sample means included (within / outside of) the critical limits, assuming the hypothesis is correct.

---

confidence

within

significance

outside of

---

42 As an example of using critical limits for testing a hypothesis concerning the population mean, suppose that the average (mean) value of a company's accounts receivable is claimed to be $187.50. An auditor selects a sample of 50 accounts randomly and determines that the sample mean is $175 and the standard deviation is $35. What are the critical limits for testing the validity of the claimed value of the population mean at the 5 percent level of significance?

$$s\bar{x} = \frac{s}{\sqrt{n-1}} =$$

$$\frac{35}{\sqrt{49}} = \frac{35}{7} = 5.0$$

$$187.50 \pm 1.96(5) = 187.50 \pm 9.80$$
$$= \$177.70 \text{ and } \$197.30$$

Critical limits $= \mu_H \pm 1.96s\bar{x} =$

43 For Frame 42, given the sample mean that was actually obtained, and using the 5 percent level of significance, the null hypothesis would be (accepted / rejected).

rejected

44 For the example in Frame 43, rejection of the null hypothesis means that the claimed average accounts receivable of $187.50 (is / is not) accepted as being correct at the 5 percent level of significance.

is not

45 Is it possible that the claimed accounts-receivable figure is actually correct? (yes / no)

yes

46 In the hypothesis-testing procedure which we have been describing, critical limits are defined in terms of the particular measurement units used (e.g., in dollars in the last example). The more popular approach to hypothesis testing, however, is to define these critical limits in terms of Z units, or number of units of the standard error of the mean, and to evaluate the sample mean accordingly. The advantage of this approach is that no matter what population mean, or other parameter, is being tested, the same critical limits are used for a given level of significance. Thus, in terms of Z units, -1.96 and $+1.96$ are the critical limits for tests at the _____ percent level of significance, and -2.58 and $+2.58$ are the critical limits for tests at the _____ percent level of significance.

5

1

47 When this approach is used, the obtained value of the sample mean has to be transformed into a Z measurement so that it can be compared to the critical values. Given that

$$Z = \frac{\bar{X} - \mu_H}{s\bar{x}}$$

calculate the value of Z for the sample mean in Frame 42, in which the hypothesized population mean was $187.50, the sample mean was $175, and the standard error of the mean was $5.

$$\frac{175.00 - 187.50}{5.00} = \frac{-12.50}{5.00} = -2.5$$

$$Z =$$

48 Would the obtained value of Z for the sample mean result in rejecting the null hypothesis at the 5 percent level? (yes / no) At the 1 percent level? (yes / no)

49 The normal probability curve below indicates the critical limits at the 5 percent level both in terms of original measurement units and in terms of Z units for the problem we have been discussing. Thus, whether the sample mean is stated as being equal to $175 or to -2.5 in terms of the equivalent Z value, the sample mean is clearly located in the region of _____.

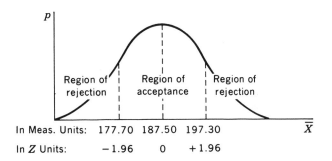

| In Meas. Units: | 177.70 | 187.50 | 197.30 | $\overline{X}$ |
| In Z Units: | -1.96 | 0 | $+1.96$ | |

50 Rejection of the null hypothesis in Frame 49 then logically leads to acceptance of the alternative hypothesis, that is, the hypothesis that the sample mean is significantly (different from / larger than / smaller than) the hypothesized population mean.

51 If there is an interest in testing for differences in one direction only, then this fact must be specified, along with the level of significance to be used, *before* the sample data to be used in making the test are collected. Thus the sample data collected for the purpose of hypothesis testing (can / cannot) be used as the basis for deciding what hypothesis should be tested and what significance level should be employed.

52 To employ sample data for this purpose would lead to a circularity in thinking and decision making, for data that suggest a certain hypothesis would then be used to test that hypothesis. On the other hand, would it be logically acceptable to formulate hypotheses on the basis of one sample of data and test them using a second, independently selected sample? (yes / no)

53 Suppose that the auditor of Frame 42 is concerned only about the possibility that the average of the accounts receivable is lower than the claimed amount. This interest would be specified before the sample is drawn, and the null hypothesis being tested is that the sample mean is not significantly (different from / smaller than) the claimed population average.

54 If the auditor is interested only in the possibility that the claimed average is too high, would he need to go through the procedure of hypothesis testing if the claimed average is $187.50 and the sample mean is $175? (yes / no)

yes

55 Continuing from Frame 54, would he need to go through the procedure of statistically testing the hypothesis if the sample mean is $200? (yes / no)

no (because the hypothesis is directed only toward the possibility that the true mean is lower than claimed)

56 Therefore, when the null hypothesis involves an assumption of "no difference," there are two critical limits, and therefore such tests are called two-tailed tests. When the null hypothesis specifies that the sample statistic is not smaller (or not larger) than the hypothesized value, there is only one critical limit, and such tests are called _____-_____ tests.

one-tailed

57 Using a randomly chosen sample of bearings being polished by a machine, we may wish to test the null hypothesis that the mean diameter of the bearings does not differ significantly, at the 5 percent level, from the production standard. This would be a _____-tailed statistical test. On the other hand, testing the hypothesis that the bearings are not significantly larger than the standard would involve a _____-tailed test.

two

one

58 The two figures below illustrate the differing locations of the regions of rejection for one- versus two-tailed statistical tests carried out at the 5 percent level. The one-tailed test is illustrated by Fig. (a / b), and the two-tailed test is illustrated by Fig. (a / b).

a   b

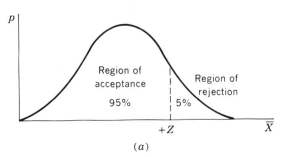

(a)

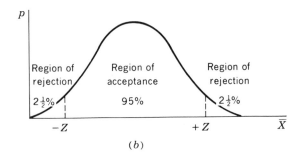

(b)

59 In Figs. *a* and *b* in Frame 58, would the critical limit $+Z$ have the same value, i.e., be at the same point, for the two distributions? (yes / no) Why or why not? _____

_____

no; because for *a* it separates the upper 5 percent of sample means, whereas for *b* it separates the upper 2½ percent

60 Thus the critical value or values of Z being used to determine the significance of a difference depends on whether a one-tailed or a two-tailed test is being employed. In Table 9.2, for example, the critical values of Z for a two-tailed test at the 1 percent level are _____, and the critical value of Z for a one-tailed test at the 1 percent level is _____.

+2.58

+2.33 (or −2.33; only one of these, depending on direction of test)

table 9.2 ▪ critical values of Z in hypothesis testing

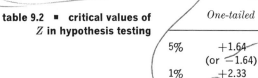

See note

	One-tailed	Two-tailed
5%	+1.64 (or −1.64)	±1.96
1%	+2.33 (or −2.33)	±2.58

61 For a shipment of cable, given that the specifications call for a mean breaking strength of 2,000 pounds, a sampling of the breaking strength of a number of segments of the cable has a mean breaking strength of 1,955 pounds with an associated standard error of the mean of 25 pounds. Using the 5 percent level, test the significance of the difference and interpret the result of your test, referring to Table 9.2 for the critical value(s) of Z to be used.

$$\frac{1,955 - 2,000}{25} = \frac{-45}{25} = -1.8$$

$$Z = \frac{\bar{X} - \mu_H}{s_{\bar{X}}} =$$

difference not significant at the 5 percent level

Interpretation: _____

_____

62 For the example in Frame 61, since we have found that the sample mean is lower in value than the hypothesized population mean, can we apply a one-tailed test instead, thus specifically determining whether the sample mean is significantly lower in value than the population mean? (yes / no) Why or why not?

no

Sample data cannot be used as the basis for deciding on the kind of test to be used with the same data.

_____

_____

63 On the other hand, suppose that before calculating the sample mean, we had stipulated that we are interested only in the possibility that the cable that has been received is weaker than called for by the specifications. What would then be the interpretation of the difference tested in Frame 61? _____

At the 5 percent level the sample cable is significantly weaker than specifications. (Z value of −1.8 is outside of critical Z limit of −1.64.)

_____

One-tailed Test. — Z value.

9.d ▪ hypotheses concerning the difference between two means

For testing differences between means, we could also illustrate two ways of setting critical limits, as we did in Sec. 9.c. However, in this section we shall proceed directly to the more popular method of defining critical limits in terms of the Z scale and computing the critical Z ratio Z_{CR} for the sample statistic involved in the test. In doing so, we shall illustrate the general nature of the critical Z ratio and how it can be used in a wide variety of hypothesis-testing situations not actually covered in this unit.

64 The general formula for the critical ratio computed in hypothesis testing is

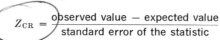

$$Z_{CR} = \frac{\text{observed value} - \text{expected value}}{\text{standard error of the statistic}}$$

Thus in Sec. 9.c the Z value, or critical ratio, computed in testing a hypothesis concerning the population mean was simply a special instance of this general formula, and it was expressed as

$$\frac{\bar{X} - \mu_H}{s_{\bar{X}}}$$

$$Z_{CR} = \frac{}{s_{\bar{X}}}$$

65 Referring to Frame 64 for the general formula of the critical ratio, given that the standard error of the median can be represented by the symbol s_{med}, construct the formula that could be used for testing a hypothesis concerning the value of the population median (med_H):

$$\frac{med - med_H}{s_{med}}$$

$$Z_{CR} =$$

66 Thus, for any hypothesis-testing situation involving the use of the normal probability distribution as the basis for the test, the general formula for the critical ratio is

$$\frac{\text{Observed value} - \text{expected value}}{\text{standard error of statistic}}$$

$$Z_{CR} =$$

67 Now, recalling that the standard error for the difference between two means is represented by $s_{\bar{X}_1 - \bar{X}_2}$ (based on sample data), complete the critical ratio that can be used for testing the assumed value of the difference between two means:

$$\frac{(\bar{X}_1 - \bar{X}_2) - (\mu_1 - \mu_2)_H}{s_{\bar{X}_1 - \bar{X}_2}}$$

$$Z_{CR} = \frac{() - ()_H}{s_{\bar{X}_1 - \bar{X}_2}}$$

68 In the large majority of cases in which the difference between means is tested, the hypothesis is that the two sample means came from the same population and thus that $(\mu_1 - \mu_2)_H = $ _____ (value).

0

69 Therefore the critical ratio used for testing the difference between means is usually presented in a simplified form (substi-

hypothesis testing ▪ 180

tuting 0 for $\mu_1 - \mu_2$):

$$\frac{\bar{X}_1 - \bar{X}_2}{s_{\bar{X}_1 - \bar{X}_2}}$$

$$Z_{\text{CR}} = \frac{(\bar{X}_1 - \bar{X}_2) - (\mu_1 - \mu_2)_H}{s_{\bar{X}_1 - \bar{X}_2}} =$$

70 In Unit 8 we estimated the "true" difference between population means with specified degrees of confidence, whereas in this unit we are testing the assumption that there actually is no difference between the means, at a specified level of significance. Given the data from Unit 8, Frame 65, if a sample of 50 employees in a particular firm has a mean wage rate of $110 per week with a standard error of the mean of $1.44, and a sample of 40 employees taken from another firm has a mean weekly wage rate of $105 and a standard error of $1.50, then

$$\sqrt{(1.44)^2 + (1.50)^2} = \sqrt{4.3236} = 2.08$$

$$s_{\bar{X}_1 - \bar{X}_2} = \sqrt{s_{\bar{X}_1}{}^2 + s_{\bar{X}_2}{}^2} =$$

71 If, for the difference between the two sample means discussed in Frame 70, we intend to test the null hypothesis at the 1 percent level of significance, then the critical values of Z are _____ and _____.

$$-2.58$$
$+2.58$ (in either order)

72 Compute the value of the critical ratio for the data of Frame 70 and interpret it.

$$\frac{\bar{X}_1 - \bar{X}_2}{s_{\bar{X}_1 - \bar{X}_2}} = \frac{110 - 105}{2.08}$$

$$= \frac{+5.00}{2.08} = +2.4$$

The hypothesis of no difference is accepted, since the critical ratio is in the region of acceptance for the test at the 1 percent level.

$Z_{\text{CR}} =$

Interpretation: _____

_____

73 Suppose, however, that before collecting the data we had predicted, or hypothesized, that the wages in the first firm would be higher than those in the second. The test then would be a _____ tailed test, and the critical value of Z to be used in evaluating the critical ratio at the 1 percent level is _____. (Refer to Table 9.2, if necessary.)

one

$+2.33$ (The sign should be included.)

9.e ▪ hypotheses concerning proportions (using the binomial distribution)

Again, as in Sec. 8.d, we need to distinguish between continuous and discrete data in the process of inference. In this section we shall illustrate the use of the binomial distribution for the purpose of hypothesis testing, as contrasted to estimation. As before, however, use of the normal probability distribution in place of the binomial distribution simplifies the required computations; this substitution will be discussed and illustrated in Sec. 9.f.

74 To take a very simple situation in which the binomial distribution can be used in hypothesis testing, suppose we toss a coin five times and the coin lands heads all five times. Can we conclude that the coin is biased at, say, the 5 percent level of significance? For developing the probability distribution by the use of Table A.2, for this problem $p =$ _____ (value) and $n =$ _____ (value).

75 Referring to Table A.2, expand the appropriate binomial distribution and list all of the terms of this expansion (but do not yet substitute any values for p and q). _____

76 Now, substituting for the values of p and q, construct the probability distribution for the various possible outcomes, in terms of number of heads.

Number of heads	p
0	0.0312
1	0.1562
2	_____
3	_____
4	_____
5	_____

77 Assume that we had reason to believe that the coin was biased in favor of heads before the five tosses were made; is the observed outcome in terms of number of heads significantly greater than the expected two or three heads at the 5 percent level? (yes / no) Why or why not? _____

78 If we had not predicted the direction of bias before data collection, would the run of heads be considered significant at the 5 percent level? (yes / no) Why or why not? _____

79 Similarly, suppose we begin with the assumption that no more than 40 percent of the students at a particular university are habitual smokers. If we survey a random sample of ten students, how many must be smokers if we must reject the hypothesis at the 5 percent level? To begin with, this will involve a _____- tailed test of the hypothesis.

80 For this problem $n = 10$ and $\pi_H = 0.4$. The most extreme outcome in nonsupport of the hypothesis would be represented in the outcome in which all ten students sampled are smokers. Since this example involves the use of the same probability distribution as the example on estimation in Unit 8, Frame 73, we can make use of a previously constructed table. According to Table 9.3, which is the same as Table 8.3, the probability of all ten students being smokers, assuming the validity of the hypothesis, is _____ (value).

Number of smokers	Proportion	Binomial term to be solved	Probability
0	0.0	q^{10}	0.0060
1	0.1	$10pq^9$	0.0403
2	0.2	$45p^2q^8$	0.1209
3	0.3	$120p^3q^7$	0.2150
4	0.4	$210p^4q^6$	0.2508
5	0.5	$252p^5q^5$	0.2007
6	0.6	$210p^6q^4$	0.1115
7	0.7	$120p^7q^3$	0.0425
8	0.8	$45p^8q^2$	0.0106
9	0.9	$10p^9q$	0.0016
10	1.0	p^{10}	0.0001

table 9.3 ▪ probability distribution for obtaining various number of smokers in a sample of 10 respondents if $\pi = 0.4$

problems will be based on normal curve computation

81 If eight of the ten students in Table 9.3 are smokers, must the hypothesis be rejected at the 5 percent level? (yes / no) Why or why not? _____

yes; because the probability of a deviation this large or larger is <0.05 (0.0106 + 0.0016 + 0.0001 = 0.0123)

82 On the other hand, suppose that seven of the ten students are smokers. Would this outcome lead to the rejection of the hypothesis that not more than a proportion of 0.4 of the student body habitually smoke, at the 5 percent level? (yes / no) Why or why not? _____

no; because the probability of a deviation this large or larger is >0.05 (0.0425 + 0.0106 + 0.0016 + 0.0001 = 0.0548)

9.f ▪ hypotheses concerning proportions (using the normal distribution)

Just as for estimation, it is more convenient computationally when the normal distribution can be used in place of the binomial in the process of hypothesis testing. As we indicated in Unit 8, this substitution can be applied whenever the sample size n is at least 50 and np and nq are each at least equal to 5.

83 If we continue with the student-survey example of Frames 81 and 82, but increase the size of the sample from 10 to 64, then the criteria for using the normal distribution in place of the binomial (have / have not) been thereby satisfied.

have

84 In developing the normal probability distribution for use with this problem, the center of the distribution is at the hypothesized value of the population proportion π_H, which is 0.4. Since the standard error of this distribution is based on the assumed population value rather than a sample proportion, it is represented by the symbol σ_p rather than s_p. Accordingly, for the data given,

$$\sigma_p = \sqrt{\frac{\pi_H(1 - \pi_H)}{n}}$$

$$\sqrt{\frac{0.4(0.6)}{64}} = \sqrt{\frac{0.24}{64}} = \frac{0.4899}{8} = 0.0612$$

(We are assuming that the sample size is less than 5 percent of the population size, and thus the finite correction factor is not necessary in the formula.)

85 According to the general formula for the critical ratio (Frame 64), what is the formula for the critical ratio which would be computed in testing the hypothesis that no more than 40 percent of the students as a whole are habitual smokers, using p for the sample proportion and π_H for the hypothesized proportion?

$$\frac{p - \pi_H}{\sigma_p}$$

$Z_{CR} =$

86 Refer to Table 9.2 if necessary. What is (are) the critical limit(s) of Z to be used in evaluating the critical ratio in Frame 85 at the 5 percent level of significance?

$+1.64$ (Sign should be included.)

$Z =$ _____ (value)

87 Suppose that 40 of the 64 students surveyed, or a proportion of 0.625, are habitual smokers. Calculate the value of the critical ratio and evaluate it, using any of the information in Frames 84 to 86.

$$\frac{0.625 - 0.4}{0.0612} = +3.68$$

$Z_{CR} =$

rejected (since the critical value of Z is $+1.64$)

Therefore the hypothesis is (accepted / rejected) at the 5 percent level (one-tailed).

88 If we had not specified any direction in the hypothesis, but had simply been testing for significance of difference in either direction, then at the 5 percent level the null hypothesis would have been (accepted / rejected).

rejected (The obtained critical ratio of $+3.68$ is also outside of the critical Z limits of -1.96 and $+1.96$.)

89 Just as for sample means, we may hypothesize that an observed difference between two sample proportions is not significant, i.e., that they could have been obtained from the same population. In this case the critical test ratio can also be simplified, so that

$$\frac{p_1 - p_2}{s_{p_1-p_2}}$$

$$Z_{CR} = \frac{(p_1 - p_2) - (\pi_1 - \pi_2)_H}{s_{p_1-p_2}} =$$

90 Given that a proportion of 0.45 of a random sample of people in an income group express approval of a product design, with a standard error of 0.04, and a proportion of 0.55 of the people in another income group express such approval, with an associated standard error of 0.03, test the null hypothesis that there is no difference between the groups at the 5 percent level of significance.

$$\sqrt{0.04^2 + 0.03^2} = \sqrt{0.0025} = 0.05$$

$$\frac{0.45 - 0.55}{0.05} = -2.0$$

rejected (since the critical values of Z are -1.96 and $+1.96$)

$$s_{p_1-p_2} = \sqrt{s_{p_1}^2 + s_{p_2}^2} =$$

$Z_{CR} =$

Therefore the null hypothesis is (accepted / rejected) at the 5 percent level (two-tailed).

91 (Frames 1–9) The assumption that is in effect tested in all applications of hypothesis testing is that the difference between the assumed value of a population parameter and the value of a sample statistic is not significantly different from _____ (value).

0

92 (Frames 10–14) The larger the difference between an assumed population parameter and a sample statistic, relative to the size of the standard error of the statistic, the (more / less) likely is it that the assumed value of the parameter is correct.

less

93 (Frames 15–20) When testing a null hypothesis at the 5 percent level of significance, if the assumed population parameter is in fact correct, then the probability is 0.05 that the sample statistic of a randomly selected sample will be in the region of _____ and the probability is 0.95 that the sample statistic will be in the region of _____.

rejection

acceptance

94 (Frames 21–26) "Level of significance" is the term always used in conjunction with _____; "degree of confidence" is always used in conjunction with _____.

hypothesis testing

estimation

95 (Frames 27–32) Type I error refers to the probability of (accepting / rejecting) a null hypothesis which is actually (true / false); type II error is the probability of (accepting / rejecting) a null hypothesis which is actually (true / false).

rejecting

true   accepting

false

96 (Frames 33–34) The level of significance used in testing a hypothesis is a direct indicator of the probability of type (I / II) error.

I

97 (Frames 35–45) In the first approach to setting critical limits for the purpose of hypothesis testing which we discussed, the limits are defined in terms of the measurement units used. Thus, for a two-tailed test at the 5 percent level, the values of the two critical limits for testing a hypothesis concerning a population mean can be determined by solving the formula $\mu_H \pm$ _____.

$\mu_H \pm 1.96 s_{\bar{x}}$

98 (Frame 46) In the more popular method of defining the critical limits, they are expressed in terms of Z units, and thus the two critical limits for a two-tailed test at the 5 percent level, regardless of the parameter being tested, are simply _____ and _____.

-1.96 $+1.96$

99 (Frames 47–50) When the critical limits are expressed in terms of Z units, then the observed value of the sample statistic, such as the sample mean, has to be converted into the Z scale in order to be evaluated. For the sample mean this conversion is accomplished by the formula, $Z =$ _____.

$$\frac{\bar{x} - \mu_H}{s_{\bar{x}}}$$

two	**100** (Frames 51–57) When we wish to test the significance of any *difference* between a sample mean and a hypothesized population mean, the hypothesis test is described as being _____-tailed, whereas a specified interest in the sample mean being only smaller, or only larger, results in a _____-tailed test.
one	

101 (Frames 58–63) As contrasted to a two-tailed test, a one-tailed statistical test includes (one / two) region(s) of rejection.

one

102 (Frames 64–73) In testing the significance of an observed difference between two sample means, the same considerations regarding one-tailed versus two-tailed hypothesis testing apply. In this case the simplified formula for computing the value of the critical ratio Z for the observed difference is

$\dfrac{\bar{X}_1 - \bar{X}_2}{s_{\bar{X}_1 - \bar{X}_2}}$ $Z_{\mathrm{CR}} =$

103 (Frames 74–82) For data that are discrete, including proportions, the probability distribution used in conjunction with hypothesis testing using small samples is the _____ distribution.

binomial

104 (Sec. 9.f, Introduction; Frame 83) However, the probability distribution for discrete data approaches the characteristics of the normal probability distribution under certain conditions. As a rule of thumb, the normal probability distribution can be used as a substitute for the binomial when the sample size n is at least equal to _____ (number) and np and nq are each at least equal to _____ (number).

50

5

105 (Frames 84–90) For testing the difference between an observed proportion and a hypothesized proportion, and using the normal probability distribution, the formula for the critical ratio is

$\dfrac{p - \pi_H}{\sigma_p}$ $Z_{\mathrm{CR}} =$

For testing the difference between two sample proportions the critical ratio is computed by

$\dfrac{p_1 - p_2}{s_{p_1 - p_2}}$ $Z_{\mathrm{CR}} =$

problems
(solutions given
on page 357)

1 The manufacturer of three-way light bulbs claims that the bulbs have an average life of 2,500 hours. A sample of 37 bulbs has an average life of 2,325 hours with a standard deviation of 600 hours. Test the null hypothesis, using the 5 percent level of significance.

2 In problems like Prob. 1, the consumer typically would be concerned only about the possibility that the bulbs do not live up to the claims made for them, not that the claims are exceeded. Accordingly, is the performance of the bulbs significantly inferior to the claimed performance, at the 0.05 level of probability?

hypothesis testing ▪ 186

3 A random sample of 65 bearings produced by a machine has a mean diameter of 0.24 inch with a standard deviation of 0.02 inch; another batch of 65 bearings produced by the same machine the next day has a mean diameter of 0.25 inch with a standard deviation of 0.04 inch. Test the hypothesis that the machine is not out of adjustment in terms of the difference in the average diameter of the bearings. using the 5 percent level of significance.

4 For Prob. 3 suppose that as this kind of machine goes out of adjustment, it invariably begins producing bearings that are too large. With this information in mind, reinterpret the result of the test, still using the 5 percent level of significance.

5 A salesman claims that on the average he obtains orders from at least 30 percent of his prospects. For a sample of ten prospects, he obtains an order from just one of them. Can the general accuracy of his claim be rejected, using the 5 percent level of significance?

6 For Prob. 5 suppose that the salesman obtains orders from 20 out of 100 randomly selected prospects.

(a) Can his claim of being able to obtain orders from at least 30 percent of his prospects in the long run be rejected at the 5 percent level of significance?

(b) Can the claim be rejected at the 1 percent level of significance?

→ one-tail test.

additional problems

7 A fertilizer manufacturer claims that the use of his product will result in a yield of at least 35 bushels of wheat per acre, on the average. Application of the fertilizer to a sample tract of 37 acres results in a yield of 33 bushels per acre with a standard deviation of 5 bushels.

(a) Can the manufacturer's claim be rejected at the 5 percent level of significance?

(b) Can the claim be rejected at the 1 percent level of significance?

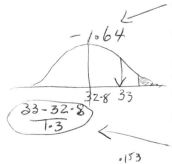

-1.64

$32.8 \quad 33$

$\dfrac{33-32.8}{1.3}$

$.153$

$Z_{CR}?$

8 Another brand of fertilizer results in a yield of 32.8 bushels of wheat per acre on a sample tract of 37 acres, with a standard deviation of 6 bushels.

(a) Does the average yield associated with the two brands of fertilizer differ significantly at the 5 percent level? *→ So, X_2 is center*

(b) Assume the first brand was predicted as being superior. Is this brand significantly superior at the 5 percent level? *no, not signif.*

(c) Assume the second brand was predicted as being superior. Is this brand significantly superior at the 5 percent level? *No.*

9 Of a randomly chosen sample of television viewers, 16 of the *No* 64 who actually had their sets turned on at a particular hour indicate

$Z_{CR} = -.13$

that they watched a specified program. The producer of the program had claimed that the program would attract at least one-third of the viewing audience. Evaluate his claim at the 5 percent level. *Yes,*

10 Twenty of the respondents in Prob. 9 indicated that they had watched a second program that was telecast at the same time. Is the difference in the proportions of people that watched the two programs significant at the 5 percent level? *No, significance.*

$$Z_{CR} = -0.75$$

unit 10 • the use of Student's t distribution

In our use of the normal probability distribution in problems of estimation and hypothesis testing, we have relied on the assumption that when a sampling distribution of a statistic, such as a distribution of sample means, is normally distributed, then the transformation of these values into values of Z will result in a distribution that is also normal. This distribution of Z values, called the standard normal distribution, is assumed to have a mean of 0 and a standard deviation of 1.0, and it is on the basis of this distribution that degrees of significance are defined in hypothesis testing. When the value of the standard error of the mean is computed on the basis of a known population standard deviation σ, then the standard error is designated by the symbol $\sigma_{\bar{X}}$, and the assumption that the associated Z distribution is normally distributed is in fact correct, regardless of sample size. However, when the value of the standard error of the mean is computed on the basis of a sample standard deviation s, then the standard error is designated by the symbol $s_{\bar{X}}$, and the assumption of normality may not be correct in this case. In this unit we shall define the conditions under which this distribution of transformed values is not normally distributed, describe the way in which such a distribution, called a t distribution, differs from the Z distribution, and illustrate the use of such a distribution in problems of estimation and hypothesis testing. "Student's t distribution" is so named because it was first described by W. S. Gosset, an employee of a brewery in Dublin, who published his work under the name Student.

10.a • characteristics of the t distribution

As indicated in the introduction above, the distribution of Z used in estimation and hypothesis testing is normally distributed whenever the standard error of the mean, designated by $\sigma_{\bar{X}}$, is based on the population standard deviation being known. This is true regardless of sample size because the Z values are computed by the formula $Z = (\bar{X} - \mu)/\sigma_{\bar{X}}$, which involves subtracting a constant from every sample mean in a normally distributed set of means and dividing the result by a constant as well. However, when the value of the standard deviation of the population is not known, then the divisor is not a constant, and the resulting transformed values are not in fact normally distributed, as we shall illustrate in this section.

1 If a sampling distribution of means is normally distributed, then the Z distribution into which it is converted is also normally distributed whenever the standard error of the mean is calculated on the basis of a known (sample / population) standard deviation.

population

2 This is so because the conversion of each mean in the (hypothetical) distribution of means into a Z value requires subtraction by a constant and division by a constant, thus preserving the normality of the original distribution of means. Specifically, in this case, each sample mean would be converted into a Z value by applying the formula

$\dfrac{\bar{X} - \mu}{\sigma_{\bar{x}}}$	$Z = \dfrac{\bar{X} -}{\rule{3cm}{0.4pt}}$
$\begin{array}{c} \mu \\ \sigma_{\bar{x}} \end{array}$	**3** In the computational formula for Z in Frame 2, the constant subtracted from every mean in the distribution is _____, and the constant by which the difference is divided is _____.

4 For an infinite population, $\sigma_{\bar{x}} = \sigma/\sqrt{n}$; for a finite population, and one in which the size of the sample is more than 5 percent of the population size,

$$\sigma_{\bar{x}} = \frac{\sigma}{\sqrt{n}} \sqrt{\frac{N-n}{N-1}}$$

is not	Thus, when σ is known, the computed value of the standard error of the mean for a given sample size (is / is not) dependent on particular sample statistics (i.e., sample standard deviations).

5 Now let us turn our attention to the calculation of $s_{\bar{x}}$, also presuming fixed sample size. In the formula $Z = (\bar{X} - \mu)/s_{\bar{x}}$ we are again subtracting a constant from every sample mean. Would we also be dividing by a constant? (yes / no)

no (This is a common, though mistaken assumption; continue with the following frames.)	

6 Assuming an infinite population in order to simplify our discussion,

$\dfrac{s}{\sqrt{n-1}}$	$s_{\bar{x}} =$

7 Now, though n in the formula in Frame 6 is presumed to be a constant, the value of s will *not* be the same for different sample means, for there is a unique sample standard deviation associated with each sample mean. That is, each sample mean is calculated on the basis of a distribution of sample values, and each of these distributions has its own standard deviation. The direct implication of this fact is that in the formula $Z = (\bar{X} - \mu)/s_{\bar{x}}$, the denominator in

does not	the fraction (does / does not) have precisely the same value for each sample mean, though all samples are of the same size.

8 Subtracting a constant from every one of a normally distributed set of values and dividing the result by a constant results in a transformed set of values that is also normally distributed. Applying this principle, the values of Z that will be normally distributed, regardless of sample size, are those that are determined by the formula (circle identifying letter):

a	**(a)** $Z = \dfrac{\bar{X} - \mu}{\sigma_{\bar{x}}}$ **(b)** $Z = \dfrac{\bar{X} - \mu}{s_{\bar{x}}}$

9 What tends to be the nature of the distribution of transformed values computed by formula **b**, above? It can be demonstrated mathematically, but we shall accept, as given, that the distribution is symmetrical and platykurtic (i.e., flat), rather than symmetrical and mesokurtic, as is the normal distribution. Because the symbol Z is reserved for use with the standard normal distribution, t will be used to designate such a transformed series of values that in fact (is / is not) normally distributed.

is not (See Unit 2, Frames 59–69, for a review of the terminology used to describe the characteristics of frequency curves.)

10 Since the departure from normality is directly related to the size of the sample in which s has been calculated, there is actually a series of t distributions. The smaller the sample used, the greater the departure from normality. In other words, the smaller the sample size, the more (platykurtic / mesokurtic / leptokurtic) is the t distribution.

platykurtic

11 Or, to consider this conclusion from another point of view, as the sample size being used is increased, the associated t distribution becomes more (platykurtic / mesokurtic).

mesokurtic

12 For large sample sizes the distribution of t becomes essentially mesokurtic. Since all t distributions are symmetrical, this also suggests that with large sample sizes the distribution of t is the same as the distribution of _____.

Z (or the normal distribution)

13 What do we mean by "large sample"? For practical purposes any sample for which the sample size n is 30 or larger can be considered to be a large sample (some statisticians say 50 or larger). For such large samples, the Z distribution can be used in place of the t distribution. Because of this, the use of the t distribution has been associated with "small-sample statistics." However, this phrase can be misleading, since the Z distribution also can be used with small samples ($n < 30$). Specifically, the Z distribution is always the appropriate distribution for use in estimation or hypothesis testing concerning the population mean when the value of _____ is known.

σ (or the population standard deviation)

14 Therefore would it be correct to say that the t distribution *must* be used whenever the sample size is small ($n < 30$)? (yes / no) Whenever the value of σ is not known? (yes / no)

no; no (The Z distribution can be used in its place when $n \geq 30$.)

15 Rather, both conditions must exist to make the use of the t distribution necessary in estimation or hypothesis testing concerning the value of the population mean, i.e., the conditions that the value of _____ is unknown *and* the sample size upon which the value of s is based is less than _____.

σ

30

16 In many sample surveys the sample sizes are considerably larger than 30, and so the use of the t distribution is not required. However, in other situations involving estimation and inference, such as in industrial sampling, small samples are often the rule rather than the exception. Consider the implications of the fact that the distribution of t is platykurtic. As compared with the Z distribution, would the t distribution have proportionally fewer or more of the possible outcomes in the tails of the distribution? (fewer / more)

17 As illustrated in the figure below, the t distribution has a proportionally greater area in the tails of the distribution. Therefore, when interval estimates are based on the use of a t distribution, as contrasted to the Z distribution, then, for a given degree of confidence, the width of the interval will be (narrower / wider).

18 Similarly, in hypothesis-testing applications the critical value of t for a given significance level, as compared to Z, is (closer to / farther from) the center of the distribution.

19 Another way of describing the difference between the t and Z distributions in hypothesis testing is that the required size of the difference between the hypothesized population value and the sample statistic that is necessary for rejecting the null hypothesis is greater for the (Z / t) distribution.

20 Suppose that the Z distribution was inadvertently used instead of the t distribution for setting confidence limits for estimating the population mean. For the stated degrees of confidence, the interval would be too (narrow / wide).

21 If the Z distribution were inadvertently used instead of the t in a series of hypothesis-testing applications, the null hypothesis would be rejected too (seldom / often).

22 Thus, when the t distribution is used, both confidence limits and critical values differ somewhat from those determined by the use of the Z distribution, the extent of the difference being related to the size of the _____.

23 We have stated that there is a separate t distribution for each possible sample size. In terms of proper statistical terminology, it is more appropriate to say that there is a separate t distribution associated with each of the possible *degrees of freedom*. Our reference to "sample size" up to this point, however, does correctly indicate that sample size and degrees of freedom (are / are not) closely related.

are

24 When the t distribution is used in conjunction with estimating the population mean or testing its assumed value, the degrees of freedom are always equal to $n - 1$. Thus, if a sample mean is based on a sample size of 25, the degrees of freedom to be used in choosing the appropriate t distribution are _____ (value).

24

25 Thus, rather than saying that there is a unique distribution of t associated with each possible sample size, it is more appropriate to state that there is a unique t distribution associated with each of the possible _____.

degrees of freedom

26 In contrast, are there separate distributions of Z according to sample size or degrees of freedom? (yes / no)

no

27 The concept of degrees of freedom is one that we shall have further occasion to use, both in this unit and in later ones. The concept is more easily illustrated than defined. Suppose that we have two measurements X_1 and X_2 and that the mean of these two values $\bar{X}$ is identified as being equal to 7.0. What are two possible values that X_1 and X_2 can have if the sample mean of 7 is correct?

any two numbers whose sum is 14

$X_1 = $ _____ and $X_2 = $ _____

28 Thus the general formula we are using in this case is

$$\frac{(X_1 + X_2)}{2} = 7$$

Once the value of X_1 is set (say, equal to 3), can X_2 take on any one of several values? (yes / no)

no (must be 11 in this case)

29 Thus, when there are two elements in a sample, and a sample statistic depending upon these values has been computed or specified, the number of sample elements whose values can vary freely is _____ (number).

1

30 Similarly, we could demonstrate that if five elements make up a sample, the number of free variables, or degrees of freedom, remaining when the sample mean has been specified is _____ (number).

4

31 In later uses of the concept of degrees of freedom, the formula to determine df will vary to reflect the number of sample statistics whose values have been specified. When there is one sample, and the value of the sample mean has been computed for use in estimation or hypothesis testing, the appropriate formula is df = _____.

$n - 1$

32 Finally, let us look at the table we shall be using in the remainder of this unit. Refer to Table A.3, "Table of Areas for t Distributions." Since there is a separate distribution of t associated with each df, in this table a separate t distribution is in effect represented by each (line / column) of the table.

line

33 Notice the illustrative figure at the top of the table and compare it to the figure at the top of Table A.1, for the distribution of Z. Whereas Table A.1 reports the proportion of area included between μ and $+Z$, Table A.3 reports the proportion of the area between +_____ and _____.

$+t; +\infty$ (read: "plus infinity")

34 In using Table A.3, it is important to note that the values of t in a particular column are associated with a given proportion of area included in (one / both) tail(s) of the distribution.

one

35 As compared to the table for the Z distribution, the table for the t distributions is quite compressed in that every line of the latter could be independently expanded into a full table of values equivalent to the table for the Z distribution. The compression of each possible table to one line of values has been achieved by presenting the t values for only selected (numbers of df / proportions of area).

proportions of area

36 We have suggested that as the degrees of freedom are increased, the t distribution approaches the Z distribution in terms of its characteristics. In order to test this statement, what line of Table A.3, in terms of df, should have values that are the same as those for the Z distribution? df = _____

∞ (infinity)

37 For example, the value of t for the 0.01 level of significance (one-tailed) with df = ∞ is equal to _____ (from Table A.3).

2.326

38 According to Table A.1, the proportion of area between μ and $+Z$ associated with a Z value of $+2.33$ is _____.

0.4901

are (If the values of Z presented in Table A.1 were carried to the third decimal place, there would be no difference between the diagrams.)

39 The two diagrams below illustrate the t and Z values that we are comparing. Inspection of these figures indicates that the values of t and Z being compared (are / are not) essentially equivalent in terms of the distributions of areas under the probability curves.

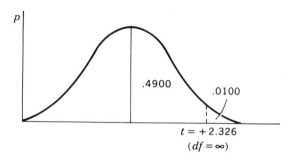

.4900   .0100

$$t = +2.326$$
$$(df = \infty)$$

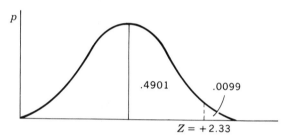

.4901   .0099

$$Z = +2.33$$

40 Similarly, the value of t for the 0.025 level of significance (one-tailed) is 1.96, which is equivalent to the 0.05 level for a two-tailed test using the Z distribution. For the 0.025 column of Table A.3, as well as for the other columns, notice that as df is reduced, the appropriate values of t become (smaller / larger).

larger (consistent with our discussion in Frames 17–22)

10.b ▪ estimation using the t distribution

In problems requiring the estimation of a population mean, total quantity, or difference between means, if the sample size is less than 30 *and* if the standard error is based on a sample standard deviation, rather than the population standard deviation, then we are required to use values of t rather than values of Z in our estimation formulas. Except for this difference, the estimation formulas are the same. Thus, for example, estimation of the population mean is accomplished by using the formula $\hat{\mu} = \bar{X} \pm ts_{\bar{x}}$. Of course, the standard error in this equation would never be designated by $\sigma_{\bar{x}}$, because a value of Z rather than a value of t would then be appropriate in the estimation formula.

41 In the production of size D cells for use as flashlight batteries, the standard deviation in operating life for all batteries is 3 hours, based on the known variability in battery ingredients. A sample of 10 batteries has a mean operating life of 20 hours. Indicate the formula to be used for estimating the average life of all batteries being produced, using an estimation interval.

$\bar{X} \pm Z\sigma_{\bar{x}}$ (since σ is known)

$\hat{\mu} =$

42 In the production of the size D cells, instead of the information given in Frame 41, suppose that the mean operating life of a sample of 35 batteries is 20 hours with a sample standard deviation of 3 hours. Indicate the appropriate formula to be used for estimating the population mean.

$\bar{X} \pm Zs_{\bar{x}}$ (since $n > 30$)

$\hat{\mu} =$

43 In the production of size D cells, instead of the information given in Frame 41, suppose that the mean operating life of a sample of 10 batteries is 20 hours with a sample standard deviation of 3 hours. Indicate the appropriate formula for estimating the population mean.

$\bar{X} \pm ts_{\bar{x}}$ (σ unknown and $n < 30$)

$\hat{\mu} =$

44 For the data of Frame 43 compute the value of the standard error of the mean.

$\dfrac{s}{\sqrt{n-1}} = \dfrac{3}{3} = 1.0$

$s_{\bar{x}} =$

45 Thus our estimation formula is $\hat{\mu} = 20 \pm t(1.0)$. For the problem in Frame 43, what is the number of degrees of freedom to be used in looking up the value of t in Table A.3? df = _____

$n - 1 = 9$

46 In using Table A.3, we must remember that the t values posted in each column of the table are associated with a proportion of area in *one tail* of the distribution, which is indicated as the column heading. If we wish to define a 95 percent confidence interval, what proportion of the distribution would remain in *each* tail of the distribution, taken by itself? $p =$ _____

0.025

47 Therefore, in defining confidence limits by using Table A.3, the value of t to be used in constructing 95 percent confidence limits would be obtained from the column headed by (0.025 / 0.05); the column to be used for defining 90 percent confidence limits is _____, and for defining 99 percent confidence limits it is _____.

0.025

0.05   0.005

48 Now, getting back to the estimation problem we introduced in Frame 41, define the 95 percent confidence limits for estimating the mean operating life of all size D cells being produced, given that

$n = 10$, $\bar{X} = 20$ hours, $s = 3$ hours, and $s_{\bar{X}} = 1.0$ hour.

$\hat{\mu} =$

$\bar{X} \pm ts_{\bar{X}} = 20 \pm 2.262(1.0) = 17.738$ to 22.262 hours

---

9
0.025

49 In the solution for Frame 48 the t value was determined by looking up that value appropriate when df = _____ and the proportion of area in each tail of the distribution is _____.

50 If we wish to estimate a total quantity in a population instead of the population mean, how would the estimation formula that we have been using be modified?

$N\bar{X} \pm Nts_{\bar{X}}$ [or $N(\bar{X} \pm ts_{\bar{X}})$]

Total quantity =

51 Using the formula in Frame 50, estimate the total hours of useful service available from 500 batteries of the type described in Frame 48, using 95 percent confidence limits.

$500(20) \pm 500(2.262)(1) = 10,000$ $\pm 1,131 = 8,869$ to 11,131 hours

Total hours service =

52 Finally, suppose we wish to estimate the difference between the means of two populations. In using the t distribution, the appropriate formula for defining the confidence limits is

$\bar{X}_1 - \bar{X}_2 \pm ts_{\bar{X}_1 - \bar{X}_2}$

Diff =

53 Again we use the t distribution for making this estimate whenever the standard deviations of the two populations are unknown and the samples are small. But note that there are two samples in this kind of problem. Unlike those of the single-sample situation, therefore, the degrees of freedom for use with the t table are equal to the accumulation of the two sample sizes with a subtraction of one degree of freedom for *each* sample mean that is computed. Thus, where n_1 is the size of the first sample and n_2 is the size of the second sample, the formula for determining the degrees of freedom is

$n_1 + n_2 - 2$

df =

54 Suppose we wish to estimate the difference in quality between the flashlight cells being produced by two firms. A sample of 17 Foreverlast batteries has a mean operating life of 22 hours with a standard deviation of 6 hours, and a sample of 10 Yamahoho batteries has a mean operating life of 18 hours with a standard deviation of 3 hours. Compute the respective standard errors of the two sample means.

$\dfrac{s}{\sqrt{n-1}} = \dfrac{6}{\sqrt{16}} = \dfrac{6}{4} = 1.5$
$\dfrac{3}{\sqrt{9}} = \dfrac{3}{3} = 1.0$

$s_{\bar{X}_1} =$

$s_{\bar{X}_2} =$

55 Recalling that $s_{\bar{X}_1 - \bar{X}_2} = \sqrt{s_{X_1}^2 + s_{X_2}^2}$, compute the standard error to be used in estimating the difference between the two population means (carry answer to three decimal places).

$$\sqrt{(1.5)^2 + 1.0)^2} = \sqrt{2.25 + 1.0}$$
$$= \sqrt{3.25} = 1.8028 = 1.803$$

$s_{\bar{X}_1 - \bar{X}_2} =$

56 For the data presented in Frames 54 and 55, if we wish to estimate the difference in mean operating life between the two brands of batteries, using 90 percent confidence limits, the number of degrees of freedom to be used in conjunction with the t table is _____, and the column heading used (proportion in each tail) is equal to _____.

$n_1 + n_2 - 2 = 27 - 2 = 25$

0.05

57 Estimate the difference between the mean operating life of the two brands of batteries, using 90 percent confidence limits and referring to any of the frames above for needed information (carry answer to two decimal places).

$X_1 - \bar{X}_2 \pm ts_{\bar{X}_1 - \bar{X}_2} = (22 - 18)$
$\pm 1.708(1.803) = 4 \pm 3.08$
$= 0.92$ to 7.08 hours

Diff $=$

58 For the solution for Frame 57, what is the probability that the difference in mean operating life between the two brands of batteries is actually less than 0.92 hour? $p =$ _____

0.05 (the proportion in the lower tail of the t distribution)

10.c ▪ hypothesis testing using the t distribution

Again, in problems involving the testing of hypotheses about the population mean or difference between means, if the sample size is less than 30 *and* the value of the standard error has been calculated on the basis of sample data, then the t distribution is used rather than the Z. The general formula which we introduced in Unit 9, Frame 64, for computing the value of the critical ratio, i.e.,

$$Z_{\mathrm{CR}} = \frac{\text{Observed value} - \text{expected value}}{\text{standard error of the statistic}}$$

remains unchanged. But we use the t table rather than the Z table in interpreting this ratio. Put another way, the critical limits used in assessing the value of the critical ratio are defined in terms of t instead of Z in this case.

59 Suppose that the production standard requires a mean battery operating life of 22 hours and the variability in ingredients is such that the standard deviation in operating life of all batteries being produced is 2.0 hours. If a sample of 10 batteries has a mean operating life of 20 hours, what are the critical values with which the critical ratio should be compared, for a two-tailed test at the 5 percent level of significance? (Refer to any of the tables in the Appendix.) $-$_____ and $+$_____

$-1.96; +1.96$ (Values of Z are used in this case, since σ is known.)

60 Instead of the information in Frame 59, suppose that the production standard requires a mean operating life of 22 hours for the D cells and that for a sample of 10 batteries the mean operating life is 20 hours with a standard deviation of 3.0 hours. Compute the critical ratio to be used in testing the population hypothesis.

$$\frac{20 - 22}{3\sqrt{9}} = \frac{-2}{1.0} = -2.0 \qquad t_{CR} = \frac{\bar{X} - \mu_H}{s_{\bar{X}}} =$$

61 Now we need to evaluate this critical ratio of -2.0. In the figure below, post the critical values of t needed for significance at the 5 percent level (two-tailed). Refer to Table A.3 for these values.

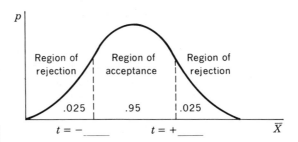

$-2.262; +2.262 \ (df = 9)$

62 Therefore the difference between the hypothesized mean and sample mean tested in Frame 60 (is / is not) significant at the 5 percent level.

is not (Obtained t of -2.0 is within the region of acceptance.)

63 Suppose that we are concerned only about the possibility that the batteries are inferior to the production standard. For this type of hypothesis, identify the general locations of the regions of acceptance and rejection on the figure below and indicate the proportion of area in each portion of the t distribution.

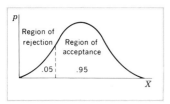

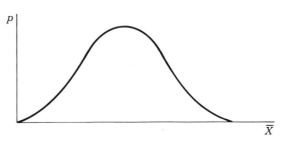

64 For testing the hypothesis that the sample mean is significantly lower than the population mean, the critical value of t for significance at the 5 percent level when $n = 10$ is _____.

-1.833 (The sign is important.)

65 Evaluating the critical ratio of Frame 60 from the standpoint of a one-tailed test, we would conclude that at the 5 percent level the sample mean (is / is not) significantly lower than the hypothesized population mean.

66 Of course, we can use the t distribution also for testing the difference between means. In Frame 54 we observed that a sample of 17 Foreverlast batteries had a mean operating life of 22 hours with a standard deviation of 6 hours and a sample of 10 Yamahoho batteries had a mean operating life of 18 hours with a standard deviation of 3 hours. In Frame 55 we found that the standard error of the difference $s_{\bar{X}_1 - \bar{X}_2} = $ _____ (value).

67 With the value identified in Frame 66, the critical ratio for testing the significance of the difference between the means is

$t_{\mathrm{CR}} = $

68 For evaluating the critical ratio computed in Frame 67 at the 1 percent level of significance, df = _____, and thus the critical values of t are equal to _____ and _____.

69 Thus, comparing the obtained critical ratio of $+2.21$ with the critical t values of -2.787 and $+2.787$, we conclude that the null hypothesis is (accepted / rejected) at the 1 percent level of significance.

70 Suppose that we had predicted the superiority of the Foreverlast batteries before seeing any of the sample results and that we wish to test the hypothesis that this brand is superior to the Yamahoho at the 1 percent level. Under these conditions can the null hypothesis be rejected? (yes / no) Why or why not? _____
_____
_____

71 Just as in the use of the Z distribution in hypothesis testing, we always run the risk of making an error when we either accept or reject the hypothesis of no difference. Incorrectly accepting a false null hypothesis is called type _____ error; incorrectly rejecting a true null hypothesis is termed type _____ error.

72 As was true for the Z distribution, the level of significance used in hypothesis testing directly indicates the probability of type _____ error associated with the critical value(s) of t.

10.d ▪ the use of the normal, binomial, and t distributions

In units 8 and 9 we have defined the appropriate use of the normal and binomial probability distributions in estimation and hypothesis testing; in this unit we have given attention to the use of the t distribution. In these discussions we have also indicated the conditions under which the normal probability distribution can be used as a substitute for both the binomial and t probability distributions. In this section we shall briefly review the use of these three types of probability distributions in statistical inference, particularly with the view of clearly distinguishing the use of the t distributions from the binomial.

73 As we have indicated in units 8 and 9, the binomial probability distribution is appropriately used in statistical inference whenever the data being studied are (discrete / continuous).

discrete

74 Thus, whenever we tabulate data in terms of counts, or in terms of proportions or percentages based on counting, the probability distribution most directly related to such data is the (normal / binomial).

binomial

75 However, as the size of the sample in which counts are made is increased, the binomial distribution approaches the normal distribution in terms of its characteristics. The rule of thumb which we have followed is that the normal probability distribution can be used as a substitute for the binomial in the process of estimation or hypothesis testing whenever $n \geq$ _____ (number) and np and nq each are at least equal to _____ (number).

50
5

76 On the other hand, in this unit we have observed that the t distribution is used solely in conjunction with statistical inference concerning (discrete / continuous) data.

continuous

77 Thus both the Z and t distributions are basically directed toward the analysis of continuous measurements and their associated means. However, the t distribution is appropriately used in statistical inference concerning the population mean whenever the _____ of the population is unknown.

standard deviation (σ)

78 Again, under certain conditions the normal probability distribution can be used as a substitute for Student's t distribution. In this case the general standard used by most statisticians is that $n \geq$ _____ (number).

30

79 The situation in which the *binomial* probability distribution must be used is the one in which data are (discrete / continuous) and $n <$ _____ or np or $nq <$ _____.

discrete
50; 5

80 The *t distribution* must be used whenever the data are (discrete / continuous), _____ is unknown, and $n <$ _____.

continuous; σ; 30

81 Thus, in statistical inference involving *discrete* data, the two probability distributions that might be used, depending on sample size, are the _____ and _____ probability distributions.

binomial; normal

normal

t

82 In statistical inference involving *continuous* data, the two types of distributions that might be used are the _____ and the _____ probability distributions.

no (Since this involves discrete data, either the binomial distribution or the normal distribution, as a substitute, would be used.)

83 Would the *t* distribution ever be used in testing a hypothesis concerning the value of a population proportion? (yes / no)

review

84 (Frames 1–4) When a set of sample means is normally distributed in its values, we can say with assurance that the conversion of these means into values of Z will result in the standard normal distribution, regardless of sample size, when the formula used for this conversion is

$$\frac{\bar{X} - \mu}{\sigma_{\bar{x}}}$$

$Z =$

85 (Frames 5–8) On the other hand, when $s_{\bar{x}}$ is the divisor in the formula in Frame 84, the value of the divisor is not a constant from sample to sample, because the value of _____ will vary from sample to sample.

s (the sample standard deviation)

86 (Frame 9) The symbol Z is used in conjunction with the standard normal distribution only; the distribution of values generated by the formula $(\bar{X} - \mu)/s_{\bar{x}}$ is designated as the _____ distribution.

t

87 (Frames 10–11) As compared to the normal probability distribution, which is symmetrical and mesokurtic, Student's *t* distribution is symmetrical and _____.

platykurtic

88 (Frames 12–14) It can be shown, however, that the *t* distribution approaches the characteristics of the normal distribution as _____ increases. For purposes of practical application, we shall substitute the normal probability distribution for use of the *t* distribution whenever $n \geq$ _____.

n (or sample size)

30

89 (Frames 15–16) On the other hand, in statistical inference concerning the population mean, the *t* distribution must be used whenever _____ is unknown and $n <$ _____.

σ 30

90 (Frames 17–22) As compared to the Z distribution, a *t* distribution has proportionally more of its area in the (center / tails) of the distribution, thus resulting in confidence intervals that are (narrower / wider) and critical values of *t* in hypothesis testing that are (larger / smaller) than those associated with use of the Z distribution.

tails

wider

larger

91 (Frames 23–31) In using the t table, we found that there is a separate distribution of t for each of the possible degrees of freedom. In testing a hypothesis concerning the value of the population mean when the sample mean is based on 25 measurements, the number of degrees of freedom is _____.

$25 - 1 = 24$

92 (Frames 32–40) The values in the t table and Z table are identical when df = _____.

∞ (infinity)

93 (Frames 41–51) The formula used for specifying the confidence interval for estimating the population mean when the standard deviation of the population of measurements is unknown and the sample size is smaller than 30 is

$\bar{X} \pm t s_{\bar{X}}$

$\hat{\mu} =$

94 (Frames 52–58) Similarly, the formula used to estimate the difference between two population means when t is used is diff $= \bar{X}_1 - \bar{X}_2 \pm t s_{\bar{X}_1 - \bar{X}_2}$. If the two sample means are each based on an n of 15, the number of degrees of freedom used in conjunction with the t table is _____.

$30 - 2 = 28$

95 (Frames 59–65) In using the t distribution for testing a hypothesis concerning the value of the population mean, the critical ratio is computed by the formula

$\dfrac{\bar{X} - \mu_H}{s_{\bar{X}}}$

$t_{CR} =$

96 (Frames 66–72) Similarly, we can test the difference between means by the formula

$$t_{CR} = \frac{\bar{X}_1 - \bar{X}_2}{s_{\bar{X}_1 - \bar{X}_2}}$$

If $n_1 = 12$ and $n_2 = 14$ and we wish to test the hypothesis that $\bar{X}_1 > \bar{X}_2$ at the 5 percent level of significance, then in using the t table (refer to Table A.3 if you wish), df = _____ and the heading of the column in the table to be used is (0.025 / 0.05 / 0.10).

$26 - 2 + 24$
0.05 (This is a one-tailed test; use $+t$ only, in this case.)

97 (Frames 73–83) Under certain conditions the normal probability distribution can be used as a substitute for both the _____ and _____ distributions. Can the t distribution ever be used as a substitute for the binomial distribution? (yes / no)

binomial
t
no

problems
(solutions given
on page 358)

1 Each of a random sample of ten packages of cereal has the contents, in ounces, listed in the table below.

Ounces per package

11.8	12.0
11.7	11.7
12.1	12.0
11.9	11.8
12.0	12.0

(a) Compute the mean for this sample.
(b) Compute the standard deviation.
(c) Compute the standard error of the mean.
(d) Estimate the average contents of cereal per package for the population from which this sample was taken, using 95 percent confidence limits.

2 For the data of Prob. 1, the required minimum average weight per package is 12.0 ounces. On the basis of this sample, can we conclude that this requirement is being satisfied at the 5 percent level of significance?

3 A random sample of 25 employees in a small firm employing 100 people earns an average hourly wage of $1.75 with a standard deviation of 25 cents.

(a) Estimate the average hourly wage of all 100 employees to the nearest cent, using 95 percent confidence limits.
(b) Is the average wage of $1.75 significantly lower than $1.85 at the 5 percent level?

4 For the first three months of the year, 15 salesmen in territory A have average weekly sales of $3,000 with a standard deviation of $500, and 10 salesmen in territory B have average weekly sales of $2,600 with a standard deviation of $600. Since a different incentive system is being used in the two territories, we consider each group to be a random sample from an infinitely large population.

(a) Is the sales performance in territory A significantly different from that in territory B at the 5 percent level?
(b) Is the performance in territory A significantly superior to that in territory B at the 5 percent level? How does this question differ from that asked in Prob. 4a?

additional problems

5 A random sample of ten No. 303 cans of peas is taken in a canning plant, and the mean weight for the drained peas is found to be 11.0 ounces with a standard deviation of 0.3 ounce. Estimate the average drained weight of the peas per No. 303 can, using 95 percent confidence limits.

6 For the data of Prob. 5, suppose that the average net weight specified per can is 11.2 ounces (drained). Assuming that we are concerned only about the contents being underweight, rather than overweight, can we accept the hypothesis that the average weight of drained peas for all cans being processed is at least 11.2 ounces, using the 5 percent level of significance?

7 As contrasted to the data in Prob. 5, ten randomly selected cans of peas at another plant have a mean drained weight of 10.8 ounces with a standard deviation of 0.2 ounce. Estimate the amount of difference in the average weight of peas included in No. 303 cans for the two plants, using 90 percent confidence limits.

8 For the data of Prob. 7, test the difference between the two sample means at the 5 percent level of significance.

⑤
$$n = 10$$
$$\bar{x} = 11$$
$$s = \cdot 3$$
$$s_{\bar{x}} = \frac{s}{\sqrt{n-1}}$$
$$S_{\bar{x}} = \frac{\cdot 3}{\sqrt{10-1}}$$
$$s_{\bar{x}} = \cdot 1$$
$$\bar{x} \pm t s_{\bar{x}}$$
$$11 \pm 2.262(\cdot 1) \rightarrow 10.8 \sim 11.2$$

⑥
$$t = \frac{\bar{x} - \mu_H}{s_{\bar{x}}}$$
$$t = \frac{11.0 - 11.2}{\cdot 1}$$
$$= -2.0$$
$$df = 9 \quad @ \; 50\%$$
$$t = -1.833.$$
Ans   reject the hypothesis.

⑦
$$n = 10$$
$$\bar{x} = 10.8$$
$$s = \cdot 2$$
$$s_{\bar{x}} = \frac{s}{\sqrt{n-1}} = \frac{\cdot 2}{\sqrt{10-1}} = \cdot 067$$
$$s_{\bar{x}_1 - \bar{x}_2} = \sqrt{s_{\bar{x}_1}^2 + s_{\bar{x}_2}^2}$$
$$= \sqrt{(\cdot 1)^2 + (\cdot 067)^2}$$
$$= \cdot 12.$$
$$\bar{x}_1 - \bar{x}_2 \pm t s_{\bar{x}_1 - \bar{x}_2}$$
$$11 - 10.8 \pm 1.734 (\cdot 12)$$

⑧
$$t = \frac{\bar{x}_1 - \bar{x}_2}{s_{\bar{x}_1 - \bar{x}_2}}$$
$$t = \frac{11.0 - 10.8}{\cdot 12}$$
$$t = 1.67.$$
$$df \; 18 @ 5\%$$
$$t = 2.101.$$
→ 18, because
we use $s_{\bar{x}_1}$ and $s_{\bar{x}_2}$.

$0 \; t_o \; 4\%$

unit 11 · the chi-square test

Whenever a tabulation of the frequencies of various outcomes is available, the chi-square (χ^2) test can be used to test the significance of the difference between the patterns of the obtained and expected frequencies. Because available data can often be expressed in the form of frequencies of categories of various outcomes, even though more precise methods of measurement were originally used, the χ^2 test is versatile in its application. This fact, combined with the relative ease of the computational procedure, has made the χ^2 test popular in statistical inference and decision making. In this unit we shall discuss some of the general assumptions underlying the use of this test, illustrate the computational procedure for one-way as well as two-way classification tables, and consider the meaning of a significant χ^2 value.

11.a · introduction

Since the χ^2 (chi-square) distribution is used in conjunction with the analysis of frequencies, it is similar to the binomial distribution in terms of some of the assumptions underlying its use. This is so because both distributions are concerned with the analysis of discrete data, though for the binomial distribution the data are manipulated in the form of proportions or percentages rather than as frequencies. One limitation of the χ^2 distribution is that it can be used only for hypothesis testing, but not for estimation (and hence this unit is entitled "The Chi-square *Test*"). On the other hand, whereas the binomial distribution can be used for testing the significance of the difference between a single expected and obtained proportion or percentage only, the χ^2 distribution can be used for testing the difference between an entire pattern of expected and obtained frequencies.

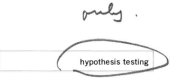

1 Like the normal, binomial, and t distributions discussed in previous units, the χ^2 test is used for the purpose of statistical inference. Unlike the distributions previously discussed, however, it can be used only for (estimation / hypothesis testing).

hypothesis testing

2 The χ^2 test is always applied to tabled data that represent frequencies, or counts, and thus is used in conjunction with (continuous / discrete) data.

discrete

3 As for any application of the methods of statistical inference, it is necessary that the sampled data being analyzed qualify as a probability sample and that the sampled and target populations (be / not be) the same.

be (See Secs. 7.a and 7.b for a review of sampling.)

4 In addition to the usual requirement of sampling, the outcome (classification) of each event or item must not be affected by other particular outcomes. That is, each event must be (independent / dependent).

independent (See Sec. 5.d for a review.)

5 Also like the binomial distribution, each outcome, or classification, must apply to only one of the possible categories. That is, the outcomes must be mutually _____.

exclusive (See Sec. 5.c for a review.)

6 Thus the frequencies being tabulated for a subsequent χ^2 test must be associated with a probability sample, and they must be for events that are _____ and outcomes that are _____ _____.

independent

mutually exclusive (But there can be more than two categories of outcomes; this is unlike the assumption for the binomial distribution.)

7 With a given number of categories of data, the larger the differences between observed and expected frequencies, the larger the value of χ^2. This being the case, the null hypothesis suggesting that there is no significant difference between the observed and expected frequencies would be rejected when the computed χ^2 is relatively (high / low) in value.

high

8 Thus the χ^2 is similar to the calculation of the critical ratio in conjunction with the Z or t distribution, in that critical values of χ^2 associated with various significance levels (can / cannot) be specified beforehand.

can

9 Furthermore the critical values of χ^2 vary with the degrees of freedom associated with the data. From this standpoint the distribution of χ^2 is similar to the (Z / t) distribution.

t (And thus there are actually a number of χ^2 distributions, one associated with each degree of freedom.)

10 In terms of its interpretation, the χ^2 test can be used to test data for goodness of fit and for the independence of two classification systems, or two variables. The goodness-of-fit test always involves the comparison of *one* row (or *one* column) of observed frequencies with the associated (observed / expected) frequencies.

expected

11 For example, comparing the observed pattern of unit sales with the expected unit sales for five sales territories would involve a goodness-of-_____ test.

fit

12 On the other hand, the null hypothesis in testing for independence suggests that there is no interaction between, say, type of product sold and sales territory. Thus the tabled observed frequencies for such a test always include (one / more than one) row and (one / more than one) column.

more than one

more than one (resulting in a two-way table)

13 We shall continue with the discussion of the interpretation of a significant χ^2 value in Sec. 11.d; Secs. 11.b and 11.c are devoted to the computation of its value. No matter what the particular purpose of the test, the value of χ^2 is dependent on the relationship between _____ frequencies and _____ frequencies of tabled data.

observed; expected (either order)

11.b ▪ comparing observed frequencies to expected frequencies

To begin with, we shall illustrate the computational procedure connected with the χ^2 (chi-square) test in the simplest situation: that in which a set of observed frequencies is tested to determine the probability that the set represents a chance deviation from an expected set of frequencies. For such a goodness-of-fit test we need to know both the observed and the expected frequencies of particular outcomes to an event, but we need not know the value of any other statistic, such as the mean or the standard deviation of measured outcomes.

14 Suppose we toss a coin 50 times and obtain 20 heads and 30 tails as the observed outcomes. Complete the table below by indicating the expected frequency of heads and tails on 50 tosses of a fair coin.

	Heads	*Tails*
Observed frequency, f_o	20	30
Expected frequency, f_e	_____	_____

25; 25

15 As observed frequencies depart more and more from expected frequencies, we are less inclined to accept the coin as being a fair coin. The significance of the difference between observed and expected frequencies can be determined by the application of the _____ test.

χ^2

16 With chi-square represented by the symbol χ^2, the formula used in computing its value is

$$\chi^2 = \sum \frac{(f_o - f_e)^2}{f_e}$$

Thus the expected frequency for each cell of the table is subtracted from the _____ frequency and the difference is squared and divided by the expected frequency (before / after) being summed with the fractions for other cells.

observed

before

17 With reference to the formula in Frame 16, can the value of χ^2 ever be negative? (yes / no)

no (since the differences are squared)

18 What would a computed χ^2 value of zero indicate? _____

that observed frequencies exactly matched expected frequencies

19 Given the following data and formula, compute the value of χ^2, recognizing that two fractions are to be summed in this case.

$$\frac{(20-25)^2}{25} + \frac{(30-25)^2}{25}$$

$$= \frac{25}{25} + \frac{25}{25} = 2.0$$

$$\chi^2 = \sum \frac{(f_o - f_e)^2}{f_e} = \underline{\hspace{2cm}} + \underline{\hspace{2cm}} =$$

20 As was true for the t test, there is a whole family of χ^2 distributions, based on the degrees of freedom involved, and the meaning of a given χ^2 value depends on the number of degrees of freedom, or df. When the observed frequencies can all be listed along one dimension (one row or one column), there are $k-1$ degrees of freedom, where k is the number of categories of *observed* frequencies. Therefore, for the χ^2 computed in Frame 19,

$2-1 = 1$ (Thus, with n specified, the frequency for just one of the two cells can vary freely.)

$$df = k - 1 = \underline{\hspace{2cm}}$$

21 Table A.4 indicates the critical values of χ^2 for differences in frequencies to be considered significant at the 5 and 1 percent levels, according to degrees of freedom. According to the table, when df $= 1$, the critical value of χ^2 for the difference to be considered significant at the 0.05 level is _____, and the value necessary for significance at the 0.01 level is _____.

3.84

6.64

22 Therefore the difference in frequency observed in the data of Frame 19 (is / is not) significant at the 1 percent level and (is / is not) significant at the 5 percent level.

is not

is not (The obtained χ^2 of 2.0 is less than either critical value.)

23 For 20 out of 60 throws of a six-sided die, the value 4 has been obtained for the face of the die. Complete the table below, indicating the obtained outcomes and the expected outcomes for a fair die.

	4	~4
f_o	_____	_____
f_e	_____	_____

	4	~4
	20	40
	10	50

24 For the data in Frame 23 calculate the value of χ^2.

$$\frac{(20-10)^2}{10} + \frac{(40-50)^2}{50}$$

$$= \frac{100}{10} + \frac{100}{50} = 10 + 2 = 12$$

$$\chi^2 = \sum \frac{(f_o - f_e)^2}{f_e} = \underline{\hspace{2cm}} + \underline{\hspace{2cm}} =$$

25 Refer to Table A.4. Is the value of χ^2 in Frame 24 significant at the 0.01 level? (yes / no) Explain: _____

yes; With df $= 1$ the critical value of χ^2 for significance at this level is 6.64.

26 Since the problems in Frames 14 and 23 had just two categories of observed frequencies, they could have been approached as hypothesis-testing problems for proportions. Refer to the data of Frame 23 and use p to represent the proportion of the outcome 4 and q for ~ 4; $\pi_H = 0.17$, $p = $ _____, and $q = $ _____.

0.33   0.67

27 Since $n > 50$, $np > 5$, and $nq > 5$, we can use the normal distribution in place of the binomial to test the null hypothesis concerning the difference between the obtained and expected proportion, with

$$\sigma_p = \sqrt{\frac{\pi_H(1 - \pi_H)}{n}} = \sqrt{\frac{(\frac{1}{6})(\frac{5}{6})}{60}} \cong 0.05$$

$$\frac{0.33 - 0.17}{0.05} = \frac{0.16}{0.05} = +3.2 \qquad Z = \frac{p - \pi_H}{\sigma_p} =$$

is (since the critical $Z = \pm 2.58$, $+3.2$ is in a region of rejection)

Therefore the difference (is / is not) significant at the 1 percent level.

28 Thus either method of testing the null hypothesis leads to its rejection. Now, turning our attention to a problem involving more than two categories of observed frequencies, suppose that a sales region has been divided into five territories, each of which was judged to have an equal sales potential. The actual sales volume, in terms of units, is indicated in the chart below. Post the expected sales volume for each territory in the chart.

| | Territory | | | | |
	A	B	C	D	E
Actual unit sales, f_o	110	130	70	90	100
Expected unit sales, f_e	___	___	___	___	___

100 for each space (since the total sales volume of 500 units was expected to be equally divided)

29 In applying the χ^2 test to the data in Frame 28, df = _____.

$\underline{k} - 1 = 5 - 1 = 4$

30 Compute the value of χ^2 for the frequencies posted in Frame 28.

$$\frac{100}{100} + \frac{900}{100} + \frac{900}{100} + \frac{100}{100} + \frac{0}{100}$$
$$= \frac{2,000}{100} = 20.0$$

$$\chi^2 = \sum \frac{(f_o - f_e)^2}{f_e} =$$

31 Are the differences between observed and expected values significant at the 0.05 level of probability? (yes / no) At the 0.01 level? (yes / no) Explain: _____
_____

yes

yes; With df = 4, χ^2 of 9.49 is needed for significance at the 0.05 level and 13.28 for significance at the 0.01 level. (Note that with the simultaneous comparison of five categories of frequencies, the binomial or normal probability distribution could *not* have been used for this problem.)

11.c ▪ contingency tables

All of the computational examples introduced thus far have involved the use of one-way classification tables, in that the categories of observed frequencies could all be indicated along a single row (or a single column). When the categories of events being analyzed fall into two or more rows *and* two or more columns, a two-way classification table, or *contingency table*, is the result. As contrasted to the one-way classification table, the contingency table always involves classification on the basis of two variables simultaneously, rather than just one. The computational method for determining the expected frequency associated with each cell of a contingency table and the determination of degrees of freedom when both columns and rows of data are involved are presented in this section.

32 When all of the classifications in a table concern a single dimension or variable, so that all categories can be listed along a single row or column, a _____-way classification table is involved in the analysis.

one

33 In contrast, a two-way classification table, or _____ table, involves analysis on the basis of two variables.

contingency

34 We shall use the expression $r \times k$ to represent the number of rows and number of columns, respectively, in the contingency table. Thus all one-way classification tables with one row of data can be represented as being _____ (number) $\times k$ tables.

1 (since there is always only one row)

35 Where $r \times k$ identifies the number of rows and columns in a contingency table, the simplest such two-way table has two rows and two columns. Therefore such a table can be designated as a _____ $\times$ _____ table.

2×2

36 For contingency tables the number of degrees of freedom is equal to $(r - 1)(k - 1)$. For a 2×2 table, therefore, the number of degrees of freedom is always equal to _____ (number).

$(2 - 1)(2 - 1) = (1)(1) = 1$

37 Table 11.1a indicates the number of favorable, neutral, and unfavorable reactions by men and women viewers of a television commercial. In terms of $r \times k$, this is a _____ $\times$ _____ table.

3×2

table 11.1a ▪ observed reactions to a television commercial

	Sex		
Reaction	*Men*	*Women*	*Total*
Favorable	28	52	80
Neutral	20	20	40
Unfavorable	52	28	80
Total	100	100	200

table 11.1b ▪ expected reactions to a television commercial

Reaction	Men	Women	Total
Favorable	―――	―――	80
Neutral	―――	―――	40
Unfavorable	―――	―――	80
Total	100	100	200

---

observed

$(3-1)(2-1) = 2$

38 The frequencies posted in the cells of Table 11.1a are all (observed / expected) frequencies. The degrees of freedom to be used in interpreting the value of χ^2 (chi-square) to be computed is ――――――― (number).

39 In order to calculate the expected frequency for each cell of Table 11.1b, we make use of the marginal totals of Table 11.1a. The general formula for f_e is $\Sigma r \Sigma k / \Sigma f$, where Σr is the sum of the frequencies posted in the row in which the cell is located, Σk is the sum of the frequencies in the column in which the cell is located, and Σf is the sum of all the frequencies in the table. Thus for the cell in row 1 and column 1 of Table 11.1b the expected frequency is

$\dfrac{(80)(100)}{200} = \dfrac{8,000}{200} = 40$

$$f_e = \frac{\Sigma r \Sigma k}{\Sigma f} =$$

40	40
20	20
40	40

40 Complete Table 11.1b by indicating the expected frequency of each cell corresponding to the observed frequency in Table 11.1a.

41 Because the marginal totals of the contingency table and of the table of expected frequencies are the same, not all of the expected cell frequencies have to be computed using the formula provided above. Instead, many of the expected frequencies can be determined by subtraction from marginal totals. For example, once the expected frequency of 40 has been computed for the cell in row 1 and column 1, the expected frequency for the adjoining cell in row 1 and column 2 can be determined by subtracting ――――― (number) from the marginal total of ――――― (number).

	40
	80

Definition of df.

ʌ¹

(¹

2 (And thus only two cell frequencies are free to vary.)

42 As a matter of fact, for a 3×2 contingency table, once we have computed the expected frequency f_e for any two cells in different columns, the other four can be determined by subtraction from marginal totals. This is a direct indication that for a 3×2 table df = ――――― (number).

43 Now, using the data in Tables 11.1a and 11.1b, calculate the value of χ^2.

$\dfrac{-12^2}{40} + \dfrac{12^2}{40} + \dfrac{0}{20} + \dfrac{0}{20} + \dfrac{12^2}{40}$

$+ \dfrac{-12^2}{40} = \dfrac{576}{40} = 14.4$

$$\chi^2 = \sum \frac{(f_o - f_e)^2}{f_e} =$$

44 Refer to Table A.4. Is the obtained χ^2 value of 14.4 significant at the 1 percent level? (yes / no) Explain: _____

yes

With df = 2, the critical χ^2 for significance at the 0.01 level is 9.21.

45 In Sec. 11.d we shall consider the meaning of a significant χ^2 value computed for a contingency table. For the present, and with reference to Table 11.1a, note that the significant χ^2 obtained in this case (does / does not) indicate that the total number of men and women respondents differed, and it (does / does not) indicate *general* favorability or unfavorability of reactions to the commercial.

does not

does not

46 As another computational example of the use of the χ^2 test in conjunction with a contingency table, Table 11.2a presents an analysis of the types of insurance policies sold by three different insurance agents. The contingency table is of the dimensions _____ $\times$ _____.

3 × 3

table 11.2a ▪ types of insurance policies sold by three agents

Type of policy		Agent		
	A	B	C	Total
A	10	6	14	30
B	5	2	2	9
C	5	12	4	21
Total	20	20	20	60

table 11.2b ▪ expected sales of insurance policies

only 4 can vary

Type of policy		Agent		
	A	B	C	Total
A	10	10	10	30
B	3	3	3	9
C	7	7	7	21
Total	20	20	20	60

47 Calculate the expected frequencies for each cell of this contingency table and enter them in Table 11.2b.

10	10	10
3	3	3
7	7	7

$$f_e = \frac{\Sigma r \Sigma k}{\Sigma f}$$

48 Now calculate the value of χ^2 for the data.

$$\frac{0}{10} + \frac{-4^2}{10} + \frac{4^2}{10} + \frac{2^2}{3} + \frac{-1^2}{3}$$
$$+ \frac{-1^2}{3} + \frac{-2^2}{7} + \frac{5^2}{7} + \frac{-3^2}{7}$$
$$= \frac{32}{10} + \frac{6}{3} + \frac{38}{7} = 10.63$$

$$\chi^2 = \sum \frac{(f_o - f_e)^2}{f_e} =$$

49 What is the value of df to be used in interpreting this χ^2? df = _____ (number).

50 Refer to Table A.4. Is the obtained χ^2 value significant at the 0.05 level? (yes / no) At the 0.01 level? (yes / no) Explain: _____
_____
_____

11.d ▪ interpretation of the χ^2 test

The computational examples of Secs. 11.b and 11.c have illustrated the kinds of data to which the χ^2 (chi-square) test can be applied. As a method of hypothesis testing, the χ^2 test is used for the two general types of purposes we introduced in Sec. 11.a, corresponding to the format of the data being analyzed. The application of the χ^2 test in a one-way classification table involves testing *goodness of fit,* whereas its application to a contingency table involves testing *for independence,* or interaction, between the two variables that serve as the basis for classification in the table.

51 As we indicated in Sec. 11.a, a χ^2 value for a one-way classification table always involves testing for (goodness of fit / independence of classification).

52 The distribution of expected frequencies for a one-way table may follow a binomial, normal, uniform, or any other distribution in applying the χ^2 test for the purpose of testing for _____
_____.

53 For the previous examples of one-way tables in this unit, the determination of expected frequencies was straightforward because the expected frequencies were all uniform in value. Refer, however, to the data of Table 11.3. Determination of the expected frequencies in this case necessitates use of the _____ distribution.

table 11.3 ▪ number of heads on 20 tosses of two coins

	Number of heads		
	0	*1*	*2*
Observed frequency	4	8	8
Expected frequency	_____	_____	_____

54 In order to determine the expected frequencies in Table 11.3, the probability of each of the three outcomes has to be determined by identifying the values of p and q, expanding the binomial to the appropriate power, and solving for each term of the expansion. With $p = 0.5$ and $q = 0.5$,

$(p + q)^2 = p^2 + 2pq + q^2 =$ _____ + _____ + _____

which are the probabilities associated with the three kinds of outcomes.

55 With $n = 20$, and using the probabilities just determined in Frame 54, calculate the expected frequencies for Table 11.3 and enter them in the appropriate cells of the table.

> 5; 10; 5

56 Now determine the value of χ^2 for the differences between observed and expected frequencies for the data of Table 11.3.

> $$\frac{-1^2}{5} + \frac{-2^2}{10} + \frac{3^2}{5} = \frac{1}{5} + \frac{4}{10} + \frac{9}{5}$$
> $$= \frac{24}{10} = 2.4$$

$$\chi^2 = \sum \frac{(f_o - f_e)^2}{f_e} =$$

57 What are the degrees of freedom to be used in interpreting this χ^2 value of 2.4? df = _____.

> $(k - 1) = (3 - 1) = 2$

58 Refer to Table A.4. Is the difference significant at the 5 percent level? (yes / no) Explain: _____

> no; With df = 2, critical χ^2 for the 5 percent level is 5.99.

_____

59 In terms of goodness of fit, therefore, the observed distribution of frequencies (would / would not) be accepted as fitting the theoretical distribution of frequencies, which in this case follows the _____ distribution.

> would
>
> binomial

60 In addition to testing for goodness of fit, the χ^2 test can be used also to test for independence of the classification systems used as the basis for categorizing the frequencies. In this case the observed frequencies are posted in a (one-way classification table / contingency table).

> contingency table

61 Any time the χ^2 test is applied to an $r \times k$ table for which r and k are greater than 1, the χ^2 test is being used as a test of (goodness of fit / the independence of two classifications).

> the independence of two classifications

62 For example, for the contingency table presenting viewer reactions to a television commercial (Table 11.1a on page 211), the χ^2 test has nothing to do with considering whether men and women were appropriately represented in the sample or with the general favorability of viewer reactions. Rather, the significant χ^2 value indicates rejection of the hypothesis that the two classification systems are (independent of / dependent on) one another.

> independent of

63 Specifically, then, the rejection of the independence assumption leads to the conclusion that there is a significant interaction between the two variables serving as the basis for classification. In Table 11.1a the reaction of the viewer can be said to be significantly related to the _____ of the viewer.

> sex

64 Similarly, the significant χ^2 value for the data of Table 11.2a (page 213) did not indicate that the individual agents differed in their total sales or that certain policies are generally more popular. Rather, it indicated that the agents differed in _____

_____.

65 If we wish to test one of the variables of a contingency table in terms of its goodness of fit with a theoretical distribution, in addition to or instead of the test for the independence of the two variables, we can do so by applying the χ^2 test to the column or row totals only. For example, the following data are the marginal totals of the observed frequencies taken from Table 11.2a. With the assumption that there is no difference in the popularity of the various types of policies, post the expected frequencies in the table below.

| | *Type of insurance policy* | | |
	A	B	C
Actual sales, f_o	30	9	21
Expected sales, f_e	_____	_____	_____

66 Now calculate the value of χ^2 for the data in Frame 65.

$$\chi^2 = \sum \frac{(f_o - f_e)^2}{f_e} = $$

67 Does this χ^2 value of 11.1 indicate that the policies differ in their popularity at the 5 percent level of significance? (yes / no) Explain: _____

68 Thus, whenever a one-way classification of observed frequencies is involved, the χ^2 test is directed toward testing _____

_____.

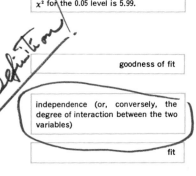

69 Whenever observed frequencies are classified in a contingency table, the χ^2 test may be used for testing the _____ _____ of the two variables. By applying the test to selected portions of the data from the contingency table, the χ^2 test may also be used to test the goodness of _____ for either of the variables taken singly, in respect to an expected pattern of frequencies.

11.e ▪ an alternative formula for computing χ^2 and the correction for continuity

For the special case of the 2 × 2 contingency table, a computational formula for χ^2 (chi-square) that does not require the determination of expected frequencies has been developed; it will be presented in this section. Another consideration in the use of the χ^2 test is the magnitude of the expected value associated with each cell of the table. When an expected cell frequency is less than 5 and there is one degree of freedom, Yates' correction for continuity, to be discussed below, should be applied in computing the value of x^2.

70 Given the labeling for the frequencies of the cells and of the row and column totals in Table 11.4, the following formula can be used to calculate directly the value of x^2:

$$x^2 = \frac{n(ad - bc)^2}{(a + b)(c + d)(a + c)(b + d)}$$

expected

The principal advantage of this formula is that it does not require the calculation of _____ frequencies as a step in determining the value of x^2.

table 11.4 ▪ coding of observed frequencies for a 2 × 2 contingency table

a	b	$a + b$
c	d	$c + d$
$a + c$	$b + d$	n

71 Given the following 2 × 2 contingency table, calculate the value of x^2, using the simplified computational formula.

viewer reactions to a television commercial

Reaction, f_o	Men	Women	Total
Favorable	1	7	8
Unfavorable	11	5	16
Total	12	12	24

$$\frac{24(5 - 77)^2}{(8)(16)(12)(12)} = \frac{124,416}{18,432} = 6.75$$

$$x^2 = \frac{n(ad - bc)^2}{(a + b)(c + d)(a + c)(b + d)} =$$

72 Now determine the expected frequencies corresponding to the data in Frame 71 and indicate these in the following table. Then compute the value of x^2, using the conventional formula.

expected viewer reactions to a television commercial

Expected reaction, f_e	Men	Women
Favorable	____	____
Unfavorable	____	____

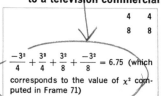

4	4
8	8

$$\frac{-3^2}{4} + \frac{3^2}{4} + \frac{3^2}{8} + \frac{-3^2}{8} = 6.75 \text{ (which corresponds to the value of } x^2 \text{ computed in Frame 71)}$$

$$x^2 = \sum \frac{(f_o - f_e)^2}{f_e} =$$

73 For the example in Frame 72 the computation of the expected frequencies was quite simple, thus resulting in little if any advantage in using the shorter computational formula. In other instances the formula may be of considerable labor-saving advantage. To use the simplified computational formula, the data must be categorized in a _____ × _____ contingency table.

2 × 2

74 At the top of Table A.4 notice the form of the x^2 distribution. The distributions have been presented as being essentially continuous because with relatively large cell frequencies, continuity of the x^2 distribution is approached, regardless of degrees of freedom. In a sense this kind of assumption is analogous to the one made when substituting the normal distribution for the _____ distribution in estimation and hypothesis testing.

binomial

75 For the x^2 distribution it has been determined that when expected frequencies are small, the size of x^2 is overestimated because of the discrete nature of the distribution in this case. This occurrence, in turn, would result in (too many / too few) rejections of the null hypothesis.

too many

76 But what is a "small expected frequency"? Most statisticians suggest that an expected cell frequency of less than 5 is too small (some say 10). What can we do about it? One possible solution is to combine adjacent classes of data with low expected frequencies, thus (increasing / reducing) the number of categories of frequencies being analyzed.

reducing

77 For example, in the following chart indicating the expected frequency of typographical errors in 100 business letters, the categories that might be combined are those for _____ (number) errors and _____ (number) errors.

4
5

	Number of errors					
	0	1	2	3	4	5
Expected frequency per 100 letters, f_e	65	15	8	5	4	3

78 Suppose the investigator prefers not to reduce the number of categories of data. There is one other alternative; that is to apply Yates' correction for continuity (it really should have been called "for discontinuity"). However, this correction can be used only when df = 1. Therefore could we have used it for the data of Frame 77? (yes / no)

no (df = 6 − 1 = 5)

79 Since Yates' correction for continuity can be used only when df = 1, it can be used with tables of two possible dimensions, in terms of $r \times k$: _____ $\times$ _____ and _____ $\times$ _____.

80 The following formula incorporates Yates' correction and should be used for *all cells* of the tabled data being analyzed, not just the particular cell or cells with low expected frequencies:

$$\chi^2 = \sum \frac{(|f_o - f_e| - 0.5)^2}{f_e}$$

In this formula $|f_o - f_e|$ means "the absolute value of the difference," without regard to arithmetic sign. The net effect of Yates' correction, then, is to reduce the size of the difference between each f_o and f_e by _____ (number) (before / after) squaring and summing.

81 Typically, Yates' correction for continuity is applied only when an expected cell frequency in a table is less than _____ (number). When used, it is applied to (all / selected) cells of the frequency table.

82 Now that we have introduced this correction, note that we should have applied it to the illustrative problem in Frames 71 and 72. Recompute the value of χ^2 for that problem, using the formula which includes Yates' correction.

83 Thus the effect of applying the correction for continuity in this case was to reduce the value of χ^2 from _____ (number) to _____ (number).

84 Suppose we were testing the null hypothesis at the 1 percent level of significance. Would the uncorrected χ^2 have indicated a significant difference? (yes / no) Does the corrected χ^2 value indicate a significant difference? (yes / no)

review

85 (Sec. 11.a, Introduction; Frames 1–2) Of the probability distributions discussed in this and previous units, the two that are oriented toward the analysis of discrete data are the _____ and _____ distributions; the two that are oriented toward data that are continuous are the _____ and _____ distributions.

86 (Frames 3–13) Among the characteristics of the χ^2 (chi-square) distribution, its use (does / does not) presume a probability sample and (does / does not) presume that the events are independent.

87 (Sec. 11.b, Introduction)   Computationally, the χ^2 test is directed toward testing the significance of differences between _____ frequencies and _____ frequencies.

88 (Frames 14–18)   The general formula used for computing the value of χ^2 is $\chi^2 = \Sigma(f_o - f_e)^2/f_e$. Therefore, given a classification table with observed frequencies, the first thing that has to be done in carrying out the χ^2 test is to determine the _____ _____ associated with each cell.

89 (Frames 14–18)   Given that 7, 10, and 13 units of products A, B, and C, respectively, were sold during a particular time period, complete the table below including all of the figures needed for the computation of χ^2. Assume that an equal sales volume was expected for the various products.

		Product	
	A	B	C
f_o	_____	_____	_____
f_e	_____	_____	_____

90 (Frames 19, 23–24, 28, 30)   Compute the value of χ^2 for the data in Frame 89.

$$\chi^2 = \sum \frac{(f_o - f_e)^2}{f_e} =$$

91 (Frames 20–22, 25–27, 29, 31)   Is the χ^2 value of 1.8 in Frame 90 significant at the 5 percent level? (yes / no) Explain: _____
_____

92 (Frames 32–38)   Of 12 workers who are 50 years of age or over, 2 had an industrial accident last year and 10 did not. Of 18 workers under 50 years of age, 8 had industrial accidents. Construct the contingency table to represent these findings.

Observed number, f_o	Under 50	50 and over	Total
Accidents	_____	_____	_____
No accidents	_____	_____	_____
Total	_____	_____	_____

93 (Frames 39–42, 47)   Construct a table indicating the expected frequencies for the data in Frame 92, using the formula

$$f_e = \frac{\Sigma r \Sigma k}{\Sigma f}$$

Expected number, f_e	Under 50	50 and over	Total
Accidents	_____	_____	_____
No accidents	_____	_____	_____
Total	_____	_____	_____

94 (Frames 43–48) Compute the value of χ^2 for the data in Frame 93, using the conventional formula.

$$\chi^2 = \sum \frac{(f_o - f_e)^2}{f_e} =$$

95 (Frames 44–46, 49–50) Is the χ^2 value of 2.5 significant at the 0.05 level of probability? (yes / no) Explain: _____

_____

96 (Sec. 11.d, Introduction; Frames 51–59) When observed frequencies are posted in a one-way classification table, the χ^2 test is used for testing _____.

97 (Frames 60–64) When observed frequencies are posted in a contingency table involving classification on the basis of the two variables, the χ^2 test is used for _____

_____.

98 (Frames 65–69) When the χ^2 test is applied to the marginal row (or column) totals of a contingency table only, it is being used for the purpose of testing _____.

99 (Frames 70–73) A simplified computational formula for χ^2, which does not require the calculation of expected frequencies, has been developed for use with 2×2 contingency tables. Using this formula, recompute the value of χ^2 for the data in Frames 92 to 94.

$$\chi^2 = \frac{n(ad - bc)^2}{(a + b)(c + d)(a + c)(b + d)} =$$

100 (Frames 74–77) The χ^2 distribution itself is presumed to be (discrete / continuous), whereas distributions of observed frequencies are (discrete / continuous). Consequently, the computed value of χ^2 tends to be somewhat overestimated. Application of a correction for continuity is particularly important when any expected cell frequency is less than _____ (number).

101 (Frames 78–82) The correction for continuity should be applied only when df = 1. Using the following formula for χ^2, which incorporates Yates' correction for continuity, recompute the value of x^2 for the data in Frames 92 and 93.

$$\left(\frac{1.5^2}{6}\right)+\left(\frac{1.5^2}{4}\right)+\left(\frac{1.5^2}{12}\right)+\left(\frac{1.5^2}{8}\right)= 1.41$$

$$\chi^2 = \sum \frac{(|f_o - f_e| - 0.5)^2}{f_e} =$$

correction for continuity

2.5; 1.41

102 (Frames 83–84) In this case the application of Yates' _____ led to a reduction of the value of x^2 from _____ to _____.

problems
(solutions given
on page 359)

1 A new promotional campaign was used in randomly selected marketing areas A and B, and the traditional method of sales promotion was used in randomly selected areas C and D during a test month. The following table, which reports present-month and previous-month sales figures for the four areas, seems to indicate that the areas using the new promotional campaign gained more in sales than did the other areas.

| | *Marketing areas* | | | |
	A	*B*	*C*	*D*
Sales prior month	75	45	30	150
Sales present month	115	75	40	170

(a) Determine the expected sales volume for each area for the present month. (*Hint:* Use the prior month's sales to calculate the proportion of total sales expected in each area this month.)
(b) Calculate the value of χ^2.
(c) Is the difference between the patterns of observed and expected frequencies for the present month significant at the 5 percent level?
(d) Is the difference between observed and expected frequencies significant at the 1 percent level?

2 In order to study shifts and movements in consumer attitudes, an automobile manufacturer arranges interviews with a random sample of 50 men and 50 women who purchased a car manufactured by the company during the preceding year. The following table summarizes the responses to one of the questions about the one most important additional safety feature desired.

| | *Additional feature desired* | | | | |
Respondents	*Disk brakes*	*Collapsible steering wheel*	*Automatic door locks*	*Speed warning buzzer*	*Total*
Men	15	25	5	5	50
Women	5	15	20	10	50
Total	20	40	25	15	100

(a) Determine the expected cell frequencies for this contingency table.

(b) Compute the value of x^2.

(c) Is the difference between the pattern of obtained and expected frequencies significant at the 1 percent level?

(d) Interpret the meaning of a significant x^2 value for contingency-table data such as these.

3   For the data of Prob. 2 suppose it had been suggested that there is no real difference in consumer preferences for the four safety features listed. Test this assumption at the 1 percent level of significance.

4   In order to test the assumption that an unemployed person represents a poor credit risk, a loan-company manager has a study of 100 randomly chosen accounts conducted with the following tabulated results.

Present status of loan	Status at time of loan		Total
	Employed	Unemployed	
In default	10	8	18
Not in default	60	22	82
Total	70	30	100

(a) Compute the value of x^2 for these data, using the usual formula.

(b) Compute the value of x^2 for this 2 × 2 contingency table, using the alternative formula.

(c) What is the result of this test at the 5 percent level of significance?

5   For Prob. 4 suppose the data had been as follows:

Present status of loan	Status at time of loan		Total
	Employed	Unemployed	
In default	5	4	9
Not in default	65	26	91
Total	70	30	100

(a) Determine the expected cell frequencies for this contingency table.

(b) Compute the value of x^2, using the appropriate formula.

(c) What is the result of this test at the 5 percent level of significance?

additional problems   6   In order to put a one-year warranty into effect, the buyers of a small appliance are required to mail a postcard on which several questions relating to the purchase are asked. From a large number of these postcards, 100 are selected for analysis. The following frequencies, based on the sample of postcards, describe the purchasers according to place of purchase and source of product knowledge.

Source of knowledge	Place of purchase			Total
	Department store	Discount store	Appliance store	
Friend	10 *6*	5 *8*	5 *6*	20
Newspaper	15 *15*	30 *20*	5 *15*	50
Magazine	5 *9*	5 *12*	20 *9*	30
Total	30	40	30	100

(a) Determine the expected cell frequencies.
(b) Compute the value of x^2.
(c) Evaluate and interpret the computed value of x^2, using the 5 percent level of significance.
(d) Would the conclusion be different if the 1 percent level were used?

$$x^2 = 34.93$$

7 In conjunction with the data of Prob. 6, the management of the company has assumed that the appliance is sold in about equal quantities in the three types of stores. Test this assumption at the 5 percent level of significance.

$$x^2 = 2.01$$

8 In conjunction with the data of Prob. 6, the management of the company has assumed that 40 percent of the purchases are influenced by friends, 40 percent by newspaper ads, and 20 percent by magazine ads. Test this assumption at the 1 percent level of significance.

$$x^2 = 17.5$$

9 Before the data for Prob. 6 had been collected, it was suggested that newspaper ads are particularly effective for discount-store buyers and magazine ads are more influential with buyers at appliance stores. Test this suggestion at the 1 percent level of significance, using the alternative formula for x^2.

10 In order to compare the quality of rheostats shipped by two subcontractors, a sample of 30 rheostats was taken from recent shipments by each supplier and the following number of defects of any type were noted. The sales representative for supplier B suggests that the difference observed is only a chance difference

$$x^2 = 2.58$$

and is not reflective of the general quality of the rheostats being supplied by his company.

Inspection result	Supplier A	B	Total
Defective	1	6	7
Nondefective	29	24	53
Total	30	30	60

$$x^2 = 2.58$$

(a) Determine the expected cell frequencies.
(b) Evaluate the sales representative's claim at the 5 percent level of significance.

use Yates Correction for continuity

$$x^2 = \frac{(|f_o - f_e| - 5)^2}{f_e}$$

Can happen in 2 cases:
① Contingency table
② goodness of fit.

9.

	30	5	35
	5	20	25
	35	25	60

$$x^2 = \frac{n(ad - bc)^2}{(a+b)(c+d)(a+c)(b+d)}$$

$$= \frac{60(600 - 25)^2}{(35)(25)(35)(25)}$$

$$= 25.91.$$

Dise.   Appl.

	Dise	Appl
New	30	5
Mag	5	20

agree with magmt?

unit 12 ▪ Bayesian inference and decision theory

Since our general introduction to probability in Unit 5, we have addressed ourselves to statistical inference, but more specifically, to what might be called the classical methods of statistical inference. Thus Units 6 and 7 developed the related concepts of probability distributions and sampling distributions, and Units 8 through 11 utilized these concepts for the purpose of estimation and hypothesis testing involving both continuous (measured) and discrete (counted) data. In relying on the concept of an underlying probability distribution, throughout these units we have followed the objective rather than subjective approach to interpreting probability values. That is, such values have been consistently interpreted as indicating relative or expected frequency rather than strength of a belief regarding a particular outcome. Indeed, both "levels of significance" and "degrees of confidence" are stated in terms of relative frequency (e.g., "significance at the 5 percent level" indicates that a difference that large will occur by chance fewer than five times in 100). In this unit we turn our attention to a relatively recent development in statistical inference, popularly referred to as *decision theory.* Decision theory is particularly addressed to identifying the criteria by which decisions made under various circumstances can be evaluated and to using these criteria to determine the best decision acts or alternatives. Though the distinction between classical statistical decision making and decision theory is not absolute, one difference is the identification and use of the values of the various possible outcomes associated with a decision in the decision-theory approach. Another distinction is the heavier reliance on subjective and conditional probability values in decision theory. Because of this, we shall first review the meanings of objective, subjective, and conditional probability and consider the use of Bayesian inference in conjunction with conditional probability values as a prelude to a discussion of decision criteria as such. Then, by discussing decision making under conditions of *risk,* under conditions of *uncertainty,* and under conditions of *conflict,* we shall introduce the *decision-theory* approach. This unit serves to introduce an area which in itself constitutes a whole field of study, and thus the unit is not exhaustive, even in categories of topics covered. For example, decision making under *certainty,* within which the mathematical applications of *operations research* to decision problems are considered, is not included in our introduction to decision theory.

12.a ▪ objective, subjective, and conditional probability

Section 5.e has already explained that, whereas the objective interpretation of a probability value is particularly oriented toward the event that can be considered an instant of many equivalent events, the subjective interpretation is oriented toward events that are considered unique. In this section we shall review this distinction and also the essential characteristics of dependent events and conditional probability before discussing Bayesian inference in Sec. 12.b.

1 When a probability value of 0.90 is interpreted as meaning that in the long run 90 percent of the occurrences of an event will have a particular outcome, the approach that is being followed is the (objective / subjective) approac.. to probability.

objective

2 Objective probability values may be determined on an *a priori* basis or on an *empirical* basis. When we observe a large number of events and tabulate the frequency of various outcomes, the method of determining probability would be described as (a priori / empirical).

empirical (See Sec. 5.a for a discussion of these and related concepts.)

3 No matter which of the two methods of determining the probability values is used, the objective approach to the interpretation of probability suggests that such a value represents (circle best choice):

(a) $\dfrac{\text{Total number of events}}{\text{Frequency of an outcome}}$

(b) $\dfrac{\text{Frequency of an outcome}}{\text{Total number of events}}$

b

4 In contrast, the subjective interpretation of probability values is not concerned with the relative or expected frequency of an outcome. Rather, it is concerned with the strength of a decision maker's belief that an outcome will or will not occur. As such, the subjective approach is particularly oriented toward decision-making situations that (occur only once / are repetitive).

occur only once

5 The computation of a probability value on the basis of either sampled events or an a priori assumption that alternative outcomes are equally likely leads to an interpretation in terms of the (objective / subjective) approach. A probability value that represents an expert's best judgment is interpreted in the context of _____ probability.

objective
subjective

6 One advantage of using the subjective approach to probability in addition to the objective approach is that methods of statistical inference can then be applied to (repetitive / unique) events.

unique

7 However, the use of the subjective approach also introduces some difficulties. For one thing, such probability values represent point estimates, but with no related standard error, and so the precision of the estimates (can / cannot) be specified.

cannot

8 Moreover, since the situation or event to which the probability value applies is unique, there is no way to test the accuracy of the value by sampling and hypothesis testing. Therefore the only alternative is to test the general accuracy of the source, or person, making such estimates by noting the correlation between the

subjective	(objective / subjective) probability values assigned by the source and the actual outcomes in a number of different events.

9 A decision maker is not typically faced with the choice of using an objective probability value which can be tested by sampling methods and a subjective value whose precision and accuracy are difficult to identify. Rather, the choice is often between using subjective probability values and using none at all, on the basis that such values are inappropriate for use in statistical inference. The statisticians who have been most willing to make use of subjective probability values are those who are interested in extending the use of statistical inference to events, or decision-making situations,

unique (one of a kind)	that can be described as being _____.

10 As we indicated in the general introduction to this unit, the methods of estimation and hypothesis testing that we have thus

objective	far discussed in this book are based on the _____ approach to probability.

11 In Unit 5 we discussed the distinction between independent and dependent events. Independent events are those in which the probability of an outcome in a particular event is unaffected by the outcomes of other events, but such an effect does occur in the case of dependent events. Thus the repeated tossing of a fair coin

independent	represents a series of (dependent / independent) events. The drawing of cards from a deck of cards *without replacement* repre-
dependent (See Sec. 5.d for a review.)	sents a series of _____ events.

12 The binomial, normal, *t*, and χ^2 (chi-square) distributions, which have served as the basis for the methods of statistical inference that we have studied, all are based on the requirement that the

independent	repetitive events be (dependent / independent).

13 By posting the missing probability values in the simple tree diagram below, illustrate the proposition that the tossing of a fair coin twice in succession represents two independent events.

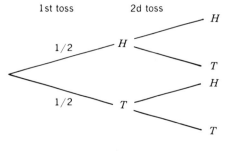

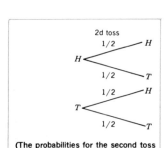

(The probabilities for the second toss are unaffected by the outcome of the first toss.)

14 On the tree diagram below post the missing probability values associated with drawing a spade from a deck of 52 cards on each of two successive draws, drawing without replacement. S signifies a spade outcome and $\sim S$ signifies a not-spade outcome.

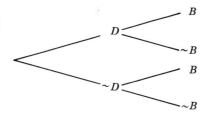

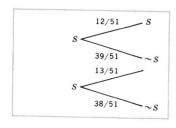

15 For independent events we can designate the probability of an outcome B by the symbol $P(B)$, regardless of the outcome of any other event. For dependent events the probability of outcome B, given that outcome A has occurred in a related event, is designated by the symbol _____.

16 The kind of probability value designated by the symbol $P(B|A)$, which can occur only for dependent events, is called _____ probability.

17 To extend the related concepts of dependent events and conditional probability to a managerial decision-making situation, suppose that the probability is 0.60 that our major competitor will decide to diversify his products, and if he does, the probability is 0.80 that he will build a new plant. If he decides not to diversify, the probability is 0.40 that he will build the plant. Enter the probability values for the various outcomes in the tree diagram below, in which D indicates the decision to diversify and B indicates the decision to build a new plant.

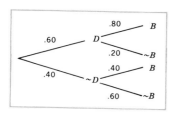

18 Since the probability of building the new plant varies with the decision of whether or not to diversify, the two decision situations, or events, can be described as being _____; all of the probability values for B and $\sim B$ posted in Frame 17 can be described as being _____ probability values.

objective, subjective, and conditional probability ▪ 229

<table>
<tr><td>

0.80
0.40

</td><td>

19 In the tree diagram in Frame 17, $P(B|D) =$ _____ (value) and $P(B|\sim D) =$ _____ (value).

</td></tr>
</table>

20 According to the data of Frame 17, the probability that our competitor will diversify *and* build a new plant is

$P(D)P(B|D) = (0.60)(0.80) = 0.48$ (See Unit 5, Frames 80–89, for a review.)

$P(\text{\_\_\_\_\_})P(\text{\_\_\_\_\_}) =$

21 Given the values in Frame 17, even if we do not know whether our competitor has decided to diversify, we can still determine the overall probability that he will build a new plant. The decision to build can be made in either of two mutually exclusive ways: with diversification or without. Thus, using the rule of addition for this either-or situation,

$$P(B) = P(D)P(B|D) + P(\sim D)P(B|\sim D) =$$

$(0.60)(0.80) + (0.40)(0.40) = 0.48 +$
$0.16 = 0.64$ (See Sec 5.c for a review of the rule of addition.)

22 Similarly, the overall probability that he will *not* build, given no information regarding his decision to diversify, is

$P(D)P(\sim B|D) + P(\sim D)P(\sim B|\sim D)$
$= (0.60)(0.20) + (0.40)(0.60) = 0.12$
$+ 0.24 = 0.36$

23 Since the possible decisions to build or not to build are mutually exclusive as well as exhaustive, in that only one of these outcomes can occur and there are no other possible outcomes, the overall probabilities of building $P(B)$ and not building $P(\sim B)$, computed in Frames 21 and 22, should add up to a value of _____.

1.0 (They do: $0.64 + 0.36$.)

24 Once a decision regarding diversification is made known, however, then we can modify the probabilities associated with building by direct reference to the tree diagram in Frame 17. Thus, if we learn that the decision has been made *not* to diversify, then $P(B) =$ _____

0.40
0.60

and $P(\sim B) =$ _____, and these values would then replace the overall values of 0.64 and 0.36, respectively, computed in Frames 21 and 22.

12.b ▪ Bayesian inference

Bayes' theorem represents the analysis of conditional probabilities for the purpose of backward inference, that is, for specifying the probability of a particular outcome in the earlier of two dependent events, given the outcome of the second event. For example, given that our competitor is in fact building a new plant, we might be interested in determining the probability that he has decided to diversify. The direction of inference is thus just the opposite of that discussed in Sec. 12.a, and this leads to applications of Bayesian inference that may not at first be obvious. The change in direction of inference permits us to take account of additional knowledge about chance events and to revise the probability values associated with an important outcome on the basis of the known outcomes of related events. In this section we shall discuss the meanings of *prior probabilities* and *posterior probabilities* as used in Bayes' theorem, introduce the computations that are associated with this approach, and finally consider the meaning or interpretation of the posterior probabilities that are determined by use of Bayes' formula.

25 Two terms used in Bayesian inference which we have not used in our previous discussions of probability values are *prior probability* and *posterior probability*. Since the essence of Bayes' approach is that it describes a procedure by which probability values can be modified on the basis of later evidence, the probability that is associated with an outcome before there is any knowledge of associated outcomes is called ＿＿＿＿＿＿ probability.

prior

26 Thus prior probabilities are the probability values prior to further information. On the other hand, when such a probability value is modified by our knowledge of the outcome of an associated (dependent) event, the resulting modified value is called ＿＿＿＿ probability.

posterior

27 As indicated in the introduction to this section, Bayesian inference is used with dependent events and conditional probabilities, but with direction of inference reversed. Refer to Fig. 12.1, which presents the tree diagram for the problem discussed in Sec. 12.a. The *prior probability* that our competitor has decided to diversify (i.e., with no knowledge of related outcomes) is ＿＿＿＿ (value).

0.60

figure 12.1 ■ tree diagram depicting the probabilities associated with a competitor's possible decisions.

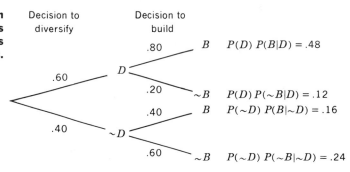

28 Now suppose that we observe that he is in fact building a new plant. Does this action on his part necessarily indicate that he has decided to diversify? (yes / no)

no (since the decision to build could also have been made along with the decision not to diversify)

29 Thus we would like to determine the probability that our competitor has decided to diversify *given that* he is building the new plant. In terms of the symbol used, this posterior probability value, which takes the new information into account, can be represented by $P(\underline{\hspace{1.5cm}})$.

$P(D|B)$

---

30 Can we directly determine the value of $P(D|B)$ by reference to Fig. 12.1? (yes / no)

---

no [The value of $P(B|D)$ is directly indicated, but *not* $P(D|B)$.]

---

31 Rather than simply presenting Bayes' formula for computing posterior probabilities, let us illustrate its derivation from the formulas already introduced in Unit 5. In that unit what formula was used to determine the *joint* probability of two outcomes, A and B, occurring in two *dependent* events?

$P(A,B) =$

$P(A)P(B|A)$ (See Unit 5, Frames 80–89.)

---

32 Arithmetically, we can reverse the two events and have the event in which B occurs considered first. In this case

$P(B,A) =$

$P(B)P(A|B)$

---

33 Referring to Frames 31 and 32, note that the conditional probabilities with which we worked in Sec. 12.a were of the $P(B|A)$ type, whereas posterior probabilities are the conditionals designated by the symbol _____.

$P(A|B)$

---

34 As the next step in developing a formula for determining $P(A|B)$, we can take advantage of the fact that $P(A,B) = P(B,A)$ in the equations

$$P(A,B) = P(A)P(B|A)$$
$$P(B,A) = P(B)P(A|B)$$

and similarly we note the equality of the right side of each equation, so that

$P(B)P(A|B) =$

$P(A)P(B|A)$

---

35 Then, solving the complete equation in Frame 34 for the value of the posterior probability,

$P(A|B) =$

$\dfrac{P(A)P(B|A)}{P(B)}$

---

36 The equation that you have just developed is a simple statement of Bayes' theorem. It is not necessary for you to memorize this equation for our purposes, but you should now be able to use it and interpret the resulting value. Getting back to the question originally posed in Frame 28, if we observe that our competitor is in fact building a new plant, and we wish to determine the probability that he has decided to diversify, substitute the appropriate symbols for the solution of this problem, referring to the formula in Frame 35:

$P(D|B) =$

$\dfrac{P(D)P(B|D)}{P(B)}$

37 Of the required values for solving this formula, the overall probability that our competitor will build a new plant, $P(B)$, is not directly represented in the tree diagram in Fig. 12.1. As we noted in Sec. 12.a, however, this value can be determined by adding the probabilities of the two circumstances under which the plant might be built; that is (in symbols),

$$\boxed{P(\sim D)P(B|\sim D)} \qquad P(B) = P(D)P(B|D) +$$

38 Therefore for computational purposes the complete general formula used to determine the posterior probability is

$$P(A|B) = \frac{P(A)P(B|A)}{P(A)P(B|A) + P(\sim A)P(B|\sim A)}$$

Using this formula for the data of Fig. 12.1, solve for the value of the posterior probability that our competitor has decided to diversify, given that he is building the new plant.

$$P(D|B) = \frac{P(D)P(B|D)}{P(D)P(B|D) + P(\sim D)P(B|\sim D)} =$$

$$\boxed{\begin{array}{c} \dfrac{(0.60)(0.80)}{(0.60)(0.80) + (0.40)(0.40)} \\[2mm] = \dfrac{0.48}{0.48 + 0.16} = \dfrac{0.48}{0.64} = 0.75 \end{array}}$$

39 In Fig. 12.1, before the additional information regarding building of the plant, the probability assigned to the decision to diversify was _____ (value), and in the language of Bayesian inference this value is designated the _____ probability. With the additional information considered, the probability that our competitor has decided to diversify is now identified as _____ (value) and is designated the _____ probability.

$$\boxed{\begin{array}{c} 0.60 \\ \text{prior} \\[4mm] 0.75 \\ \text{posterior} \end{array}}$$

40 Incidentally, a posterior probability may be either higher or lower in value than the associated prior probability. If our competitor had decided not to build the new plant, then the posterior probability assigned to his having decided to diversify would be (less than 0.60 / equal to 0.60 / greater than 0.60).

$$\boxed{\text{less than 0.60}}$$

41 To satisfy yourself in this regard, determine the posterior probability that our competitor has decided to diversify, given that he is *not* building a new plant and given the formula below.

$$P(D|\sim B) = \frac{P(D)P(\sim B|D)}{P(D)P(\sim B|D) + P(\sim D)P(\sim B|\sim D)} =$$

$$\boxed{\begin{array}{c} \dfrac{(0.60)(0.20)}{(0.60)(0.20) + (0.40)(0.60)} \\[2mm] = \dfrac{0.12}{0.12 + 0.24} = \dfrac{0.12}{0.36} = 0.33 \end{array}}$$

42   Thus the value of the Bayesian approach to inference is that it provides a basis for modifying probabilities based on evidence from related events. Some statisticians, however, have expressed concern about the direction and type of reasoning inherent in this approach. First, probability values are being assigned to an outcome that has, in fact, already either occurred or not occurred (though the decision maker is not in the position of knowing the outcome). Furthermore, not only has the event already taken place, but it will not take place again. According to our previous discussion, these kinds of concerns are most likely to be expressed by those who believe that statistical inference should be based only on the (objective / subjective) approach to interpreting probability values.

43   If one applies a strength-of-belief interpretation to the posterior probability values, then the "backward reasoning from effect to cause" inherent in the Bayesian approach does not present any additional difficulties other than those always encountered in the _____ approach to interpreting probability values.

12.c ▪ decision making under conditions of risk: expected payoff

Decision theorists have identified four types of situations: decision making under conditions of *certainty, risk, uncertainty,* and *conflict.* By conditions of *certainty* we mean that the decision maker can specify the consequence of a particular decision, or act. The necessity of using the quantitative methods of operations research, such as linear programming, in such situations stems from the fact that combinations of effects are not easily identified without the use of a mathematical model to handle the various interactions that occur in complex situations. In decision making under conditions of *risk,* discussed in this section, the outcomes cannot be specified with certainty but can be specified with known probability values. In *uncertainty,* discussed in Sec. 12.d, the possible outcomes of a decision act can be specified, but the probabilities associated with these outcomes are unknown. Under *competitive* conditions, discussed in Sec. 12.e, the consequences of a decision act are dependent on the actions of one or more adversaries, all of whom are assumed to be fully informed regarding possible payoffs stemming from their decisions. Under conditions of *risk* the usual criterion used by decision theorists to evaluate the available decision alternatives, or acts, is the *expected value of the payoff* associated with each act. The expected payoff associated with a decision act is the sum of the value of each possible outcome times its associated probability, as we shall demonstrate below. As a decision-making criterion, use of this approach maximizes the expected payoff (or minimizes the expected loss) over the long run, and thus the *average* payoff over a series of decisions, rather than the payoff in any particular instance, is what is maximized.

44 If X represents the value of each of the possible outcomes of a decision act and $P(X)$ represents the probability of that outcome, then the expected value of the payoff is equal to $\Sigma XP(X)$. That is, the value of each outcome is multiplied by the _____ of that outcome (before / after) summation.

45 Suppose that a retailer has the opportunity to sell a portion of his slow-moving stock to a liquidator for $1,200. Since the items in question happen to be primarily children's toys, he is also aware that they *may* yield a greater payoff if he does not sell now but keeps them in stock through the approaching Christmas shopping season. Table 12.1 indicates four possible payoffs associated with the decision to keep the merchandise and the probability of each outcome occurring, based on the retailer's previous experience with this type of merchandise. In the table each possible payoff is designated by the symbol _____, and the probability of each outcome is designated by _____.

table 12.1 ▪ possible payoffs and probability values associated with the decision to hold the slow-moving merchandise

Payoff X	Probability $P(X)$
$800	0.20
$1,000	0.20
$1,200	0.40
$1,400	0.20

46 In this decision problem involving just two decision alternatives (to sell the stock to the liquidator or not to sell it), from the standpoint of the *expected-value-of-payoff* criterion, the retailer should keep the merchandise only if the expected payoff associated with this decision is greater than _____.

47 Given the formula expected payoff $= \Sigma XP(X)$, determine the expected value of payoff associated with holding the merchandise by completing the calculations below:

Payoff X	Probability $P(X)$	$XP(X)$
$800	0.20	$160
$1,000	0.20	_____
$1,200	0.40	_____
$1,400	0.20	_____
		$\Sigma XP(X) =$ $_____

48 In terms of the criterion of expected payoff, then, the appropriate action for the retailer to take is to (sell now / hold the merchandise).

49 The following question should help to clarify the meaning of the expected-payoff criterion: In this particular decision-making instance is a payoff of $1,120 actually one of the possible outcomes? (yes / no)

no

50 $1,120 is the expected *average* payoff if the retailer were to make a number of such decisions involving the same possible payoffs and probability values. From this standpoint the interpretation of expected payoff is similar to the (objective / subjective) approach to interpreting probability values.

objective

51 The decision problem in Frames 45 to 48 was relatively simple, in that only two decision alternatives were available and the expected payoff had to be determined for just one of the alternatives. When the *expected-payoff* criterion is applied to a situation in which there are several decision alternatives, we would carry out several independent summations represented by the symbol $\Sigma XP(X)$, each for a different (outcome / decision act).

decision act (The summation represents the expected payoff associated with a *decision.*)

52 Suppose that the revenue associated with the use of each car in a commuter train is $200 and the cost associated with the use of each car is $80. What is the payoff related to the use of five commuter cars if five are in fact needed? _____
What is the payoff associated with the use of five cars if only two are in fact needed? _____

5($200) − 5($80)
        = $1,000 − $400 = $600

2($200) − 5($80)
        = $400 − $400 = 0

53 Thus both revenue and cost figures have to be considered in determining the value of each payoff in this kind of problem. Table 12.2 presents the values associated with every possible combination of decision acts and outcomes ranging from zero through five commuter cars, each payoff having been computed in the same way as in Frame 52. Thus Table 12.2 indicates that if two cars are provided and two cars are needed, the payoff is _____, whereas if three cars are provided and one is needed, the payoff is _____.

$240

−$40 (a loss)

table 12.2 ■ **decision acts, outcomes, and payoffs for the commuter-car problem (payoffs stated in dollars)**

Number provided	0	1	Number needed 2	3	4	5
0	$ 0	$ 0	$ 0	$ 0	$ 0	$ 0
1	− 80	120	120	120	120	120
2	− 160	40	240	240	240	240
3	− 240	− 40	160	360	360	360
4	− 320	− 120	80	280	480	480
5	− 400	− 200	0	200	400	600

54 In terms of the expected value of the payoff that we wish to maximize, as represented by the symbol $\Sigma XP(X)$, all of the numbers entered in Table 12.2 represent values of (X / $P(X)$).

X

55 Table 12.3 presents the probability associated with the need for commuter cars, based on a study of previous demand patterns. Thus the values in this table are all values of $(X / P(X))$.

$$P(X)$$

table 12.3 ■ outcomes and associated probabilities for the commuter-car problem

Number needed	Probability
0	0
1	0.10
2	0.20
3	0.30
4	0.30
5	0.10

56 Since all values of X and $P(X)$ are identified in Tables 12.2 and 12.3, respectively, the task now remaining is to determine the expected payoff associated with each of the decision alternatives of attaching zero through five commuter cars to the train. The table below illustrates the computation of the expected payoff associated with the decision to provide five cars for the train. Complete the calculations and determine the expected payoff associated with this decision.

Number needed	Payoff X	Probability $P(X)$	$XP(X)$
0	$-\$400$	0	$0
1	-200	0.10	-20
2	0	0.20	0
3	200	0.30	60
4	_____	_____	_____
5	_____	_____	$\Sigma XP(X) = \$\_\_\_\_$

400*	0.30†	120
600	0.10	60
		$220

* From Table 12.2.
† From Table 12.3.

57 Note, again, that an expected payoff does not directly indicate the outcome of a particular event or its value. Rather, it indicates the average payoff in the long run, assuming the probability distribution used as the basis of the decision continues to apply. Thus, given the payoff values of Table 12.2 and the probability distribution of Table 12.3, the expected (average) payoff associated with providing five commuter cars is _____.

$220

58 Table 12.4 presents the expected payoffs for all six decision alternatives, each of the values having been computed in the same way as for the decision to provide five cars in Frame 56. According to this table, the decision by which the criterion of maximum expected payoff is satisfied is that of providing _____ (number) commuter cars.

table 12.4 ▪ expected payoffs associated with providing zero to five commuter cars

Number provided	Expected payoff
0	$ 0
1	120
2	220
3	280
4	280
5	220

59 Note, however, that in maximizing expected payoff, we have not necessarily considered all variables that in fact influence long-run success. If we consistently provide four cars, in what percentage of the train runs will there be more demand for commuter cars than there are cars provided? _____ percent

60 It is conceivable that one commuter reaction to a shortage of cars might be to switch to another mode of travel, thereby changing the probability distribution associated with the possible outcomes. Thus the criterion of expected payoff is one possible criterion and (does / does not) substitute for managerial responsibility for evaluating the decision criteria themselves.

61 As another kind of illustration indicating that the expected-payoff criterion may not always be the appropriate one, note the data given in Table 12.5. Using these data, determine the expected payoffs for the two decision alternatives in the table below.

Out-come	X	Decision A $P(X)$	$XP(X)$	X	Decision B $P(X)$	$XP(X)$
a	$-2,000	0.5	$_____	$-40,000	0.5	$_____
b	12,000	0.5	_____	60,000	0.5	_____
			$\Sigma XP(X) = $_____			$\Sigma XP(X) = $_____

table 12.5 ▪ outcomes, probabilities, and payoffs associated with two decision alternatives

Decision	Possible outcomes and probability Outcome a, $p = 0.5$	Outcome b, $p = 0.5$
A	$ -2,000	$12,000
B	-40,000	60,000

62 From the standpoint of expected payoff, decision B is clearly superior to decision A. But why might a businessman with modest

financial resources make decision A instead? _____
_____

the risk of high loss associated with B

63 As our final computation in this section, we shall illustrate the use of Bayesian inference in decision making under risk. By the application of Bayes' theorem the probabilities associated with each possible outcome can be modified on the basis of sample evidence. The original probability values are prior probabilities in this case, and the modified values are _____ probabilities.

posterior

64 In order to simplify computations, we shall define a problem that includes only two decision alternatives and two possible outcomes. Extending the commuter-car problem, suppose that for a given run the probability is 0.70 that one commuter train (with five cars) will be sufficient to meet demand and the probability is 0.30 that two trains will be needed. Given that there is an average of $1,000 in revenue associated with each needed train and $500 in costs for each train provided, complete the payoff table below.

Number of trains scheduled	Number of trains needed	
	1 $p = 0.70$	2 $p = 0.30$
1	$500	$500
2	_____	_____

0; $1,000

65 Now determine the expected payoff associated with each decision by completing the table below.

Number of trains needed	One train scheduled			Two trains scheduled		
	X	$P(X)$	$XP(X)$	X	$P(X)$	$XP(X)$
1	$500	0.70	$ 350	$ 0	0.70	$ 0
2	500	0.30	_____	1,000	0.30	_____
			$\Sigma XP(X) = $_____			$\Sigma XP(X) = $_____

150 300
$500 $300

66 Without considering other long-run factors in this simplified example, the best decision from the standpoint of the maximum payoff criterion is that of scheduling one train. Suppose, however, that the decision to schedule an additional train can be made up to 15 minutes before departure time. Moreover, when only one train will be needed, the probability is just 0.20 that three or more cars of the train are filled at that time, whereas when two trains are needed the probability is 0.60 that at least three commuter cars have been filled 15 minutes before departure time. Complete the tree diagram below illustrating the relationship between the two events.

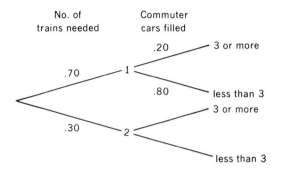

No. of
trains needed

Commuter
cars filled

.20 — 3 or more

.70 ___ 1

.80 — less than 3

3 or more

.30 ___ 2

less than 3

.60 — 3 or more

2

.40 — < 3

67 Given no sample information, we concluded that providing one train will maximize the expected value of payoff. But what if we have the additional information that at least three commuter cars have been filled 15 minutes before departure? Within the context of the present problem, this information would have the effect of (decreasing / increasing) the probability that only one train will be needed.

decreasing

68 We can of course compute the revised probability values by using Bayes' theorem. The posterior probability that only one train will be needed, given that three commuter cars have been filled, is (refer to Frame 66 for values)

$$p(1|3) = \frac{p(1)p(3|1)}{p(1)p(3|1) + p(2)p(3|2)} =$$

$$\frac{(0.70)(0.20)}{(0.70)(0.20) + (0.30)(0.60)}$$

$$= \frac{0.14}{0.14 + 0.18} = \frac{0.14}{0.32} = 0.44$$

69 Similarly, the posterior probability that two trains will be needed, given that at least three commuter cars are filled 15 minutes before departure, is

$$p(2|3) = \frac{p(2)p(3|2)}{p(2)p(3|2) + p(1)p(3|1)} =$$

$$\frac{(0.30)(0.60)}{(0.30)(0.60) + (0.70)(0.20)}$$

$$= \frac{0.18}{0.18 + 0.14} = \frac{0.18}{0.32} = 0.56$$

70 Now use the revised probability values to compute the expected payoff for each decision below.

Number of trains needed	One train scheduled			Two trains scheduled		
	X	P(X)	XP(X)	X	P(X)	XP(X)
1	$500	0.44	$_____	$ 0	0.44	$_____
2	500	0.56	_____	1,000	0.56	_____
		ΣXP(X) =	$_____		ΣXP(X) =	$_____

$220	$ 0
280	560
$500	$560

71 The use of Bayesian inference in this problem serves to exemplify its contribution in making it possible to modify probability values on the basis of related sample information. Given no sample information, the decision that maximizes expected payoff in the problem is that of scheduling (one / two) trains. With the information that three cars have been filled 15 minutes before departure time, the decision that maximizes expected payoff is that of scheduling (one / two) trains.

one

two

72 In Sec. 12.d, on decision making under conditions of uncertainty, we shall expand our consideration of decision-making criteria. As covered in this section, a popular decision criterion that has been used when both the possible payoffs and the applicable probability distribution are known, or can be estimated, is the criterion of maximizing _____.

expected payoff

12.d ▪ decision making under conditions of uncertainty: further decision criteria

Sec. 12.c dealt with decision making under conditions of risk, but the situations we are now concerned with are those in which the decision maker does not know the probabilities associated with the possible outcomes, though he has been able to identify the possible outcomes and their related payoffs. This is not the same as decision making under conditions of complete ignorance, in which even the possible outcomes and their payoffs cannot be identified. Since payoffs are identified but probabilities are unknown under conditions of uncertainty, the criterion of maximizing expected payoff cannot be used in evaluating the decision alternatives, or acts. Three other bases that can be used, however, are the *maximin, maximax,* and *minimax-regret* criteria.

73 Suppose that an electronics firm has perfected a television receiver with a three-dimensional picture and now faces several alternative choices regarding the scheduling of production and related market-promotion activities for the receiver. Consumer acceptance of the product within the next 10 years is considered certain, but the timing of that acceptance is considered an unknown, partly because of the receiver's necessarily high price. Table 12.6 presents four decision alternatives, ranging from immediate full-scale production and promotion to limited production in 5 years.

Similarly, the possible consumer reactions range from immediate acceptance to acceptance in 8 years. Thus each figure in Table 12.6 represents the payoff associated with each possible combination of _____ and _____.

decision; outcome (or production decision and consumer acceptance)

table 12.6 ▪ decision acts, outcomes, and payoffs for the television-receiver problem (payoffs stated in millions of dollars)

Decision act	Consumer acceptance			
	Immediate	2 years	5 years	8 years
Immediate production and promotion	$80	$40	$ −10	$ −50
Limited production now	30	40	30	10
Limited production in 2 years	20	30	40	15
Limited production in 5 years	5	10	30	30

74 Since we have no probability figures available, we cannot determine the expected payoff for each decision act. However, several other decision criteria can be considered. For example, the manufacturer might be rather pessimistic, or cautious, and choose that decision act which *maximizes* the *minimum payoff* that can occur. This is called the *maximin* criterion. For the decision to go into immediate production, what is the minimum payoff that can occur? _____ million dollars

−50 (a loss)

75 Similarly, the minimum payoff possible for limited production now is _____ million dollars; for limited production in 2 years it is _____ million dollars; and for limited production in 5 years it is _____ million dollars.

10
15
5

76 Therefore, if we use the *maximin* criterion as the basis for the decision, the decision alternative in Table 12.6 that would be chosen is _____.

limited production in 2 years (since the minimum payoff of 15 million dollars is greater than any other minimum payoff)

77 Hence use of the *maximin* criterion results in maximizing the _____ that can occur.

minimum payoff

78 Another criterion, which might be used by a decision maker who is more optimistic, is the *maximax*. As the name implies, the objective in this case is to *maximize* the *maximum payoff* that can occur. For the decision to begin immediate production and promotion, the maximum payoff indicated in Table 12.6 is _____ million dollars.

80

79 Similarly, consider the maximum payoffs that can occur for the other three decision acts. If the *maximax* criterion is used as the basis for the decision, the alternative that would be chosen is _____.

immediate production and promotion

80 Thus the criterion whereby the maximum possible payoff is maximized is called the _____ criterion; the criterion whereby the minimum possible payoff is maximized is called the _____ criterion.

maximax

maximin

81 Finally, the third possible criterion, called *minimax regret,* looks at the decision problem from a point of view that is neither so pessimistic nor so optimistic as the maximin and maximax criteria, respectively. After the outcome in question has occurred, to the extent that the decision act was not "perfectly matched" with that outcome, there will be an opportunity loss, or regret, associated with the decision. As the name again implies, the *minimax-regret* criterion is the one by which the decision maker minimizes the _____ that can occur, no matter what the outcome.

maximum regret

82 To illustrate the meaning of an opportunity loss, or regret, suppose that the 3-D television receiver wins consumer acceptance in 5 years. The highest payoff associated with this outcome is _____ million dollars.

40 (for the decision limited production in 2 years)

83 If any decision other than limited production in 2 years had been made, there would be an opportunity loss, or regret, in terms of the difference between the payoff for the best decision act under the circumstances and the decision that was actually made. For the outcome of acceptance in 5 years, the amount of regret associated with the decision to go into immediate production is _____ million dollars; for limited production now it is _____ million dollars; and for limited production in 5 years it is _____ million dollars.

$40 - (-10) = 50$ $40 - 30 = 10$
$40 - 30 = 10$

84 Table 12.7 presents the opportunity losses, or regrets, associated with each possible combination of decision act and outcome. In terms of the *minimax-regret* criterion, the decision maker attempts to minimize the maximum regret that can occur. For the decision to go into immediate production and promotion, for example, the maximum regret that can occur is _____ million dollars.

80 (i.e., if the outcome is acceptance in 8 years, the best-matched decision for this outcome results in a payoff of 30 million dollars instead of a loss of 50 million dollars.)

table 12.7 ■ opportunity losses, or regrets, for the television-receiver problem (stated in millions of dollars)

| | *Consumer acceptance* | | | |
Decision act	*Immediate*	*2 years*	*5 years*	*8 years*
Immediate production and promotion	$ 0	$ 0	$50	$80
Limited production now	50	0	10	20
Limited production in 2 years	60	10	0	15
Limited production in 5 years	75	30	10	0

85 Review the opportunity losses associated with each of the decision alternatives in Table 12.7. The decision act that satisfies the *minimax-regret* criterion is _____.

86   In Sec. 12.c, on decision making under conditions of risk, when the probability distribution associated with the possible outcomes could be identified, the decision criterion used was that of maximizing _____.

87   In this section, on decision making under conditions of uncertainty, we have illustrated the use of three additional criteria, called the _____, _____, and _____.

88   Depending on the criterion used, different decision acts might be considered best. For the case illustration involving the production of the new 3-D television receiver, for example, use of the *maximin criterion* would result in the decision _____ _____; the *maximax* would result in the decision _____ _____; and the *minimax regret* would result in the decision _____.

89   It has been suggested that one solution to the dilemma of which criterion to use under conditions of uncertainty is to get expert opinion regarding the probability associated with each outcome; that is, to use subjective probability values rather than no values at all. If we were to follow such a procedure consistently, then all decisions under conditions of uncertainty would become decisions under conditions of _____.

90   However, one could also argue the matter from the other point of view. Since the expected-payoff criterion represents a long-run expected average, the decision maker may not consider it as being appropriate for a one-shot situation in which, for example, there may be a risk of high loss. Even though probability values have been identified, if he wants to avoid the risk of high loss, he would very likely choose to satisfy the _____ criterion.

12.e ▪ decision making under conditions of conflict: game theory

In addition to the conditions of certainty, risk, and uncertainty, conditions of conflict, or competitive conditions, influence decision making. Some decision theorists have discussed decisions under uncertainty as a special case of conflict, with nature rather than an intelligent adversary as the antagonist. Of the several decision-making situations, the condition of conflict is most complex and least developed from the standpoint of the formulation of decision-making criteria that have won general acceptance. Conflict represents a vast range of possibilities in terms of number of competitors, conditions of competition, and kind of interactions and outcomes that can ensue. This kind of situation has become the focal point of interest in a branch of mathematics called *game theory;* its analytical techniques are potentially applicable to any situation involving competition between intelligent adversaries, such as collective bargaining, business competition, and international conflict. In this section we shall discuss what is probably the simplest type of competitive situation: the *zero-sum two-person game.* As such, our discussion of game theory is introductory, aimed at illustrating the approach of this method of analysis.

91 Whereas the other decision-making situations that we have discussed in this unit have always involved a single decision maker (or decision-making organization), in game theory the objectives and possible decision strategies of at least _____

two

(number) competing decision makers have to be considered.

92 The particular type of competitive situation that we shall discuss has been referred to as a *zero-sum two-person game.* The "two-person" in this name indicates that there are just two adversaries, and the "zero-sum" indicates that one player's gain becomes the other player's loss and that the sum of the gains and losses experienced by the two adversaries equals _____

zero

(value).

93 Put another way, in a zero-sum game there is no percentage of individual gain paid to an outside agency (such as a tax), and there is no opportunity for market development by which both adversaries might gain. Thus the general assumption is made that the total amount of assets held by the two players taken together is (fixed / variable) during the period of play.

fixed

94 As a case illustration of the use of game theory, suppose that two department stores have had about an equal share of the consumer market in a relatively isolated community. With a growth in local population and proposed development of a suburban shopping center, each store manager has the decision alternatives presented in Table 12.8 regarding the type of store expansion, if any, to undertake. The row and column headings of this decision matrix indicate the decision alternatives available to each of the

table 12.8 ■ **decision acts available to two department stores and payoffs in terms of percentage of the market gained or lost by store A**

competitors; the values in the table indicate the various possible _____ for store (A / B).

Decision alternatives, store A	No expansion	Enlarge present store	Build branch store	Row minima
		Decision alternatives, store B		
No expansion	0%	−25%	−15%	−25%
Enlarge present store	25%	0%	−10%	−10%
Build branch store	15%	10%	0%	0%
Column maxima	25%	10%	0%	

95 Thus a decision matrix always presents the possible gains or losses, or payoffs, from the standpoint of one of the two antagonists. But since any gain in the percentage of market for store A is a loss for store B, and vice versa, simply reversing the signs in Table 12.8 would make this the payoff table for store _____.

96 Refer to Table 12.8. If store A does not expand and store B also does not expand, A will gain _____ percent of the market and B will lose _____ percent of the market. However, if store A does not expand and B builds a branch store, A will (gain / lose) _____ percent of the market and B will (gain / lose) _____ percent of the market.

97 In most competitive situations the antagonists are not in identical positions in terms of resources and the like, as they happen to be in this example, and so the decisions available to one may not be the same as those available to the other. In any case, however, the game-theory approach does assume perfect information on each side. Thus the payoffs entered in Table 12.8 would be known to (neither / one / both) competitor(s).

98 Refer to Table 12.8. Since each decision maker has to choose an alternative act before the action of his competitor can be known, is he likely to use the *maximax* criterion as the basis for his decision in this case? (yes / no)

99 Since the decision maker operates under the assumption that his adversary is also fully informed regarding possible payoffs, one possible strategy is to maximize the minimum payoff that can be obtained no matter what his competitor does. That is, a frequently used decision criterion in zero-sum two-person games is the _____ criterion.

maximin

100 In situations in which the maximum of the minimum payoffs is a loss rather than a gain, the decision maker can be described as minimizing his maximum loss, or using the *minimax* strategy. Thus the *minimax* and _____ criteria are equivalent in terms of their meaning.

build branch store

101 Using the maximin (or equivalent minimax) criterion, what decision would you make as the manager of store A? _____
_____

102 Note that the row minima posted in Table 12.8 serve to summarize the information needed for applying the maximin criterion for store A. On the other hand, the column maxima indicate the maximum payoff that store A can obtain for each of the decision acts of store (A / B).

B (as represented by the column headings)

103 The *smallest* of the column maxima represents the minimum of the maximum payoffs for store (A / B). Therefore, when their signs are reversed, the column maxima indicate the minimum payoffs that can be obtained by store (A / B).

A

B

104 Or put another way, whereas the maximum of the row minima represents that decision alternative which satisfies the _____ criterion for player A, the minimum of the column maxima represents that value which satisfies the _____ criterion for player B.

maximin (or minimax)

maximin (or minimax)

105 Thus, for the competitive situation portrayed in Table 12.8, the decision which satisfies the maximin criterion for store A is build branch store (row 3). The decision which satisfies the maximin criterion for store B is also build branch store (column 3). In this example the competition is *equitable* in that the payoff of 0 percent that occurs when each· decision maker uses the maximin criterion does not favor either store. If the value in the cell at the intersection of row 3 and column 3 had been −5 percent, for example, the advantage in the competitive situation would be held by store (A / B).

B

106 The decision matrix we have presented has another important characteristic in that the maximum of the row minima is equal to the minimum of the column maxima. Such a payoff is called the *saddle point* of the decision matrix. When a saddle point exists, then a player can do no better than satisfy the maximin criterion, since any other strategy inevitably leads to a lower payoff if his opponent uses the maximin criterion. For example, given that store A follows the maximin criterion and builds the branch store, if store B does not expand, it will lose _____ percent of the market, and if it simply enlarges the present store, it will lose _____ percent of the market.

15

10

does not (The best that one of the players may be able to do is to minimize his loss.)

107 When a saddle point exists, the situation represents a standoff, and the strategies of the two opponents tend to become fixed. The existence of a saddle point (does / does not) necessarily suggest that the game is equitable.

maximum   minimum

108 Thus a saddle point exists whenever the (minimum / maximum) of the row minima is equal to the (minimum / maximum) of the column maxima.

109 As another brief example of a decision matrix for a zero-sum two-person game, see Table 12.9. The decision act that satisfies the maximin criterion (really minimax, in this case) for player A is decision (1 / 2), and the decision that satisfies the maximin criterion for B is (I / II).

2

II

table 12.9 ■ decision acts available to two adversaries and the payoffs to player A

Player A	Player B		Row
	I	II	minima
1	−5	7	−5
2	12	−4	−4
Column maxima	12	7	

no (The maximum of the minima is not equal to the minimum of the maxima.)

110 Is there a saddle point in Table 12.9? (yes / no)

111 Now note the implications of the absence of a saddle point in payoff. If player A consistently uses the maximin criterion and chooses act 2 while player B chooses act II, then player B finds himself in the pleasant position of gaining a payoff of 4 instead of the loss of 7 he had anticipated. On the other hand, if A can depend on B to follow the maximin criterion, his best strategy would be to choose decision act (1 / 2).

1 (thus gaining a payoff of 7 instead of −4)

112 But if A switches to decision act 1 and B subsequently abandons the maximin decision strategy and chooses act I instead, player A's loss will then be 5 instead of 4. Thus, in the absence of a saddle point, use of the maximin criterion does not result in the best decision strategy for both players, and hence the competing strategies used (do / do not) tend to become fixed.

do not

113 Given two equally informed and skilled adversaries, when there is no saddle point, a *mixed* or *randomized* strategy can be used to maximize the minimum gain in the long run, no matter what strategy is followed by the competitor. However, a mixed strategy can be used only when the competitive decisions to be made are for a (single and unique event / repetitive event).

repetitive event (And in this sense, the maximin criterion satisfied is an average, as is true for the expected-payoff criterion which is used under conditions of risk.)

114 (Frames 1–10) Of the two approaches to interpreting the meaning of a probability value, the one that is particularly applicable when the value applies to an event that is unique and will occur only once is the _____ approach; a repetitive event lends itself to being interpreted by the _____ approach.

subjective

objective

115 (Frames 11–13) The methods of inference heretofore discussed have required that the events whose outcomes are studied be (dependent / independent) and have led to the interpretation of probabilities in terms of the (objective / subjective) approach.

independent

objective

116 (Frames 14–24) The conditional probability that B will occur, given that A did not occur, is designated by the symbol _____.

$P(B|{\sim}A)$

117 (Sec. 12.b, Introduction; Frames 25–27) In the language of Bayesian inference, the probability value that is identified before any knowledge of the outcome of a related event is called the _____ probability. When the value is modified on the basis of a known outcome in a related event, the revised probability value is called the _____ probability.

prior

posterior

118 (Frames 28–41) Where the general symbol which is used to represent a conditional probability value is $P(B|A)$, the probability whose value is determined by use of Bayes' formula is represented by the symbol _____.

$P(A|B)$

119 (Frames 42–43) The meaning of the posterior probability computed in Bayesian inference is most readily interpreted within the (objective / subjective) approach to probability.

subjective

120 (Sec. 12.c, Introduction) Under conditions of risk, when both the possible financial outcomes and the probability distribution related thereto have been identified, the criterion used as the basis for choosing the decision alternative is that of maximizing the expected _____.

value of payoff (or simply payoff)

121 (Frames 44–56) The expected payoff associated with a particular decision act is determined by taking the sum of each possible payoff associated with the act times its respective _____.

probability

122 (Frames 57–62) The expected payoff refers to the expected value of the gain or loss (in a particular event / as a long-run average).

as a long-run average

123 (Frames 63–72) The probability values that serve as the basis for computing the expected payoff can be modified when related sample evidence is available by the use of _____ inference.

Bayesian

124 (Sec. 12.d, Introduction) In decision making under conditions of uncertainty, in which the probability distribution associated with the possible payoffs is unknown, the three decision criteria that might be used are referred to as the _____, _____, and _____ criteria.

> maximax; maximin; minimax-regret
> (any order)

125 (Frames 73–80) Of the three criteria in Frame 124, the one that might be described as being most optimistic is the _____, and the one that is most conservative is the _____.

> maximax
>
> maximin

126 (Frames 81–90) Comparing the payoff for each decision act with the best-matched decision for a particular outcome concerns use of the _____ criterion.

> minimax-regret

127 (Sec. 12.e, Introduction; Frame 91) The branch of mathematics whose techniques are applied for the purpose of analyzing the decision acts of intelligent adversaries is called _____ theory.

> game

128 (Frames 92–105) In the zero-sum two-person game the possible payoffs available to a given player are known by (neither / one / both) of the adversaries and one player's gain (is / is not) invariably the other player's loss.

> both   is

129 (Frames 106–108) The existence of a saddle point for a decision matrix is exemplified by the fact that the (minimum / maximum) of the row minima is equal to the (minimum / maximum) of the column maxima.

> maximum   minimum

130 (Frames 109–113) When a saddle point exists, the strategies of the adversaries tend to become fixed, with each using the _____ criterion. In the absence of a saddle point, the objective of maximizing the minimum gain in the long run, no matter what actions the adversary takes, can be attained by following a _____ strategy.

> maximin
>
> mixed (or randomized)

problems
(solutions given
on page 362)

1 If a manufacturer plans a major change in the new model of his product, the probability is 0.70 that he will begin making production-line modifications before September 1, whereas if he does not plan a major change, the probability is 0.20 that he will begin such changes before September 1. In terms of the previous pattern of model changes, the probability of a major change this year is assessed as being 0.40.

(a) Construct a tree diagram to represent the relationship among the outcomes of these two dependent events and their probabilities, using M for major change, $\sim M$ for no major change, P for production-line changes before September 1, and $\sim P$ for no production-line changes before September 1.

(b) Refer to the tree diagram. If the manufacturer has decided not to institute a major model change, what is the probability that production-line modifications will not be made before September 1?

(c) What is the overall probability that production-line modifications will begin before September 1, given no information regarding the type of model change being made?

(d) What is the prior probability that a major model change will be made?

(e) What is the posterior probability that a major change is being made, given that production-line modifications have begun before September 1?

(f) What is the posterior probability that a major change is being made, given that September 1 has passed and production-line modifications have not yet begun?

2 A small retailer estimates that the probabilities associated with his selling 0, 1, 2, or 3 stereo sets within a specified time are 0.10, 0.40, 0.30, and 0.20, respectively. The markup on each component is $90, and the loss on any set he does not sell is $120.

(a) Construct a table indicating the payoff associated with each possible combination of stocking action and customer demand for zero to three stereo sets.

(b) Compute the expected payoff associated with each decision act and identify the decision that maximizes the expected value of payoff.

3 For Prob. 2 suppose that no basis exists for determining the probabilities associated with the possible outcomes.

(a) Identify the decision act that satisfies the maximax criterion.
(b) Identify the decision act that satisfies the maximin criterion.
(c) Identify the decision act that satisfies the minimax regret criterion.
(d) In this kind of stock-ordering situation in which the probabilities are unknown, which criterion would you use? Why?

4 The following table indicates the payoffs available to player A in a zero-sum two-person game.

	Player B	
Player A	*Act 1*	*Act 2*
Act 1	40	−10
Act 2	90	−20

(a) Does a saddle point exist for this problem?
(b) What decision act is player A likely to make in this situation? Why?

(c) What decision act is player B likely to make? Why?

(d) Is the game equitable? Why or why not?

5   In order to submit a bid for a government contract, a considerable investment is entailed in determining the basis for the bid and performing initial research and development aimed at providing operational goals for the project. If our firm submits a bid and our major competitor does not, the probability that we will obtain the contract is 0.80. However, if our competitor also carries out preliminary research and development activities and submits a bid, the probability is just 0.40 that our bid will be accepted. Because of our competitor's other commitments, we have estimated that the probability is 0.30 that he will submit a bid on a coming project.

(a) Construct a tree diagram to represent the situation described above, using B and $\sim B$ to indicate whether or not our competitor submits a bid and A and $\sim A$ to designate whether our bid is accepted.

(b) What is the probability that our competitor does not enter a bid for the contract and our bid is accepted?

(c) What is the overall probability that our bid will be accepted, given no information regarding our competitor's decision?

(d) What is the probability that our bid is not accepted, given that our competitor does not bid?

(e) Suppose that our bid is in fact accepted. What is the probability that our competitor submitted a bid?

(f) Suppose that our bid is not accepted. What is the probability that our competitor submitted a bid?

6   For the contract described in Prob. 5, the estimated profit that can be realized over the life of the contract itself is 1.5 million dollars and the required investment associated with entering a bid is $600,000, thus representing a potential gain of $900,000. If we have no information regarding our competitor's decision, should we plan to submit a bid if we use the criterion of expected value?

7   Refer to Prob. 6. Suppose we have information from a reliable source indicating that our competitor plans to submit a bid. Should we also plan to submit a bid?

8   Suppose that the payoffs associated with the decision to bid or not to bid are those indicated in Prob. 6, but that no probability values regarding acceptance of the bid are available.

(a) What decision would be made if the maximax criterion is used?

(b) What decision would be made if the maximin criterion is used?

(c) What decision would be made if the minimax-regret criterion is used?

9 If we assume that each competitor in Prob. 8 is faced with the same decision situation and pattern of possible payoffs, can the competitive situation be described as a zero-sum two-person game? Why or why not?

10 Suppose that a number of small contracts are available, rather than one major contract, and that both our firm and our competitor have the choice of carrying out no preliminary research and development, selective research and development, or full-scale research and development. The following table indicates the payoffs, in terms of percentage of available contracts awarded to our firm.

payoffs to our firm

	Competitor's decision acts		
Our decision acts	No res. and dev.	Selective res. and dev.	Extensive res. and dev.
No res. and dev.	50%	20%	10%
Selective res. and dev.	60%	40%	20%
Extensive res. and dev.	70%	45%	30%

(a) Does a saddle point exist in this competitive decision-making situation?

(b) What decision act is our firm likely to make? Why?

(c) What decision is our competitor likely to make? Why?

(d) Which firm, if any, appears to have a competitive advantage in this situation?

unit 13 · linear-regression analysis

When two variables are related, so that a change in one variable is associated with a systematic change in the other variable, *regression analysis* can be used to derive an equation by which the value of one variable can be estimated when the value of the other variable is known. In contrast, *correlation analysis*, which will be covered in Unit 14, is concerned with measuring and expressing the closeness of the relationship between the two variables. In this unit we shall consider the graphic and algebraic methods of determining the equation for a straight line, the uses of the equation for purposes of estimation, and measurement of the reliability or accuracy of these estimates.

The term *simple regression* indicates that the value of a variable is being estimated on the basis of a known value in one other variable only. In contrast, *multiple regression*, which we shall not cover in this unit, is concerned with estimation on the basis of known values in two or more other variables. As is indicated by the title of this unit, all of the computational procedures that are discussed are concerned only with linear relationships rather than curvilinear relationships. This point is illustrated in Sec. 13.a.

13.a · the graphic analysis of simple linear regression

Suppose that the score on a preemployment selection test and the performance rating after six months on the job are available for each of a group of apprentices working in a manufacturing firm, as indicated in Table 13.1. In this section we shall use the *scatter*

table 13.1 · selection test scores and performance ratings for a group of industrial apprentices

Apprentice identification number	Selection test score	Performance rating, 20-point scale
01	88	17
02	85	16
03	72	13
04	93	18
05	70	11
06	74	14
07	78	15
08	93	19
09	82	16
10	92	20
11	79	14
12	84	15
13	71	12
14	77	13
15	87	19
16	87	17
17	72	10
18	77	12
19	82	14
20	76	13

diagram as a graphic method of describing the relationship between selection test scores and performance ratings and illustrate the meaning of a regression line.

1 In regression analysis we always identify at least two variables such that systematic changes in the value of one variable are associated with changes in the value of the other variable. In Table 13.1, for example, the two variables being considered are _____ and _____.

selection test score
performance rating

2 The principal objective in regression analysis is that of estimating the value of one variable when the value of at least one other variable is known. For the data of Table 13.1 the values of which variable would most likely be estimated (i.e., which one would we be interested in predicting? _____

performance rating

3 In regression analysis the *independent variable* is the one used as the basis for estimating the value of another variable. For the data of Table 13.1 the independent variable is _____ _____.

selection test score

4 The *dependent variable,* on the other hand, is the variable whose values are being estimated. For the data of Table 13.1 the dependent variable is _____.

performance rating

5 If the net profit earned by a number of business firms is estimated on the basis of published gross-sales figures, net profit would be the _____ variable and gross sales would be the _____ variable in the regression analysis.

dependent
independent

6 *Simple-regression analysis* involves estimation on the basis of known values in one other variable, whereas *multiple-regression analysis* involves estimation on the basis of known values in two or more other variables. Therefore regression analysis for the data of Table 13.1 would involve (simple / multiple) regression analysis.

simple

7 Estimating net profit on the basis of gross sales involves (simple / multiple) regression analysis.

simple

8 Estimating consumer spending in a number of communities on the basis of number of people employed and the average wage level in each community involves (simple / multiple) regression analysis.

multiple

9 In regression analysis there can be just one (independent / dependent) variable, but there may be more than one (independent / dependent) variable.

dependent
independent

10 In this unit we shall be concerned only with regression problems involving one independent and one dependent variable. Thus all problems presented in this unit are directed toward _____ regression analysis.

11 For simple regression analysis the values for the independent and dependent variables can be represented on a two-dimensional graph. Typically, the horizontal axis, or *X* axis, is used to present the values for the independent variable, and the vertical axis, or *Y* axis, is used for values of the _____ variable.

12 On the blank graph below enter the appropriate labels for the two axes, using the variables of Table 13.1.

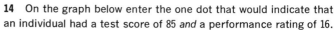

13 Thus the horizontal axis, or _____ axis, always designates values of the _____ variable, and the vertical axis, or _____ axis, always designates values of the _____ variable.

14 On the graph below enter the one dot that would indicate that an individual had a test score of 85 *and* a performance rating of 16.

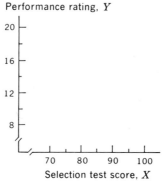

Performance rating, *Y*

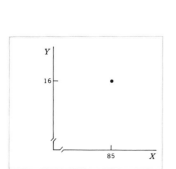

independent; dependent (or vice versa)

15 Thus each dot on the graph represents a *pair* of values: one for the _____ variable and one for the _____ variable.

X

Y

16 The value of the independent variable is represented by the position of the dot in respect to the (X / Y) axis; the associated value of the dependent variable is represented by its position relative to the (X / Y) axis.

17 On the graph below enter the dot representing a selection test score of 75 and a performance rating of 12.

Performance rating, Y

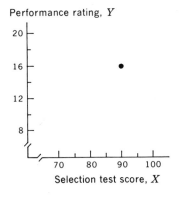

Selection test score, X

90; 16

18 What are the values of the X and Y variables indicated by the dot entered on the graph below? X = _____ and Y = _____

Performance rating, Y

Selection test score, X

19 Figure 13.1 presents a graphic portrayal of all of the pairs of values reported in Table 13.1. As in this figure, a graph indicating

graphic analysis of simple linear regression ▪ 257

all of the associated values for an independent and a dependent variable is called a _____ diagram.

scatter

figure 13.1 ▪ scatter diagram relating selection test scores to performance ratings for a group of industrial apprentices.

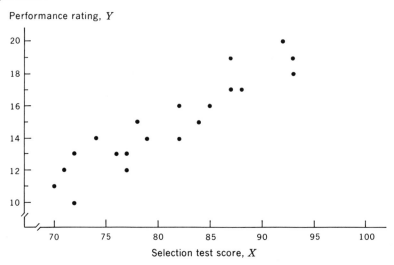

Performance rating, Y

Selection test score, X

20 Because it visually portrays the nature of the relationship between the independent and dependent variables, construction of a _____ diagram is typically the first technical step in regression analysis.

scatter

21 Preceding any of the technical steps of regression analysis, of course, is the choice of variables to be analyzed and the collection of sample data. Thus regression analysis is typically applied for the purpose of statistical (description / inference).

inference (Thus the apprentice test scores and performance ratings represent a sample of values.)

22 Construction of the scatter diagram provides visual evidence regarding the shape of the relationship between the sample data for two variables. The relationship may be linear, that is, tending to follow a straight line, or curvilinear. The scatter diagram in Fig. 13.1, for example, portrays a relationship that appears to be essentially (linear / curvilinear).

linear

23 In order to estimate the value of the Y variable on the basis of the X variable, we need to locate the position of the line that best represents the relationship between X and Y, as indicated by the location of the dots in the scatter diagram. This line can then be used for estimating the value of the Y variable for any given value of the _____ variable.

X

linear-regression analysis ▪ 258

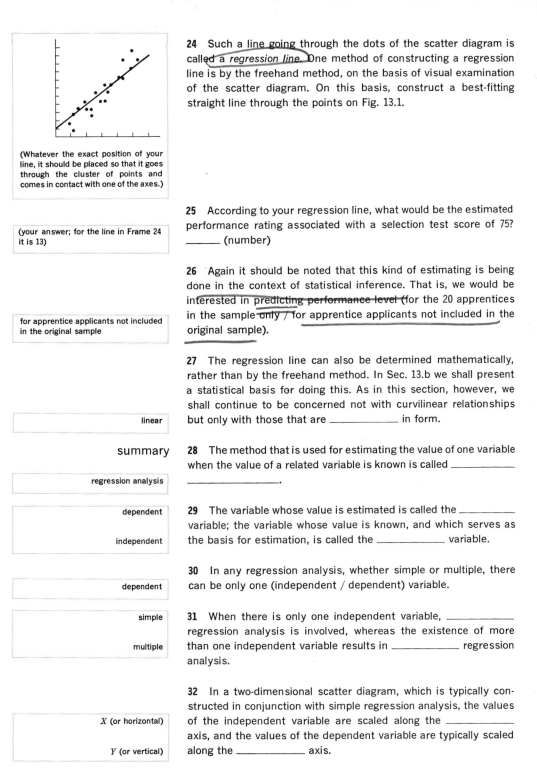

24 Such a line going through the dots of the scatter diagram is called a *regression line.* One method of constructing a regression line is by the freehand method, on the basis of visual examination of the scatter diagram. On this basis, construct a best-fitting straight line through the points on Fig. 13.1.

(Whatever the exact position of your line, it should be placed so that it goes through the cluster of points and comes in contact with one of the axes.)

25 According to your regression line, what would be the estimated performance rating associated with a selection test score of 75? _____ (number)

(your answer; for the line in Frame 24 it is 13)

26 Again it should be noted that this kind of estimating is being done in the context of statistical inference. That is, we would be interested in predicting performance level (for the 20 apprentices in the sample only / for apprentice applicants not included in the original sample).

for apprentice applicants not included in the original sample

27 The regression line can also be determined mathematically, rather than by the freehand method. In Sec. 13.b we shall present a statistical basis for doing this. As in this section, however, we shall continue to be concerned not with curvilinear relationships but only with those that are _____ in form.

linear

summary

28 The method that is used for estimating the value of one variable when the value of a related variable is known is called _____ _____.

regression analysis

29 The variable whose value is estimated is called the _____ variable; the variable whose value is known, and which serves as the basis for estimation, is called the _____ variable.

dependent

independent

30 In any regression analysis, whether simple or multiple, there can be only one (independent / dependent) variable.

dependent

31 When there is only one independent variable, _____ regression analysis is involved, whereas the existence of more than one independent variable results in _____ regression analysis.

simple

multiple

32 In a two-dimensional scatter diagram, which is typically constructed in conjunction with simple regression analysis, the values of the independent variable are scaled along the _____ axis, and the values of the dependent variable are typically scaled along the _____ axis.

X (or horizontal)

Y (or vertical)

33 In order to estimate the value of the Y variable on the basis of knowing the value of the X variable, the location of the _____ line in the scatter diagram must be determined.

regression

13.b ▪ the least-squares criterion in fitting a straight line

Depending on the statistical standard, or criterion, that is used, a number of different straight lines could be considered the best-fitting lines for the data of a scatter diagram. In fitting a line, the most frequent basis used by statisticians is the *least-squares criterion.* By this standard the best-fitting line is the one for which the sum of all of the squared differences between the estimated and actual values of the dependent variable is minimized. Of course, the least-squares criterion also serves as the basis for determining the value of the arithmetic mean for a set of measurements, as discussed in Unit 3. There is thus a direct tie-in between the mean, as a sample statistic, and the least-squares regression line. The regression line relating two variables can be thought of as a "mean" line in the sense that it represents the average relationship between X and Y for all possible values of these variables.

34 The general form of the equation for a regression line which we shall use is $Y_c = a + bX$, in which Y_c is the estimated, or computed, value of the dependent variable and X is the known value of the _____ variable.

independent

35 The two constants a and b in the regression equation

$$Y_c = a + bX$$

also have a specific meaning. a indicates the value of Y_c when $X = 0$. Therefore, for the regression equation $Y_c = 5 + 2X$, the regression line intersects the Y axis at the point where $Y =$ _____.

5 (since $X = 0$ at this point)

36 For $Y_c = a + bX$, b indicates the slope of the regression line. The regression equation $Y_c = 5 + 2X$ indicates that for each increase of one unit in the value of X, Y_c increases by _____ units.

two

37 On the graph below enter the regression line represented by the equation $Y_c = 5 + 2X$.

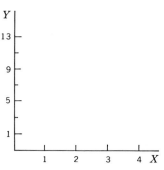

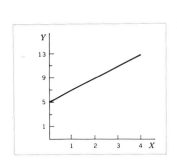

38 On the graph below enter the regression line represented by the equation $Y_c = 3 + X$.

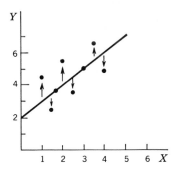

39 Thus, for $Y_c = a + bX$, Y_c is the estimated value of Y, a indicates the value of Y_c at the point where $X = $ _____, b is the rate of change of _____ with respect to X, and X is the known value of the _____ variable.

0

Y_c

independent

40 If the points entered on a scatter diagram are somewhat dispersed and do not all fall precisely along a single straight line, is it possible to avoid all errors, or discrepancies, in the estimated values of Y based on a straight-line regression equation? (yes / no)

no

41 For example, the regression line entered on the following graph represents the equation $Y_c = 2 + X$. However, most of the points in the scatter diagram do not lie exactly on the line, indicating that for these points the actual values of Y differ from the _____ values of _____.

estimated (or computed)

Y

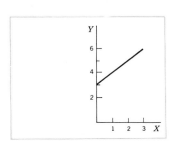

42 In the graph in Frame 41 the direction and size of the discrepancies between the estimated and actual values of the Y variable are indicated by the small _____ entered on the diagram.

arrows

43 One criterion that we could use for determining the location of the best-fitting straight line for a scatter diagram is to choose that line for which the *sum of the absolute values of the discrepancies* (errors) between estimated and actual values of the dependent variable is minimized. As in our discussion of measures of central tendency in Unit 3, this criterion is represented by (N_e = min / $\Sigma|e|$ = min / Σe^2 = min).

$\Sigma|e|$ = min (See Unit 3, Frames 67–80, for a review.)

44 The most frequently used criterion for determining the location of the regression line, however, is the least-squares criterion. This criterion is represented by (N_e = min / $\Sigma|e|$ = min / Σe^2 = min).

Σe^2 = min

45 Thus the mathematical criterion typically used as the basis for locating the regression line is the same as the criterion underlying the computation of the (mean / median / mode) as a measure of central tendency.

mean

46 The least-squares regression line can therefore be thought of as a kind of mean line through the points of the scatter diagram. What is minimized by the location of this line is the sum of the squared discrepancies between the _____ and _____ values of the Y variable.

estimated; actual

47 Using the equation for a straight line $Y_c = a + bX$, we can satisfy the least-squares criterion by using the following formulas to solve for b and a in this equation:

$$b = \frac{\Sigma XY - n\bar{X}\bar{Y}}{\Sigma X^2 - n\bar{X}^2}$$
$$a = \bar{Y} - b\bar{X}$$

In the formula for finding the value of b, n refers to the number of pairs of measurements of the independent and dependent variable. For the simplified data of Table 13.2, for example, n = _____ (number).

5

table 13.2 ■ partial data relating two variables

Person	X	Y
A	3	9
B	2	8
C	1	5
D	3	10
E	1	8

n

48 As a step toward finding the value of b for the regression-line equation for the data of Table 13.2, complete the following calculations:

Person	X	Y	XY	X²
A	3	9	27	9
B	2	8	16	4
C	1	5	5	1
D	3	10	___	___
E	1	8	___	___
	$\Sigma X = 10$	$\Sigma Y = 40$	$\Sigma XY = $ ___	$\Sigma X^2 = $ ___

$\Rightarrow \bar{X} = 2$ $\Rightarrow \bar{Y} = 8$

30	9
8	1
86	24

49 Now substitute the appropriate values from the table in Frame 48 in the following equation and solve for b:

$$\frac{86 - 5(2)(8)}{24 - 5(4)} = \frac{6}{4} = 1.5$$

$$b = \frac{\Sigma XY - n\bar{X}\bar{Y}}{\Sigma X^2 - n\bar{X}^2} =$$

50 Using the figures in Frames 48 and 49, solve the equation for a:

$$8 - 1.5(2) = 5$$

$$a = \bar{Y} - b\bar{X} =$$

51 Thus, according to the regression-line formula $Y_c = a + bX$, the best-fitting straight line in terms of the least-squares criterion for the data of Table 13.2 is represented by the equation

$$5 + 1.5X$$

$$Y_c = \underline{\quad} + \underline{\quad}$$

52 On the graph below plot the scatter points for the data of Table 13.2.

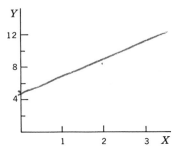

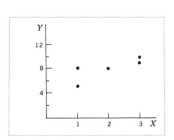

53 Now enter the regression line represented by the equation $Y_c = 5 + 1.5X$ on the graph in Frame 52.

54 Whereas the location of the scatter points in respect to the Y axis indicates actual values of the dependent variable, the regression line indicates the estimated values of the dependent variable based on the regression equation. For each of the five available values of X given in Table 13.2, compute the estimated value of the dependent variable Y_c, using the equation

$$Y_c = 5 + 1.5X$$

X	Y	Y_c
3	9	————
2	8	————
1	5	————
3	10	————
1	8	————

55 In Frame 53 the fact that the scatter points did not all coincide with the location of the regression line indicated the existence of some discrepancy between actual and estimated values of the dependent variable. In the table in Frame 54 this discrepancy is indicated by the difference in values (if any) between the column labeled ———— and the column labeled ————.

56 With the data of the table in Frame 54, the sum of the errors squared can thus be computed by using the equation

$$\Sigma(Y - Y_c)^2 = \text{————} + \text{————} + \text{————} + \text{————} + \text{————}$$
$$= \text{————}$$

57 Can any other regression line result in a smaller sum of squared deviations between the estimated and actual values of the dependent variable (Y) for the data of Table 13.2? (yes / no)

58 Thus, for the data of Table 13.2, the equation $Y_c = 5 + 1.5X$ and the regression line that it represents can be said to satisfy the ———————————————— criterion.

59 Typically, we would collect many more pairs of sample measurements of the independent and dependent variables than the five reported in Table 13.2, but the format of the solution for finding the regression equation would be identical to the solution just completed. As another simplified exercise, complete the following table as the first step in determining the regression equation for the data.

X	Y	X^2	XY
6	8	36	48
7	10	49	70
4	4	——	——
3	2	——	——
$\Sigma X = 20$	$\Sigma Y = 24$	$\Sigma X^2 =$ ——	$\Sigma XY =$ ——

16	16
9	6
110	140

60 Solve for b, using the following formula:

$$\frac{140 - 4(5)(6)}{110 - 4(25)} = \frac{20}{10} = 2$$

$$b = \frac{\Sigma XY - n\bar{X}\bar{Y}}{\Sigma X^2 - n\bar{X}^2} =$$

61 Using the values from Frames 59 and 60, solve for a:

$$6 - 2(5) = -4$$

$$a = \bar{Y} - b\bar{X} =$$

62 Thus the equation for this least-squares regression line is

$-4 + 2X$

0

$Y_c =$ —— $+$ ——. The value of -4 for a indicates that the value of the dependent variable is -4 when the value of the independent variable is equal to —— (number).

63 On the graph below enter the regression line represented by the equation $Y_c = -4 + 2X$.

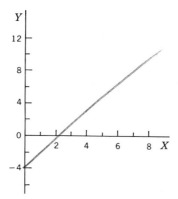

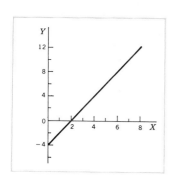

13.c ■ use of the regression equation

If we were to use the regression equation simply to estimate values of the dependent variable that are in fact already known, there would be little point to determining this equation. Typically, however, the data used as the basis for constructing the regression equation constitute a sample from a larger population of values for which the equation is to be used. Of course, the appropriateness of the regression equation for use with other samples from the same population is dependent on the representativeness of the original sample on which it is based, which, in turn, is related to the sampling procedure used.

64 In Sec. 13.a we illustrated a scatter diagram relating apprentice selection test scores with performance ratings on the job. What is the possible value of a regression equation based on these data; i.e., for what purpose might this regression equation be used?

_____

_____

65 Thus the values of a and b in the regression equation

$$Y_c = a + bX$$

are based on analysis of a particular sample, although they are then used as the estimated values for the regression equation representing an entire population of relationships. For our purpose we need not go into a detailed consideration of this point, except to note that just as a sample mean $\bar{X}$ is used as the unbiased estimate of the population mean μ, so also the population values α and β are estimated by the sample regression coefficients _____ and _____, respectively.

66 Once a regression equation is determined, we would use it as the basis for estimating the value of the _____ variable when the value of the _____ variable is known.

67 There are numerous reasons why the value of a dependent variable might not be known. For example, if we are estimating the useful life of batteries on the basis of knowing the quantity of a certain ingredient, the only way to obtain the actual value of the dependent variable (battery life) would be to subject the batteries to a destructive test. Similarly, why might apprentice selection tests be used to estimate the level of job performance? _____

_____

_____

68 Another factor that needs to be considered in the use of a regression equation is the meaning of the words "independent" and "dependent." These words are used in a statistical sense only and are not meant to imply that one variable somehow causes another. In other words, the possibility of estimating or predicting the value of the dependent variable when the value of the independent variable is known (does / does not) necessarily imply causation.

69 For example, since the amounts of personal spending _and_ personal saving tend to increase as income increases, one could determine the regression equation by which the amount of personal spending could be estimated when the amount of personal saving is known (or vice versa). In this case the independent variable is so labeled simply because its value happens to be (known /

known

unknown). It is clear that saving does not cause spending.

70 If we wish to reverse our direction of prediction and estimate the value of the variable represented along the X axis, which is typically the independent variable, we need to exercise some caution. In spite of what might be an intuitive expectation, one cannot usually use the same regression line for predicting X from Y as is used for predicting _____ from _____.

Y   X

71 The reason for this is that the regression line that satisfies the least-squares criterion when the actual and estimated values of the Y variable are compared is usually not the same as the regression line that satisfies the least-squares criterion for the X variable. In the graph below, for example, the line which would be used to estimate Y when X is known is represented by the equation _____, but the line which would be used to estimate X when Y is known is represented by the equation _____.

$Y_e = a + bX$

$X_e = a' + b'Y$

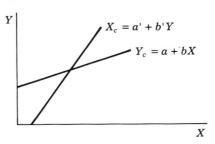

72 To illustrate the point further, the regression line represented by the equation $X_c = a' + b'Y$ on the graph below minimizes the sum of the squared deviations between the actual and estimated values of X, as indicated by the (horizontal / vertical) deviations posted on the graph, whereas the equation $Y_c = a + bX$ minimizes the (horizontal / vertical) deviations on the graph.

horizontal

vertical

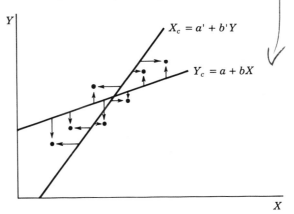

73 The only case in which a modification of the same regression equation (i.e., by solving for the other variable) can be used to estimate *either* Y from X *or* X from Y is when the two regression lines exactly coincide. This occurs only when every scatter point entered on the graph falls exactly along the line in question, resulting in (no / some / extensive) deviation between estimated and actual values of either variable.

no

74 For example, the scatter diagram below represents the functional relationship between two variables, labeled X and Y. Such precise functional relationships are unusual for business and economic data, but they do occur in the physical sciences. In this case the regression line satisfies the least-squares criterion when predicting either Y from X or _____ from _____.

X; Y

75 For data in the social sciences, business, and economics, there is invariably a degree of error involved in making predictions of one variable based on knowledge of another variable. The standard, or criterion, that is used for locating the best line to be used for making such estimates is the _____ criterion.

least-squares

76 One might ask: Just how good is a given estimate using a regression equation? The computation of the *standard error of estimate,* discussed in Sec. 13.d, provides us with the basis for answering this type of question. It represents the degree of scatter of the (estimated / actual) values of the dependent variable around the regression line.

actual (The estimated values are represented along the regression line itself.)

13.d ▪ the standard error of estimate

The standard error of estimate is a measure of the degree of scatter of the actual values of a dependent variable around the regression line used for estimating that variable. As such, this measure provides us with the basis for determining just how closely the actual value of the dependent variable is likely to correspond to its estimated value. There are three possible symbols for the standard error of estimate, depending on whether population or sample data serve as the basis for its value and whether sample data are being used to estimate the population standard error of estimate. Thus

77 The value of the standard error of estimate is indicative of the amount of discrepancy between the estimated and actual values of the _____ variable.

dependent (Y)

78 The graph below presents a visual portrayal of the relationship of the standard error of estimate to the regression line used to estimate values of the dependent variable. Thus the standard error of estimate represents the degree of scatter of the (estimated / actual) values of the dependent variable around the _____ line.

actual; regression

$Y_c = a + bX$

in vertical direction.

79 The computational formulas for $\sigma_{Y.X}$ and $s_{Y.X}$ are very similar. The former represents the standard error of estimate for a (population / sample), and the latter is applicable to a (population / sample).

population

sample

80 The computational formula for the population standard error of estimate is *

$$\sigma_{Y.X} = \sqrt{\frac{\Sigma(Y - Y_c)^2}{N}}$$

The computational formula for the sample standard error of estimate also requires the squaring and summing of discrepancies, with the only difference being that this sum is divided by sample size rather than population size. Therefore the formula for the sample standard error of estimate is

$$\sqrt{\frac{\Sigma(Y - Y_c)^2}{n}}$$

$$s_{Y.X} = \sqrt{\frac{\Sigma(Y - Y_e)^2}{n}}$$

* The formulas used in this book for the standard error of estimate are approximations; they are based on the assumption that the true, rather than an estimated, regression line has been identified. For formulas which take this factor into account, see E. C. Bryant, *Statistical Analysis*, 2d ed., Chap. 7, McGraw-Hill, New York, 1966.

81 When the population standard error of estimate is estimated on the basis of *sample* values, the symbol that we shall use to represent this estimate is _____.

82 Because both a and b in the regression equation are statistics, two degrees of freedom are lost in estimating the population standard error of estimate $s_{Y.X}$ on the basis of sample data. Accordingly, indicate the denominator in the following formula:

$$s_{Y.X} = \sqrt{\frac{\Sigma(Y - Y_c)^2}{n-2}}$$ *very important.*

83 Because regression equations are typically used in conjunction with *sampling* and for the purpose of statistical inference, the symbol for the form of the standard error of estimate which is most frequently computed is ($\sigma_{Y.X}$ / $s_{Y.X}$ / $\hat{s}_{Y.X}$).

84 Match the appropriate formulas with the symbols below, using the code letters.

$\hat{s}_{Y.X} =$ _____ $a = \sqrt{\dfrac{\Sigma(Y - Y_c)^2}{N}}$ where the values of Y constitute all such values in the population

$s_{Y.X} =$ _____ $b = \sqrt{\dfrac{\Sigma(Y - Y_c)^2}{n}}$ where the values of Y are sample values

$\sigma_{Y.X} =$ _____ $c = \sqrt{\dfrac{\Sigma(Y - Y_c)^2}{n - 2}}$ where the values of Y are sample values

85 The following are the actual and estimated values of the dependent variable Y for the data presented in Table 13.2. Considering this to be a random sample taken from a larger population of values, compute the missing values in the table below.

Y	Y_c	$Y - Y_c$	$(Y - Y_c)^2$
9	9.5	-0.5	0.25
8	8.0	0	0
5	6.5	_____	_____
10	9.5	_____	_____
8	6.5	_____	_____
		$\Sigma(Y - Y_c)^2 =$ _____	

86 For the data in Frame 85, and by the appropriate formula from Frame 84,

$\hat{s}_{Y.X} =$

87 Just as for any standard error, either the normal probability (Z) table or the t table is used in conjunction with using the standard error of estimate. When the population standard error of estimate is based on analysis of population data, the _____ _____ table is used. When the value of the population standard error of estimate is based on sample data, the _____ table is appropriately used.

88 The appropriate table for using the standard error of estimate of 1.3 computed in Frame 86 is the _____ table.

89 In estimating the population mean on the basis of sample data, the point estimate used is $\bar{X}$ and the interval estimate is $\bar{X} \pm ts_{\bar{x}}$. Similarly, in estimating the value of Y when X is known, the appropriate point estimate is Y_c and the interval estimate that incorporates the use of $s_{Y.X}$ is _____ $\pm$ _____ .

90 Thus, with $n - 2$ degrees of freedom and a standard error of estimate of 1.3, within what limits would 95 percent of the actual values of the dependent variable Y be located with respect to the expected regression line value Y_c?

Limits =

91 Or to put it another way, and using the data from Frame 90, the probability that an actual value of the dependent variable will differ by more than 4.1 measurement units in either direction from the estimated, or predicted, value of the dependent variable is _____ (value).

92 What would be the principal disadvantage of using a regression equation for the purpose of estimation without computing and making use of the associated standard error of estimate? _____ _____ _____

review

93 (Introduction to Unit 13; Frames 1–10) The term "simple regression analysis" indicates that _____ (number) independent variable(s) and _____ (number) dependent variable(s) are involved in the analysis.

94 (Frames 11–15) In the graphic portrayal of the relationship between two variables, values of the independent variable are typically represented along the _____ axis and values of the dependent variable are represented along the _____ axis.

95 (Frames 16–22) A graph on which all of the related values of the independent and dependent variable are represented by dots entered in a coordinate system is called a _____

scatter diagram

_____ .

96 (Frames 23–33) The one best line that can be drawn through the pattern of dots entered in a scatter diagram is called the _____ line.

regression

97 (Sec. 13.b, Introduction) The statistical standard that is most frequently used for determining the equation, and location, of the regression line is the _____ criterion.

least-squares

98 (Frames 34–36) In the equation for the regression line $Y_c = a + bX$, a represents the value of Y_c when $X = $ _____, and b represents the rate of change of _____ with respect to _____.

0

Y_c; X

99 (Frames 37–41) For the equation $Y_c = 4 + 0.5X$, enter the regression line on the graph below.

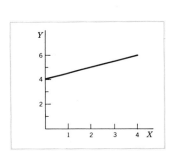

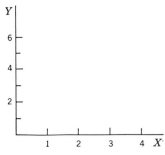

100 (Frames 42–46, 57–58) What value is minimized by the use of the least-squares criterion for determining the equation for a regression line? _____

the sum of the squared deviations between estimated and actual values of
the dependent variable

101 (Frames 47–56, 59–63) The values of a and b in the equation $Y_c = a + bX$ can be determined by solving the appropriate formulas. Given the simplified sample data and computational formulas below, determine the values of a and b and indicate the complete regression equation.

X	Y	XY	X^2
9	5	45	81
6	3	18	36
8	5	___	___
5	3	___	___
$\Sigma X = 28$	$\Sigma Y = 16$	$\Sigma XY = $ ___	$\Sigma X^2 = $ ___

40   64
15   25
118   206

$$b = \frac{\Sigma XY - n\bar{X}\bar{Y}}{\Sigma X^2 - n\bar{X}^2} =$$

$$a = \bar{Y} - b\bar{X} =$$

Therefore $Y_c =$

---

102 (Sec. 13.c, Introduction; Frames 64–69) Once a regression equation is determined, for what purpose is it typically used?

for estimating values of the dependent variable when these values are unknown

_____

_____

---

103 (Frames 70–76) If we wish to reverse our direction of estimation, can we usually use the established regression equation for the dependent variable Y by solving it for X? (yes / no) Why or why not? _____

no (unless it is a functional relationship with no error of estimate)

This equation would not satisfy the least-squares criterion in estimating X.

_____

---

104 (Sec. 13.d, Introduction; Frames 77–78) The measure which provides us with the basis for determining the amount of expected discrepancy associated with the use of the regression equation is the standard error of _____.

estimate

---

105 (Frames 79–84) There are three symbols for the standard error of estimate, representing the source of the data used in computing it and its intended use. Match the appropriate formulas with the symbols listed below, using the code letters.

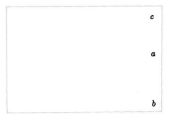

c $s_{Y.X} =$ _____

a $\hat{s}_{Y.X} =$ _____

b $\sigma_{Y.X} =$ _____

$a = \sqrt{\dfrac{\Sigma(Y - Y_c)^2}{n - 2}}$ where the values of Y are sample values

$b = \sqrt{\dfrac{\Sigma(Y - Y_c)^2}{N}}$ where the values of Y constitute all such values in the population

$c = \sqrt{\dfrac{\Sigma(Y - Y_c)^2}{n}}$ where the values of Y are sample values

---

106 (Frames 85–86) The following sample data are based on the information presented and the regression equation determined in Frame 101. Using the appropriate formula from the listing in Frame

105, determine the estimated value of the population standard error of estimate.

X	Y	Y_c	$Y - Y_c$	$(Y - Y_c)^2$
9	5	5.2	−0.2	0.04
6	3	3.4	−0.4	0.16
8	5	4.6	_____	_____
5	3	2.8	_____	_____
			$\Sigma(Y - Y_c)^2 =$	_____

$$\hat{s}_{Y.X} =$$

0.4	0.16
0.2	0.04
	0.40

$$\sqrt{\frac{\Sigma(Y - Y_c)^2}{n - 2}} = \sqrt{\frac{0.40}{2}}$$

$$= \sqrt{0.20} = 0.447$$

107 (Frames 87–92) Whereas Y_c represents the point estimate of the value of the dependent variable, the interval estimate which incorporates the use of the estimated population standard error of estimate is represented by _____ ± _____. The number of degrees of freedom used in conjunction with this estimation formula is $n -$ _____ (number).

$$Y_c \pm t\hat{s}_{Y.X} \text{ (or } \pm Z\hat{s}_{Y.X} \text{ if } n \geq 30)$$

2

problems
(solutions given
on page **364**)

1 For the simplified data relating the values of two variables in the table below, construct a scatter diagram.

X	Y
3	5
4	10
6	9
7	12

2 Determine the least-squares regression equation for estimating Y when X is known and enter the associated regression line on the scatter diagram of solution 1.

3 Determine the regression equation for estimating X when Y is known and enter the associated regression line on the scatter diagram of solution 1. How is it possible for *both* this line and the one determined in Prob. 2 to satisfy the least-squares criterion?

4 Assuming that the data in Prob. 1 represent a random sample from a large population of values for which estimates are to be made, compute the standard error of estimate to be used with the regression equation determined in Prob. 2.

5 As a point estimate, what is the expected value of the Y variable when $X = 8$?

6 Using 95 percent confidence limits, estimate the value of the Y variable when $X = 8$.

additional problems **7** For the simplified data relating the values of two variables in the table below, construct a scatter diagram.

X	Y
1	9
3	7
5	5
7	3

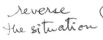

$b = -1$

$a = 10$

8 Algebraically determine the least-squares regression equation for estimating Y when X is known and enter the associated regression line on the scatter diagram of Prob. 7.

reverse the situation

9 Algebraically determine the least-squares regression equation for estimating X when Y is known and enter the associated regression line on the scatter diagram of Prob. 7. Compare this equation with the one developed in Prob. 8 and explain the relationship between the two equations.

10 Assuming that the data in Prob. 7 represent a random sample from a large population of values for which estimates are to be made, compute and interpret the value of the standard error of estimate to be used with the regression equation determined in Prob. 8. *no error. , fall exactly the same value. by chance → random sampling.*

11 Estimate the value of the Y variable when $X = 9$, using 95 percent confidence limits. Explain.

unit 14 ▪ correlation

In Unit 13 we discussed the use of regression analysis to derive the equation by which values of one variable can be estimated when the values of an associated variable are known. In this unit we shall discuss the technique of correlation, which is concerned with measuring and expressing the closeness of the relationship between two variables. After introducing the meaning of the correlation coefficient in terms of the least-squares regression line, we shall review the historical development of the Pearson correlation coefficient r and its computation, present the computational procedure for determining the correlation between ranked variables, and consider the use of multiple and partial correlation. Finally, we shall address ourselves to the interpretation of correlation values as signifying causation.

14.a ▪ the meaning of the correlation coefficient

The coefficient of correlation indicates the degree of association between an independent and a dependent variable. In this section we shall consider the possible values that a correlation coefficient can have, relate these to the characteristics of the scatter diagram for the data being studied, and interpret its value in terms of the associated coefficient of determination r^2.

1 The value of a correlation coefficient can vary between -1.0 and $+1.0$. The *sign* attached to the correlation coefficient indicates the *direction* of the change in the dependent variable as the size of the independent variable is increased. Thus a *positive* correlation coefficient indicates that as the value of the independent variable increases, the value of the associated dependent variable (increases / decreases).

increases

2 Similarly, a *negative* correlation coefficient indicates that as the value of the independent variable increases, the value of the dependent variable (increases / decreases).

decreases

3 For example, since the expenditure on education by family unit tends to go up with increase in income level, the correlation coefficient expressing the degree of relationship between these two variables would have a (positive / negative) sign.

positive

4 At a given income level, as the present level of personal debt increases the amount of planned purchases for a subsequent period decreases. The coefficient of correlation representing this relationship would have a (positive / negative) sign.

negative

5 Whereas the sign of the correlation coefficient indicates the direction of the relationship, its *absolute value* (value without regard to sign) indicates the extent of the relationship. As we have already indicated, the largest absolute value the correlation coefficient can have, indicating perfect correlation, is _____ (number).

1.0

6 Of the following correlation coefficients, the one that indicates the highest extent of relationship is (circle your choice) (+.70 / −.80 / +.25).

> −.80 (since the absolute value without regard to sign is the indicator of *extent* of relationship)

7 A perfect correlation indicates that if the value of the independent variable is known, the value of the associated dependent variable can be determined without error. Therefore the *two* values of the correlation coefficient that indicate perfect correlation between two variables are _____ (number) and _____ (number).

> −1.0; +1.0

8 The *one* value of the correlation coefficient that indicates absolutely no relationship between the values of the two variables is _____ (number).

> 0

9 Though we do not use the scatter diagram to compute the value of the correlation coefficient, it can be used as an indicator of the extent and direction of the correlation. According to the definitions of positive and negative correlation given above, the diagram below which indicates perfect negative correlation is (a / b).

> a

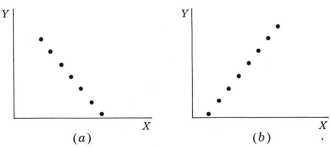

(a) (b)

10 The value of the coefficient of correlation for the data of Fig. *b* in Frame 9 would be _____ (number).

> +1.0

11 The closer the points on a scatter diagram are clustered around the regression line used for estimating the dependent variable, the higher is the absolute value of the correlation coefficient. Of the following scatter diagrams, the one that indicates no correlation is (a / b / c); the one that indicates moderate correlation is (a / b / c); and the one that indicates a relatively high degree of correlation is (a / b / c).

> c
> b
> a

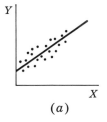 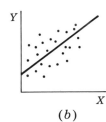 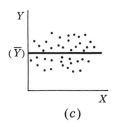

(a) (b) (c)

the meaning of the correlation coefficient ▪ 277

12 In the diagrams in Frame 11 notice also that when the correlation is zero, no matter what the known value of the independent variable X, the estimated value of the dependent variable is always
$\bar{Y}$ equal to _____ (symbol).

13 In the regression line represented by the equation

$$Y_c = a + bX$$

b indicates the slope of the best-fitting line, as discussed in Unit 13 (Frames 35–38). Therefore, whenever the correlation coefficient has a negative value, the value of b in the associated regression equa-
negative   tion will be (positive / negative).

14 In Unit 13, on regression analysis, we discussed the standard error of estimate, whose value indicates the degree of scatter of
regression line   the points in a scatter diagram around the _____.

15 As we observed, the smaller the value of the standard error of estimate, the closer will be the correspondence between the pre-
dependent   dicted and actual values of the (independent / dependent) variable.

16 Therefore the smaller the value of the standard error of esti-
larger   mate, the (smaller / larger) is the absolute value of the associated correlation coefficient.

coef of determination.

17 The fact that this kind of relationship exists makes it possible to define the correlation coefficient in terms of the standard error of estimate, though it would seldom be computed on this basis. With r representing the correlation coefficient, for sample data it can be stated that

$$r^2 = 1.00 - \frac{s_{Y.X}{}^2}{s_Y{}^2}$$

Thus this formula indicates that when the standard error of esti-
1.00   mate for predicting Y from X ($s_{Y.X}$) is equal to zero, $r^2 = $ _____ (number).

18 Along these lines we can also note that if $r^2 = 1.00$, then
$-1.00; +1.00$ $r = $ _____ (number) or _____ (number).

19 s_Y in the formula in Frame 17 is the standard deviation of the Y variable. Though it is not obvious in that formula, there is a definite limit to the possible value of $s_{Y.X}$. To begin with, if there is no relationship at all between the X and Y variables, then the best estimate for Y, no matter what the value of X, is $\bar{Y}$, and the standard deviation about this estimate is represented by the symbol
s_Y _____.

1.00

20 Since $s_{Y.X} = s_Y$ when there is absolutely no relationship between the two variables, $s_{Y.X}$ can never be larger than s_Y itself. Accordingly, the largest value that the fraction $s_{Y.X}^2/s_Y^2$ can have is _____ (number).

0
0

21 Since $r^2 = 1.00 - s_{Y.X}^2/s_Y^2$, if $s_{Y.X} = s_Y$, then $r^2 =$ _____ (number) and $r =$ _____ (number).

22 More significant than the arithmetic manipulations we have been presenting is the essential meaning that the formula in Frame 17 conveys. In Unit 4, on measuring dispersion, we suggested that the standard deviation squared is particularly useful in certain advanced applications of statistics; it is referred to as the

variance (See Unit 4, Frames 65–68.)

_____ (name).

23 The formula for r^2 being discussed is essentially dependent on the ratio between two variances. Since the term "total variance" is used to refer to the largest amount of variance that we can have in estimating the value of the Y variable, the total variance is represented by the symbol (s_Y^2 / $s_{Y.X}^2$).

s_Y^2

24 In that $s_{Y.X}^2$ represents the variance remaining in our estimate of the Y variable even after use of our knowledge regarding the value of the X variable, it is referred to as the (explained / unexplained) variance.

unexplained

25 Thus the appropriate verbal formula for r^2 is (**a** / **b**) below:

a

(**a**) $r^2 = 1 - \dfrac{\text{unexplained variance}}{\text{total variance}}$

(**b**) $r^2 = 1 - \dfrac{\text{total variance}}{\text{unexplained variance}}$

26 Since the fraction in the formula in Frame 25 represents the *proportion of unexplained variance* when values of the dependent variable are being estimated based on knowledge of the independent variable, then subtracting this proportion from 1.00

explained

identifies the proportion of _____ variance.

27 Thus the value of r^2 directly indicates the proportion of the variance in the dependent variable explained by knowledge of the

independent

_____ variable.

28 Because r^2 is actually easier to interpret in general terms than is the value of the coefficient of correlation r itself, it has been given its own name and is referred to as the coefficient of determination. For a correlation coefficient of .50 the associated coefficient

.25 (= .50²)

of determination is _____ (number).

29 For a correlation coefficient of $+.70$, the associated coefficient of _____ r^2 is .49.

determination

30 If the correlation between a test of finger dexterity and work errors is $-.40$, then knowledge of the independent variable serves to explain _____ percent of the variance in the dependent variable.

16

31 Whereas s signifies a sample standard deviation and r signifies a coefficient of correlation, s^2 signifies a sample _____ and r^2 signifies a coefficient of _____.

variance

determination

summary

32 The direction of relationship between two variables is indicated by the _____ of the correlation coefficient, and the extent of the relationship is indicated by its _____.

sign

absolute value

33 As the degree of dispersion around the regression line of a scatter diagram is decreased, the value of the standard error of estimate is (increased / decreased) and the absolute value of the correlation coefficient is (increased / decreased).

decreased

increased

34 The proportion of the variance in the dependent variable that is explained by knowledge of the independent variable is directly indicated by the value of the coefficient of _____.

determination (r^2)

35 In symbols, the value of the coefficient of determination can be defined as:

$$r^2 =$$

$1.00 - \dfrac{s_{Y.X}^2}{s_Y^2}$

14.b ▪ development of the Pearson correlation coefficient r

In Sec. 14.a we illustrated the relationship between the standard error of estimate and the correlation coefficient, and we introduced and discussed the interpretation of the coefficient of determination. In this section we shall briefly trace the historical development of correlation analysis and the development of the computational formula for the correlation coefficient. Though a number of correlation methods now exist, the Pearson product-moment correlation coefficient r is the most important in that all of the others represent modifications of this method. Specifically, the Pearson formula requires that (1) both of the variables be on a continuous scale, that is, that they be measured rather than categorized; (2) there be only one independent and one dependent variable; and (3) the relationship between the two variables be linear. To take care of the situations in which one or more of these requirements cannot be satisfied, alternative correlation procedures have been developed as substitutes for the Pearson r.

36 The development of the correlation coefficient is related to the work of Sir Francis Galton during the latter part of the nineteenth century. Being interested in problems of heredity, he investigated the relationship between the height of parents and the height of their offspring. To begin with, since no statistical technique was available to measure this relationship, he entered the pairs of measurements on a two-dimensional graph, thus essentially constructing a _____ diagram.

scatter

37 Figure 14.1 illustrates the type of scatter diagram that Galton constructed. Then, as is also indicated in the figure, he entered the best-fitting _____ to be used for the purpose of estimation.

regression lines (or straight lines)

figure 14.1 ▪ scatter diagram and regression lines depicting the relationship between height of parent and height of offspring.

Height of offspring, Y

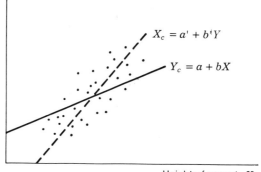

$X_c = a' + b'Y$

$Y_c = a + bX$

Height of parent, X

38 The tools of regression analysis, discussed in Unit 13, were not available at the time. In determining the regression line for predicting Y from X, Galton computed the mean of each column of values in the scatter diagram and connected them with the best-fitting straight line by the freehand method. Similarly, to determine the regression line for predicting X from Y, he computed the mean of each (row / column) and connected these by a straight line.

row

39 Galton then solved for the values of a and b in the equation $Y_c = a + bX$ by using his graph. As indicated in Unit 13, a is the value of Y_c on the graph when $X =$ _____ (number), and b indicates the _____ of the regression line in respect to the X axis.

0

slope (See Unit 13, Frames 34–39.)

40 Similarly, he used the other regression line to determine the values of a' and b' in the equation $X_c = a' + b'Y$. In this case a' is the value of X on the regression line when $Y =$ _____ (number), and b' indicates the _____ of this regression line on the Y axis.

0

slope

41 Galton was apparently the first to refer to these lines as *regression lines.* He so named them because he thought they indicated that there is a regression toward the group mean in inherited characteristics. Specifically, he noted that short parents tended to have children (shorter / taller) than themselves and tall parents tended to have children (shorter / taller) than themselves.

42 Thus Galton concluded that "nature abhors extremes" and named the best-fitting lines on the graph _____ lines. (*Note:* But what about the average-sized parents, who had children both taller and shorter than themselves?)

43 In passing, it should be noted that Sir Francis Galton was concerned about the "regression toward the mean" not just in regard to height, but in regard to a number of human characteristics, including intelligence. Why would a characteristic like height particularly lend itself to statistical study? _____

44 Refer to Fig. 14.2. By using the deviation values x and y instead of the original measured values X and Y, he was able to simplify the regression equations. As you should recall from our discussion in Unit 4, on measures of dispersion, given $\bar{X}$ and a particular value of X, $x = $ _____ $-$ _____.

figure 14.2 ■ regression lines depicting the relationship between height of parent and height of offspring in terms of deviation values.

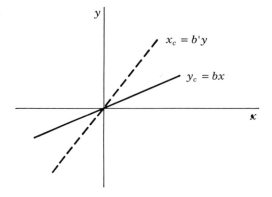

45 From Fig. 14.2 the regression equation for predicting y_c when x is known is $y_c = $ _____.

46 Galton now began to wonder whether the extent of the relationship between the two variables could not be expressed by some one number, rather than by two separate regression equations. In order to represent the two axes of his graph in terms of a common scale, he transformed the deviation values to values on the Z scale by dividing each deviation value by the appropriate standard deviation. Thus $Z_X = x/s_X$ and $Z_Y = $ _____.

Marginal answers (left column):

taller
shorter

regression

easily measured

$X - \bar{X}$ (See Unit 4, Frames 21–24.)

bx

$\dfrac{y}{s_Y}$

---

47 The regression lines for the Z values of X and Y are illustrated in Fig. 14.3. In this case the regression equations for predicting Z_Y from Z_X and Z_X from Z_Y are, respectively:

$Z_{Yc} =$

$Z_{Xc} =$

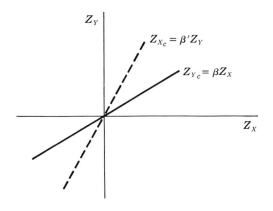

48 On the basis of these series of transformations and graphic analyses, Galton found that β almost equaled the value of β' in the equation in Frame 47, and he believed that the difference (in the second decimal place) was due entirely to graphic reading error. If true, this discovery would be significant because it would provide the basis for expressing the degree of relationship between two variables in terms of (only one / two distinct) value(s).

49 Galton turned to Karl Pearson, a mathematician and biologist, and asked him to prove that β is equal to β' in the regression equations given in Frame 46. Pearson was able to demonstrate that both β and β' are equal to $\Sigma Z_X Z_Y / n$ and are thus equal to one another. Pearson chose r as the symbol for the measure of relationship because both he and Galton referred to this value as the "regression coefficient." Since then it has come to be referred to as the _____ coefficient.

50 Specifically, the symbol r refers to the "Pearson product-moment correlation coefficient." It has been so named because the word "moment" refers to the sum of something divided by n, and in the formula $r = \Sigma Z_X Z_Y / n$ the sum of the product of each pair of _____ is divided by _____.

51 It would be very cumbersome to have to transform every value of X and Y into a Z value in order to compute r. Therefore the alternative computational formula normally used, which is directly equivalent to the product-moment formula and can be used with the measured values of X and Y, is

$$r = \frac{n\Sigma XY - \Sigma X \Sigma Y}{\sqrt{n\Sigma X^2 - (\Sigma X)^2}\ \sqrt{n\Sigma Y^2 - (\Sigma Y)^2}}$$

Unless a computational error has been made, the value of r determined by the use of this formula can never be less than $-$_____ (number) or more than $+$_____ (number).

summary

52 In Sec. 14.c we shall illustrate the use of the computational formula with a simplified example. Reviewing the material above, the early work in regression analysis which paved the way for the development of the concept of correlation was carried out by _____ (name).

Sir Francis Galton

53 The mathematician who developed the formula for the coefficient of correlation and used the symbol r to represent it was _____ (name).

Karl Pearson

54 Whereas the equation for a regression line permits us to estimate the value of a dependent variable given the value of the independent variable, the correlation coefficient expresses the degree of _____ between two variables.

relationship

14.c ▪ computations in simple correlation analysis

In this section we shall illustrate the computation of the Pearson r for simple linear correlation and consider the basis for concluding that a given sample correlation value does or does not represent a statistically significant relationship between two variables. Use of the correlation coefficient to determine the value of the standard error of estimate to be used with the associated regression equation will also be illustrated.

55 Given the data of Table 14.1, which is the same simplified example used to illustrate the computation of the least-squares regression line in Unit 13, substitute the appropriate values in the equation below, but do not carry out any of the computations.

$$\frac{5(86) - (10)(40)}{\sqrt{5(24) - (10)^2}\ \sqrt{5(334) - (40)^2}}$$

$$\left(= \frac{430 - 400}{\sqrt{20}\ \sqrt{70}} = \frac{30}{\sqrt{1400}} \right.$$

$$\left. = \frac{30}{37.417} = +.80 \right)$$

$$r = \frac{n\Sigma XY - \Sigma X \Sigma Y}{\sqrt{n\Sigma X^2 - (\Sigma X)^2}\ \sqrt{n\Sigma Y^2 - (\Sigma Y)^2}} =$$

table 14.1 ▪ partial data relating two variables

Person	X	Y	XY	X^2	Y^2
A	3	9	27	9	81
B	2	8	16	4	64
C	1	5	5	1	25
D	3	10	30	9	100
E	1	8	8	1	64
	$\Sigma X = 10$	$\Sigma Y = 40$	$\Sigma XY = 86$	$\Sigma X^2 = 24$	$\Sigma Y^2 = 334$

56 For the computational result in Frame 55, since $r = +.80$, the proportion of the variance in the dependent variable Y, which is explained by knowledge of the independent variable, is _____ (number).

.64 (= r^2)

57 The statistic r^2, which serves as one basis for interpreting the value of the correlation coefficient, is referred to as the coefficient of _____ .

determination

58 In addition to interpreting the value of the correlation coefficient in terms of the coefficient of determination, we might also ask whether the size of the sample correlation coefficient is large enough to indicate that the population correlation coefficient is different from zero. Would you expect that the sample size needs to be considered in evaluating a correlation coefficient from this standpoint? (yes / no) Why or why not? _____

yes

There is a greater likelihood of a chance relationship in a small sample.

59 Accordingly, Table A.5 lists the various values of the sample correlation coefficient needed to conclude that it is significantly different from 0 at the 0.05 and 0.01 levels, based on sample size as reflected in the degrees of freedom. Refer to Table A.5; for the data of Table 14.1, df = _____ (number).

$n - 2 = 5 - 2 = 3$

60 Refer again to Table A.5; when df = 3, the value of r needed to conclude that it is different from 0 at the 5 percent level of significance is _____ (number).

.8783

61 Therefore the obtained r of $+.80$ (is / is not) significantly different from 0 at the 5 percent level. How large does the sample size have to be before a correlation coefficient of this size is significant at the 5 percent level? $n =$ _____

is not

7 (df = 5)

62 In Unit 13 we reported selection test scores and performance ratings for a sample of 20 apprentices. If we were to calculate the correlation coefficient representing the degree of association between the two variables, the minimum value of r needed to consider it as being significantly different from 0 at the 0.05 level is _____ (number).

.4438 (df = 18)

63 Suppose that we obtain a correlation coefficient of $+.18$ for a *population* of 100 pairs of measurements. Would we use Table A.5 in evaluating this correlation coefficient? (yes / no) Why or why not? _____

no

Table A.5 is used to test hypotheses about the population given sample data.

64 Thus, when we conclude that a given sample correlation coefficient is significant at some probability level by using Table A.5, we

important —

| | 0 |

are concluding that the population correlation coefficient is different from _____ (value).

| is not (since simply being different from 0 may not constitute enough relationship for a particular purpose) |

65 If we wish to ascertain further whether the value of a correlation coefficient is high enough for some applied purpose, this (is also / is not) directly indicated by use of Table A.5.

66 In addition to its principal use in expressing the extent of relationship, the sample correlation coefficient can be used to determine the value of the standard error of estimate $s_{Y.X}$ by a computational procedure that is considerably simpler than the one introduced in Unit 13. Given that $s_Y = 1.67$ for the distribution of Table 14.1, substitute the appropriate values in the following formula by referring to any of the frames above, but do not carry out the computations.

| $1.67 \sqrt{1 - (.80)^2} [= 1.67(.6) = 1.002]$ |

$$s_{Y.X} = s_Y \sqrt{1 - r^2} =$$

67 Now, if we wish to estimate the population standard error of estimate based on the standard error of estimate obtained from a particular sample, we need to multiply the obtained $s_{Y.X}$ by $\sqrt{n/(n-2)}$. Thus in this case (substitute appropriate values only)

| $1.002 \sqrt{\dfrac{5}{3}} [= 1.002(1.2832)$
 $= 1.286 = 1.3]$ (See Unit 13, Frame 84, for the relationships among $s_{Y.X}$, $\hat{s}_{Y.X}$, and $\sigma_{Y.X}$.) |

$$\hat{s}_{Y.X} = s_{Y.X} \sqrt{\frac{n}{n-2}} =$$

68 Thus the computed value of 1.3 for $\hat{s}_{Y.X}$ corresponds to the value computed in Frame 85 of Unit 13. Notice, however, that in the present procedure for computing the standard error of estimate the only sample statistic that we have to compute when r has already been determined is _____ (symbol).

| s_Y (the standard deviation of the Y variable) |

69 On the other hand, as the first step in computing $\hat{s}_{Y.X}$ in Frame 85 of Unit 13, *for every value of* X we had to determine the value of _____ (symbol).

| Y_c (Consider the amount of effort this would involve for, say, a sample of 50 pairs of measurements.) |

70 Because the sample standard deviations are normally also computed when the Pearson r is computed, the most frequently used formula for computing $\hat{s}_{Y.X}$ is **(a / b)** below.

$$\text{(a)} \quad \hat{s}_{.YX} = \sqrt{\frac{\Sigma(Y - Y_c)^2}{n-2}}$$

| **b** (Since the use of $\hat{s}_{Y.X}$ was illustrated in Unit 13, Frames 87–92, it will not be repeated here.) |

$$\text{(b)} \quad \hat{s}_{Y.X} = s_Y \sqrt{1 - r^2} \sqrt{\frac{n}{n-2}}$$

71 In addition to using the equations for solving for the values of a and b in $Y_c = a + bX$, as presented in Frames 47 to 51 of Unit 13, these values for the regression line that satisfies the least-squares criterion can also be determined by an alternative formula that utilizes the value of r. Unlike the computation of the standard error of estimate, however, the present formula does not present any special computational advantage over the procedure presented in Unit 13 and thus is presented here only to inform you of its existence. Using r, the least-squares regression equation for estimating Y when X is known can be defined as

$$ Y_c = \left(\bar{Y} - r \frac{s_Y}{s_X} \bar{X} \right) + \left(r \frac{s_Y}{s_X} \right) X $$

Using the equation for a straight line, $Y_c = a + bX$, in the equation above,

$$\bar{Y} - r \frac{s_Y}{s_X} \bar{X} \qquad a =$$

$$r \frac{s_Y}{s_X} \qquad \text{and } b =$$

14.d ▪ rank correlation

Among the alternative correlation procedures used for the Pearson r under special circumstances, one of the most popular in terms of extent of use is the rank correlation. It is often referred to as Spearman's rank correlation coefficient, in honor of the statistician who first developed the procedure in the early 1900s. As the symbol we shall use suggests, r_{rank} is a measure of the extent of relationship between two variables, X and Y, each of which is expressed as a series of ranks rather than measurements.

72 Like the Pearson correlation coefficient, the Spearman rank correlation coefficient ranges in possible value from -1.0 to $+1.0$. Therefore the value of r_{rank} that indicates the lowest degree of relationship between the two ranked variables is _____ (number).

0

table 14.2 ▪ a ranking of investment alternatives in terms of degree of risk (rank 1 = highest risk)

Investment	Rank by analyst 1	Rank by analyst 2
A	7	6
B	8	4
C	2	1
D	1	3
E	9	11
F	3	2
G	12	12
H	11	10
I	4	5
J	10	9
K	6	7
L	5	8

73 Table 14.2 lists the ranks assigned by two securities analysts to twelve investment opportunities in terms of the degree of investor risk involved. The formula for the rank correlation coefficient is

$$r_{\text{rank}} = 1 - \frac{6\Sigma D^2}{n(n^2-1)}$$

For the data of Table 14.2, $n =$ _____ (number).

12 (In correlation analysis n always refers to the number of pairs of values.)

74 The only other value we need in order to determine the rank correlation coefficient is ΣD^2. Given that D equals the difference between the two ranks given to each investment opportunity, complete the table below and determine the value of ΣD^2.

Investment	Rank by analyst 1	Rank by analyst 2	D	D^2
A	7	6	1	1
B	8	4	4	16
C	2	1	1	1
D	1	3	-2	4
E	9	11	-2	4
F	3	2	1	1
G	12	12	____	____
H	11	10	____	____
I	4	5	____	____
J	10	9	____	____
K	6	7	____	____
L	5	8	____	____
			$\Sigma D^2 =$	____

0	0
1	1
-1	1
1	1
-1	1
-3	9
	$\overline{40}$

75 Refer to the completed table in Frame 74; for the data of Table 14.2

$$r_{\text{rank}} = 1 - \frac{6\Sigma D^2}{n(n^2-1)} =$$

$$1 - \frac{6(40)}{12(143)} = 1 - \frac{20}{143} = \frac{123}{143} = +.86$$

76 Whenever measured data are transformed into ranks, the value of r_{rank} will usually differ somewhat from the value of r that could have been computed. However, the r_{rank} may be "good enough" for certain purposes, or it may be used as the basis for deciding whether or not to proceed to a computation of r itself. For the data below, indicate the ranks assigned to each variable, from highest to lowest. *In case of tied observations, each of the tied observations is assigned the average of the ranks which would have been assigned if no ties had occurred.*

Supervisor	Overall performance rating		Rank	
	Of the supervisor	Of his subordinates	Of the supervisor	Of his subordinates
A	70	75	_____	_____
B	95	83	_____	_____
C	85	92	_____	_____
D	95	95	_____	_____
E	90	80	_____	_____

5	5
1.5	3
4	2
1.5	1
3	4

77 Using the ranks which are reproduced below, determine the value of ΣD^2.

Supervisor	Supervisor's rank	Subordinates' rank	D	D^2
A	5	5	_____	_____
B	1.5	3	_____	_____
C	4	2	_____	_____
D	1.5	1	_____	_____
E	3	4	_____	_____
			$\Sigma D^2 =$	_____

0	0
−1.5	2.25
2	4
0.5	0.25
−1	1
	7.50

78 Finally, solve for the value of r_{rank} using the data in the table in Frame 77.

$$r_{\text{rank}} = 1 - \frac{6\Sigma D^2}{n(n^2 - 1)} =$$

$$1 - \frac{6(7.5)}{5(24)} = 1 - \frac{45}{120} = \frac{75}{120}$$
$$= .625 = +.62$$

79 The Spearman rank correlation coefficient is used whenever the pairs of values for the two variables are ranked rather than measured. As compared to r, r_{rank} requires (more / less) computational effort and is (more / less) accurate.

less

less (since it is essentially a substitute for r)

14.e ▪ multiple and partial correlation and the meaning of correlation values

In this section we shall define and give examples of the coefficient of multiple correlation and the coefficient of partial correlation, but we shall not discuss computational procedures as such. Beyond this, we shall consider the meaning of correlation values in general, particularly in terms of their being used to indicate causation.

80 The coefficient of multiple correlation R is useful as an extension of the Pearson r whenever we wish to measure the relationship between two or more independent variables on the one hand with one dependent variable on the other. Thus the coefficient of *multiple* correlation always involves more than one (independent / dependent) variable.

independent

multiple and partial correlation ▪ 289

81 The symbol for the coefficient of multiple correlation, R, is usually written with a subscript, and in the subscript the number 1 always refers to the single dependent variable. Thus $R_{1.23}$ indicates that the coefficient is a measure of the relationship between the dependent variable and two other variables, arbitrarily numbered _____ and _____.

2; 3

82 Similarly, $R_{1.234}$ indicates the correlation between the dependent variable and (two / three / four) other variables, taken as a group.

three

83 Thus, if an economist wishes to ascertain the amount of relationship between the level of consumer debt and the levels of household income and interest rates taken together, the coefficient that would be appropriately computed is the coefficient of _____ correlation.

multiple

84 Similarly, the personnel manager interested in assessing the correlation between the performance ratings for a group of apprentices and a general ability test and a test of mechanical comprehension taken together could also make use of the coefficient of multiple correlation. The appropriate symbol and subscripts for the correlation coefficient would in this case be _____ (symbol).

$R_{1.23}$

85 Instead of measuring the relationship between a single dependent variable and a number of independent variables, the technique of *partial correlation* permits us to measure the extent of relationship between one dependent variable and one independent variable with other specified independent variables "held constant" statistically. In simple correlation, such as the correlation between general-ability test scores and performance ratings, are other independent variables, such as extent of mechanical comprehension, held *constant*? (yes / no)

no (Other variables are ignored, but not controlled.)

86 The lowercase r is used as the symbol for the coefficient of partial correlation, with the subscripts indicating the two principal dependent and independent variables by listing them first and then designating the variables held constant. Thus $r_{14.23}$ indicates that the correlation reported is between variables _____ and _____ and that the variables held constant are those numbered _____ and _____.

1; 4

2

3

87 If we want to determine the relationship between the height of corn and the amount of rainfall, with days of sunshine held constant, the appropriate statistic to compute is the coefficient of _____ correlation.

partial

88 Where variable 1 is the level of personal debt, variable 2 is the level of household income, and variable 3 is the level of interest rates, the coefficient of partial correlation indicating the relationship between personal debt and interest rates, with income held constant, is designated as _____ (symbol).

$r_{13.2}$

89   The material presented in this section thus far may be summarized: The relationship between a single dependent variable and several independent variables taken as a group can be determined by computing a coefficient of _____.
The relationship between a single dependent variable and a single independent variable, with other specified independent variables held constant, can be determined by computing a coefficient of _____.

multiple correlation

partial correlation

90   No matter what type of correlation coefficient is computed, whether the Pearson r, Spearman r_{rank}, coefficient of multiple correlation, or coefficient of partial correlation, interpretation of the coefficient as indicating causation has to be done with caution. If a coefficient expresses the relationship between amount of rainfall and height of corn, or level of income and level of savings, is a cause-effect relationship implied? (yes / no)

yes

91   If a positive correlation were found between level of expenditure and level of savings, would you consider this as an indication of cause and effect? (yes / no)

no

92   Thus the correlation coefficient indicates the extent of the relationship as such, but it does not necessarily indicate the existence of a cause-effect relationship between the variables. Among other reasons, two variables may have a high relationship with one another because they are effects of a common cause. For example, in Frame 91 the levels of personal expenditure and savings might both be the effects of the level of _____.

personal income

93   In addition to having a common cause, two variables that are positively related may be separated by several steps in a cause-effect chain of events. For example, in the medical field it has been discovered that: warm, humid air → breeding of mosquitoes → activity of mosquitoes in an area → transportation of malaria microorganisms → incidence of malaria. In terms of this sequence, then, would the existence of warm, humid weather in certain geographic areas be positively related to the incidence of malaria? (yes / no) Are these weather conditions the cause of malaria? (yes / no)

yes ("Malaria" literally means "bad air.")

no (though they make it possible for the causative factors to operate)

94   In addition to the possibility of a common cause or being separated by several steps in a cause-effect sequence, many correlations in business and economics represent *mutual cause-effect*

relationships. For example, investor optimism may affect stock-market price changes and stock-market price changes may, in turn, affect _____.

95 A sample correlation coefficient indicating a significant degree of relationship can represent:

(a) a direct cause-effect relationship
(b) two variables influenced by a common cause
(c) two variables that are several steps removed in a cause-effect sequence
(d) two variables with a mutual cause-effect relationship within certain limits
(e) sampling error

In terms of the last possibility, if an obtained correlation coefficient is significant at the 5 percent level, the probability that the coefficient represents nothing but a chance relationship is _____ (number).

96 Of the five possible meanings of a correlation coefficient reviewed in Frame 95, write the identifying letters of those that would have possible value in business decision making and economic forecasting: _____ (letters).

97 Thus, even though two variables do not enter into a direct cause-effect relationship, knowledge of a relatively stable relationship between them may nevertheless be highly useful. For example, cyclical changes in demand for a product may invariably follow similar changes for another product. Though the reason for the correlation may be debatable, its existence may be useful for the purpose of _____.

98 Similarly, if a relationship is found between performance on a test of mechanical comprehension and performance ratings on a particular job, a direct cause-effect relationship is certainly not implied, because both the test score and the ratings represent evaluations of performance. Rather, both are probably effects of a common set of _____.

99 Thus a correlation coefficient need not represent a direct cause-effect relationship in order to have practical value, for the existence of a relationship may be useful in any event. Put another way, the only correlation coefficient that cannot be useful in decision making or forecasting is one whose value represents _____ _____.

100 (Frames 1–12) The sign of a correlation coefficient indicates the _____ of relationship between two variables; its absolute value indicates the _____ of relationship.

direction

extent

101 (Frames 13–16) As the degree of dispersion around the regression line of a scatter diagram is increased, the value of the standard error of estimate is (increased / decreased) and the absolute value of the correlation coefficient is (increased / decreased).

increased

decreased

102 (Frames 17–25) Where $s_{Y.X}^2$ is the unexplained variance and s_Y^2 is the total variance, one way to define the value of the correlation coefficient is to note that

$$r^2 = 1.00 - \underline{\hspace{1cm}} \quad \text{(symbol)}$$
$$\text{(symbol)}$$

$\dfrac{s_{Y.X}^2}{s_Y^2}$

103 (Frames 26–35) Since the value of r^2 represents the proportion of the variance in one variable that is explained by knowledge of the other variable, it has been called the coefficient of _____.

determination

104 (Frames 36–43) In his work which led to the formulation of the coefficient of correlation, Sir Francis Galton entered pairs of values representing the heights of parents and their children on a _____ diagram, and he called the best-fitting straight lines entered on this diagram _____ lines.

scatter

regression

105 (Frames 44–48) In his attempt to transform each scale of measurement to a common base, Galton first computed the deviation values for each measured height and plotted these on a scatter diagram, and then he transformed the heights into _____ values and plotted these on the diagram.

z

106 (Frames 49–54) Karl Pearson, the mathematician, was able to prove that in the equations $Z_{Y_c} = \beta Z_X$ and $Z_{X_c} = \beta' Z_Y$, both β and β' are equal to $\Sigma Z_X Z_Y / n$. He then designated this by the symbol _____ and called it the _____ coefficient.

r

regression (Since then it has been called the Pearson product-moment correlation coefficient.)

107 (Frames 55–65) Suppose a sample of 20 pairs of measurements yields a correlation coefficient of .60. Would this indicate that the population correlation coefficient is different from zero at the 1 percent level of significance? (yes / no) Why or why not?

yes (According to Table A.5, the required coefficient is .5614.)

108 (Frames 66–71) In addition to its use as a measure of relationship, r can be used in determining the regression equation for predicting Y from X (or X from Y) and in computing the value of the associated standard error of estimate. Of these two, the use of

r particularly simplifies the computation of the (regression equa-tion / standard error of estimate).

109 (Frames 72–79) The Spearman rank correlation coefficient (r_{rank}) is used whenever (one / both) of the variables in the corre-lation analysis is (are) ranked and, as compared to the Pearson r, requires (more / less) computational effort.

110 (Frames 80–84) If we want to know the extent of the relation-ship between a single dependent variable and several independent variables taken as a group, we would appropriately compute the coefficient of _____.

111 (Frames 85–89) If we want to know the extent of the relation-ship between a single dependent variable and a single independent variable, but at the same time hold the effects due to one or more other independent variables constant, we would appropriately compute the coefficient of _____.

112 (Frames 90–95) In this unit we identified five possible mean-ings of a sample correlation coefficient in terms of causation. Give two meanings, other than a direct cause-effect relationship, that a correlation coefficient can represent.

(a) _____

(b) _____

113 (Frames 96–99) Of the five possible meanings of the sample correlation coefficient that were discussed, the only one that indi-cates a lack of usefulness for economic forecasting or business decision making is the one that represents only _____ _____.

problems
(solutions given
on page 366)

1 For the simplified data below, which also served as the basis for the problems of Unit 13, on regression analysis, compute the value of the product-moment coefficient of correlation. Assuming that these data represent a random sample of associated values from a large population, is the obtained coefficient significantly different from zero at the 5 percent level?

X	Y
3	5
4	10
6	9
7	12

2 Compute the value of the coefficient of determination for the data in Prob. 1 and indicate its meaning.

3 Transform the values into ranks and compute the rank correlation coefficient.

4 Develop the least-squares regression equation for estimating the value of Y when X is known by use of the formula presented in Frame 71 of this unit. Compare the equation with the one developed in Prob. 2, Unit 13.

5 Compute the value of the standard error of estimate to be used in conjunction with the equation developed in Prob. 4 by use of the formula presented in Frame 70 of this unit. Compare its value with the one computed for Prob. 4, Unit 13.

additional problems

6 For the simplified data relating the values of two variables in the table below, compute the value of the product-moment correlation coefficient. Assuming that these data are a random sample from a large population, is the obtained coefficient significantly different from zero at the 1 percent level? What effect does the sign of the correlation value have on its interpretation?

X	Y
1	9
3	7
5	5
7	3

7 Compute the value of the coefficient of determination for the data in Prob. 6 and interpret it.

8 Transform the values into ranks and compute the rank correlation coefficient.

9 Develop the least-squares regression equation for estimating the value of Y when X is known by the formula that utilizes the known value of r.

10 Compute the value of the standard error of estimate to be used in conjunction with estimating the value of Y when X is known by the formula that utilizes the known value of r.

unit 15 · time-series analysis

A time series is made up of a set of observations taken at specified, and usually equal, intervals of time. The principal approach to the analysis of time-series data has involved the attempt to identify the component factors that influence each of the periodic values in the series. In turn, these components are identified so that the time series can be projected into the future and used for both short-run and long-run forecasting. Unfortunately, future events and their outcomes are not necessarily from the same population as past events and their outcomes, and hence the methods of statistical inference cannot be used in conjunction with forecasting. The result is that the accuracy of forecasts cannot be evaluated, or described, in terms of probability values, and time-series analysis is a statistical procedure whose accuracy and success depend to a considerable extent on the appropriateness of the judgments made by the statistical analyst. In the sections below we shall present the classical, or conventional, approach to identifying the components of a time series and consider the use of these components in forecasting.

15.a · the components of a time series

As indicated in the introduction above, there is no way by which to evaluate contrasting approaches to time-series analysis in terms of the methods of statistical inference. A widely used approach to time-series analysis is that of identifying the major factors that appear to influence the individual values in a time series. From this standpoint the principal components of a time series are the trend, seasonal, cyclical, and irregular components.

1 A series of measurements taken at specified times, and listed in tabular form, is called a _____.

time series

figure 15.1 ■ the components of a time series.

Level (e.g., production sales, etc.), Y

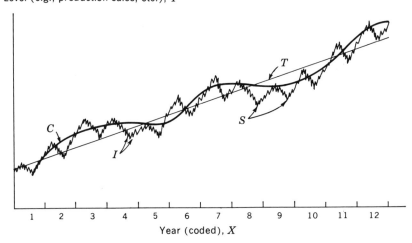

Year (coded), X

2 Time-series data also are often portrayed graphically, as the hypothetical series of Fig. 15.1. On such a graph the time periods are represented along the (horizontal / vertical) axis, and the possible quantities are represented along the (horizontal / vertical) axis.

horizontal
vertical

3 Of the components that affect the individual values in a time series, the most important is usually *trend,* which is defined as the long-term underlying growth movement in a time series. Thus the component of trend can be determined only if time-series data are available for a number of (weeks / months / years).

years

4 The long-term component in a time series that underlies the growth movement (or decline) in the series and is usually attributed to advances in population or technology is called _____.

trend

5 In Fig. 15.1 the data of the time series are represented by the jagged line extending toward the upper right-hand corner of the graph. The straight line which represents the trend line for the series is identified by the symbol _____.

T

6 The seasonal component of the time series refers to a pattern of change which recurs regularly over time. Furthermore this movement must be completed within the duration of a year, and repeat itself year after year, in order to qualify as a seasonal change. It follows, therefore, that in order to identify the seasonal component in a time series, it is necessary to collect data (for one year only / for a period of more than one year).

for a period of more than one year

7 The increase in the sale of lawn fertilizer each spring and its decline during certain other months exemplifies the _____ component in a time series.

seasonal

8 In Fig. 15.1 the seasonal component of the time series is identified by the symbol _____.

S (There is a seasonal increase near the middle of each year and then a seasonal drop.)

9 In addition to the trend and seasonal components of a time series, the cyclical component can be identified. Cyclical movements are similar to the seasonal, in that they also are repetitive wavelike movements, but they differ in that the movements are of longer duration and are less predictable in duration and amplitude. Thus a cyclical movement requiring a total of four years for its completion (would / would not) be an unusual phenomenon.

would not

10 The fairly long-term movement in a time series, not so persistent as trend, which often requires several years for its completion is the _____ component.

cyclical

11 The business cycle is the prime example of a cyclical component that has had considerable attention devoted to it by economists. In Fig. 15.1 the cyclical component is identified by the symbol _____.

C

12 Finally, the movements that represent quick changes that are normally of short duration, and are not characterized by smooth regular patterns, make up the irregular component of the time series. Is it conceivable that through analysis the causes underlying irregular movements in a time series could be identified? (yes / no)

yes (e.g., specific government actions, price increases, industrial disputes)

13 The day-to-day and week-to-week fluctuation in the level of lawn-fertilizer sales that is related to variations in the weather would constitute some of the short-term changes contributing to the _____ component of the time series.

irregular

14 In Fig. 15.1 the irregular component of the time series is identified by the symbol _____.

I

15 Thus in Frames 3 to 14 we have introduced the four conventional components identified in time-series analysis: the _____, _____, _____, and _____ components.

trend; seasonal; cyclical; irregular

16 To complete an introduction to the classical model of time-series analysis, we need to specify how the trend T, seasonal S, cyclical C, and irregular I components interact in their effect on specific values in the series. The most generally accepted model assumes that any given value Y in the time series is a *product* of the effects of components T, S, C, and I at that point in time. Thus, symbolically stated, $Y = $ _____.

$TSCI$ $(T \times S \times C \times I)$

17 An alternative approach to combining the components of a time series is to assume that their effects are additive rather than multiplicative, resulting in the equation $Y = $ _____.

$T + S + C + I$

18 Under the additive assumption the contribution of the seasonal component, for example, remains at the same level of magnitude for a given part of the year, no matter what the overall level of time-series values. Under the multiplicative assumption, as overall time-series values increase, the absolute size of the seasonal fluctuation from period to period (remains at the same level / also increases).

also increases

19 Throughout this unit we shall follow the more popular assumption regarding the relationship among the components of the time series, that is, that they are (additive / multiplicative) in their interaction.

multiplicative

20 Much of time-series analysis consists of identifying and eliminating the effect in time-series values of each of the components in turn; this process is often referred to as the *decomposition* of the time series. The first component typically identified is that which represents the long-term, slowly moving forces affecting the time-series values, that is, the component of _____.

trend

21 In our analysis of trend, presented in Sec. 15.b, it will be represented as a line, and in this respect its calculation is similar to that for fitting a regression line. Therefore one of the methods by which the trend line can be located is by the use of the _____ _____ criterion.

least-squares

22 The next component we shall identify in the major illustration of this unit is that which underlies the regular and relatively short-term upward and downward movements in the series, that is, the _____ component.

seasonal

23 Finally, if the trend T and seasonal S influences on time-series values are removed or averaged out, the remaining unknowns whose effects are thus highlighted by the process of decomposition are the _____ (____) and _____ (____) components.

cyclical (C)	irregular (I)

24 Because the cyclical and irregular components may follow no systematic regularity, they are often identified as the remainder, or residual, of the decomposition of a time series. Algebraically, since $Y = TSCI$, then if Y, T, and S are known, we can solve for the combined components C and I by the equation

$\dfrac{Y}{TS}$

$CI =$

25 In the remainder of this unit we shall illustrate the computational procedures that can be represented by such algebraic formulas. The basic approach of identifying and removing the effect of time-series components, particularly important for identification of the cyclical and irregular components, is often referred to as the _____ of a time series.

decomposition

15.b ▪ trend analysis

Because the material of this unit represents an introduction to the methods of time-series analysis, rather than a coverage in depth, we shall describe several of the techniques available for determining the location of the trend line without extended discussion of the particular circumstances under which each would be most appropriate. Again, the analyst's judgment as to which technique to use is particularly crucial because there is no way of evaluating one approach as contrasted to another by the use of the methods of statistical inference. Rather, all methods and judgments have to await the test of time, assuming that they play a role in forecasting. In this section we shall illustrate the use of the freehand method, the method of semiaverages, the method of moving averages, and the method of least squares as approaches to identifying the one best trend line for the number of new automobiles registered annually in the United States from 1951 to 1965, inclusive.

26   The method of identifying the location of the trend line which is mathematically least sophisticated is the *freehand method.* By this approach the location of the line on the time-series graph is entirely dependent on the judgment (or whim) of the analyst studying the data, with no numerical calculations necessarily involved. Is it possible that a trend line so constructed might turn out to be more useful for forecasting purposes than one identified by one of the more sophisticated mathematical methods? (yes / no)

yes (The decision to use a particular mathematical method is itself a judgment, and one which may prove to be incorrect.)

27   Figure 15.2 portrays the yearly number of new-car registrations in the United States between 1951 and 1965. On this graph enter the best-fitting trend line, either as a straight line or otherwise, and extend this line for the year 1966. Ignore your actual knowledge of automobile sales in 1966, if at all possible, and construct your trend line entirely on the basis of the data for the years 1951–1965. Based entirely on your freehand trend line, the forecast new-car registrations for 1966 would have been approximately _____ units.

(Your answer, read from the graph; label this freehand line entered on Fig. 15.2 with an *F.*)

figure 15.2 ▪ registration of new passenger cars in the United States, 1951 to 1965.

Registration, in millions of units

28 Now let us apply some of the mathematically more sophisticated techniques to the same data. The *method of semiaverages* consists of separating the data into two parts, preferably equal in terms of the time span involved, averaging the values within the two parts, and thus establishing two points for locating the trend line. As typically used, therefore, the method of semiaverages results in trend lines that are (straight lines only / either straight or curved).

straight lines only (since only two points determine the location of the line)

29 The first column of Table 15.1 lists the annual number of new-car registrations, in millions of units, for the years 1951–1965. As indicated in the footnote of the table, the average number of registrations for the years 1951–1958 was _____ million units, and the average registration for the years 1959–1965 was _____ million units.

5.532

7.195

	Annual registration, in millions of units†	Five-year moving total	Five-year moving average
Year	(1)	(2)	(3)
1951	5.061		
1952	4.158		
1953	5.739	27.663	5.533
1954	5.535	28.557	5.711
1955	7.170	30.381	6.076
1956	5.955	29.297	5.859
1957	5.982	29.803	5.961
1958	4.655	29.210	5.842
1959	6.041	29.110	5.822
1960	6.577	30.067	6.013
1961	5.855	32.983	6.597
1962	6.939	35.007	7.001
1963	7.571	37.744	7.549
1964	8.065		
1965	9.314		

table 15.1 ▪ registration of new passenger cars in the United States, 1951 to 1965, and computation of five-year moving averages*

* Alaska is included beginning with 1958 and Hawaii is included beginning with 1959.
† For the method of semiaverages, the arithmetic mean for 1951 to 1958 (eight years) is 5.532, and for 1959 to 1965 (seven years) it is 7.195.
Source of data: Department of Commerce, *Survey of Current Business*.

30 Our next step is to enter these two points on Fig. 15.2 and construct the appropriate straight line. In reference to the horizontal (time) axis of Fig. 15.2, each average value should be entered over the midpoint of the span of years that it represents. For example, the average of 5.532 million units for the eight-year period of 1951 through 1958 should be entered on the graph above the midpoint between the two adjoining years _____ and _____.

1954; 1955 (If an odd number of years had been involved, the point would have been entered directly over the middle year of the series.)

31 Now connect these two points on Fig. 15.2, forming a straight line, and label this trend line SA. Following this trend line, the projected new-car-registration figure for 1966 is approximately _____ million units.

32 As contrasted to the method of semiaverages, the *method of moving averages* typically results in the plotting of several points and therefore does not usually result in a straight trend line. Its major purpose is to accomplish a smoothing of data when there are cyclical or other irregular year-to-year variations in the value of the time series. On the basis of the data of Table 15.1 and Fig. 15.2, does it appear that the method of moving averages would have any use in this case? (yes / no)

33 We normally choose to use an odd number of years for the computation of a moving average so that the averages will be centered at particular years, rather than between years. Accordingly, columns 2 and 3 of Table 15.1 present the five-year moving totals and five-year moving averages for the data of column 1. Thus, of the first two totals in column 2, 27.663 million units is the total for the five years from _____ through _____, and 28.557 million units is the total for the five years from _____ through _____.

34 Similarly for the moving averages, 5.822 million units is the average for the years _____ through _____, and 6.013 is the average for the years _____ through _____.

35 Now plot the values in column 3 of Table 15.1 on the graph of Fig. 15.2, connect these points by a series of straight lines, and label the result $5M$. If we were to project the five-year moving average to 1966 as the basis for forecasting, the method at this point would be most similar to that of the (freehand method / method of semiaverages).

36 One consideration regarding the method of moving averages is that the number of categories of data is reduced by its application. For example, whereas we began with 15 categories of data in Table 15.1, calculation of the five-year moving averages results in a reduction to _____ (number) categories of data.

37 Thus far we have considered the freehand, semiaverage, and moving-average methods of describing trend. Now we shall illustrate the application of the method of least squares, as described in Unit 13, for determining the values of a and b in the equation for the straight line. In this application of regression analysis Y_c is the trend value to be estimated and X is the specified year. Thus the general equation for the straight line being used in this analysis is

$$Y_c = \underline{\hspace{2cm}}$$

38 Table 15.2 contains the necessary worksheet data for this linear-regression analysis. Solving first for b, substitute the appropriate values in the following formula but do not carry out the arithmetic solution.

$$\frac{65.347 - 15(0)(6.308)}{280 - 15(0)^2}$$

$$\left(= \frac{65.347}{280} = 0.233\right)$$

$$b = \frac{\Sigma XY - n\bar{X}\bar{Y}}{\Sigma X^2 - n\bar{X}^2} =$$

table 15.2 ■ worksheet for the computation of the values needed for fitting a least-squares straight line, the resulting expected annual registration figures, and the cyclical relatives

Year (1)	Year, coded, X (2)	Registration, in millions, Y (3)	XY (4)	X² (5)	Expected registration, Y_c (6)	Cyclical relative, 100Y/Y_c (7)
1951	−7	5.061	−35.427	49	4.677	108.2
1952	−6	4.158	−24.948	36	4.910	84.7
1953	−5	5.739	−28.695	25	5.143	111.6
1954	−4	5.535	−22.140	16	5.376	103.0
1955	−3	7.170	−21.510	9	5.609	127.8
1956	−2	5.955	−11.910	4	5.842	101.9
1957	−1	5.982	−5.982	1	6.075	98.5
1958	0	4.655	. . .	0	6.308	73.8
1959	+1	6.041	6.041	1	6.541	92.4
1960	+2	6.577	13.154	4	6.774	97.1
1961	+3	5.855	17.565	9	7.007	83.6
1962	+4	6.939	27.756	16	7.240	95.8
1963	+5	7.571	37.855	25	7.473	101.3
1964	+6	8.065	48.390	36	7.706	104.7
1965	+7	9.314	65.198	49	7.939	117.3
	$\Sigma X = 0$	$\Sigma Y = 94.617$	$\Sigma XY = 65.347$	$\Sigma X^2 = 280$		

39 Similarly,

$$6.308 - 0.233(0) = 6.308$$

$$a = \bar{Y} - b\bar{X} =$$

40 Thus the equation for the trend line based on the method of least squares is

$$6.308 + 0.233X$$

$$Y_c = a + bX =$$

41 Using this equation, determine the forecast trend value for 1966. Do not forget to substitute the appropriate coded value for 1966, by reference to columns 1 and 2 of Table 15.2.

$$6.308 + 0.233(8) = 6.308 + 1.864$$
$$= 8.172$$

$$Y_c = 6.308 + 0.233X =$$

42 Enter the value just computed and any other value from column 6 of Table 15.2 in the appropriate locations on the graph of Fig. 15.2, connect the two points to form the trend line, and label this trend line LS. Of the freehand, semiaverage, and least-squares methods, which one resulted in the most conservative projection for 1966, in this particular case? _____

Which method resulted in the most optimistic projection? _____ _____ Which projected trend value turned out to be closest to the actual number of new-car registrations for 1966?[1]

_____

43 In addition to the freehand method, we have discussed three mathematical methods used in the analysis of trend: the methods

of _____, _____, and _____.

44 In using the methods of semiaverages and least squares for the purpose of forecasting in this unit, we have assumed that the

trend line is (linear / curvilinear).

45 If the trend component of a time series appears to be curvilinear, two kinds of approaches to its analysis are possible: (1) transforming the values in the time series into logarithms, to investigate the possibility that the logarithmic values will follow a linear trend, and (2) using the least-squares method to solve for the unknowns in equations for higher-order curves. Look at the original time-series values plotted on Fig. 15.2. Does it appear that a

curvilinear assumption would lead to better long-term projection of trend? (yes / no / uncertain)

15.c ▪ seasonal variation

Whereas the analysis of trend has implications for long-term managerial planning, the analysis of the seasonal component of a time series has more immediate short-term implications. Manpower and marketing plans, for example, have to take into consideration expected seasonal patterns in the employment market and in consumer purchases. The identification of the seasonal component in a time series differs from trend analysis in at least two ways. First, whereas trend is determined directly from all available data, the seasonal component is determined by eliminating the other components from the data so that only the seasonal remains. Second, whereas trend is represented by one best-fitting line, or equation, a separate seasonal value has to be computed for each month (or season, etc.) of the year, usually in the form of an index number. As was true for trend analysis, several methods of measuring seasonal variation have been developed. However,

[1] Actual registration for 1966 was 9.016 million units.

because most of the seasonal index computations now used are variations of the *ratio-to-moving-average method,* we shall describe this method exclusively.

46 The seasonal component in a time series is measured in the form of an *index number* for each segment of the year being studied. In contrast to this, the *trend* component of a time series is described by determining the equation for, or the location of, the _____ for all the time-series data.

47 The interpretation of the index number that represents the extent of seasonal influence for a particular segment of the year involves a comparison of the measured or expected values for that segment (month, quarter etc.) with the overall average for all the segments of the year. Thus, a seasonal index of 100 for a particular month indicates that the expected time-series value for that month is exactly one-twelfth of the total for the annual period centered at that month. Similarly, a seasonal index of 110 for another month would indicate that the expected value for that month is 10 percent (greater / less) than one-twelfth of the annual total.

48 A monthly index of 80 indicates that the expected level of activity that month is _____ percent (greater / less) than one-twelfth of the total activity level for the year centered at that month.

49 Thus the monthly index number indicates the expected ups and downs in monthly (or quarterly, etc.) levels of activity, with effects due to trend T, cyclical C, and irregular I time-series components (also included / removed).

50 In Sec. 15.a we used annual automobile-registration data as the basis for our trend analysis. As contrasted to this, why is it necessary to use monthly (or quarterly) data for the analysis of the seasonal component of the time series? _____

51 In our analysis of new-car registrations we shall use the monthly data for the years 1962 through 1965 as the basis for the analysis of the seasonal component, rather than using the monthly data for the entire 1951–1965 time period. One reason for this reduction is to simplify the computations in this illustration. Another more important reason is that if there has been any significant shift in the seasonal pattern of new-car purchases in recent years, using the entire 1951–1965 period for the seasonal analysis would result in (better / poorer) projections of expected seasonal patterns for 1966 than using the data for only 1962–1965.

52 Table 15.3 presents the monthly new-car registrations, in thousands, for the period from January, 1962, through December, 1965. The first step in the ratio-to-moving-average method, when using monthly data, is to compute a twelve-month moving average (using quarterly data, a four-quarter moving average would be computed). Because all of the months of the year are included in this moving average, differential effects due to the seasonal component itself are thus removed, leaving the effects due to longer-term _____, _____, and _____ components in the moving averages.

trend; cyclical; irregular

table 15.3 ▪ registration of new passenger cars in the United States: worksheet for computation of seasonal indexes by the ratio-to-moving-average method

Year	Month	Registra-tions, in thousands (1)	Twelve-month moving total (2)	Two-year moving total of column 2 (3)	Twelve-month centered moving average (4)	Percent of twelve-month centered moving average (5)
1962	Jan.	506				
	Feb.	473				
	Mar.	592				
	Apr.	635				
	May	644				
	June	602				
			6,939			
	July	614		13,926	580.25	105.82
			6,987			
	Aug.	540		13,999	583.29	92.58
			7,012			
	Sept.	374		14,056	585.67	63.86
			7,044			
	Oct.	678		14,212	592.67	114.40
			7,168			
	Nov.	637		14,407	600.29	106.12
			7,239			
	Dec.	644		14,568	607.00	106.10
			7,329			
1963	Jan.	554		14,750	614.58	90.14
			7,421			
	Feb.	498		14,853	618.88	80.47
			7,432			
	Mar.	624		14,896	620.67	100.54
			7,464			
	Apr.	759		14,965	623.54	121.72
			7,501			
	May	715		15,005	625.21	114.36
			7,504			
	June	692		15,076	628.17	110.16
			7,572			
	July	706		15,202	633.42	111.46
			7,630			

Year	Month	Registrations, in thousands (1)	Twelve-month moving total (2)	Two-year moving total of column 2 (3)	Twelve-month centered moving average (4)	Percent of twelve-month centered moving average (5)
	Aug.	553		15,314	638.08	86.67
			7,684			
	Sept.	404		15,381	640.88	63.04
			7,697			
	Oct.	715		15,447	643.62	111.09
			7,750			
	Nov.	640		15,566	648.17	98.74
			7,816			
	Dec.	712		16,694	695.58	102.36
			7,878			
1964	Jan.	612		15,774	657.25	93.12
			7,896			
	Feb.	552		15,888	662.00	83.39
			7,992			
	Mar.	637		16,145	672.71	94.69
			8,153			
	Apr.	812		16,249	677.04	119.93
			8,096			
	May	781		16,116	671.50	116.31
			8,020			
	June	754		16,085	670.21	112.50
			8,065			
	July	724		16,185	674.38	107.36
			8,120			
	Aug.	649		16,319	679.96	95.45
			8,199			
	Sept.	565		16,560	690.00	81.88
			8,361			
	Oct.	658		16,806	700.25	93.97
			8,445			
	Nov.	564		16,950	706.25	79.86
			8,505			
	Dec.	757		17,098	712.42	106.26
			8,593			
1965	Jan.	667		17,296	720.67	92.55
			8,703			
	Feb.	631		17,524	730.17	86.42
			8,821			
	Mar.	799		17,667	736.12	108.54
			8,846			
	Apr.	896		17,780	740.83	120.95
			8,934			
	May	841		18,098	754.08	111.53
			9,164			

Year	Month	Registra- tions, in thousands (1)	Twelve- month moving total (2)	Two- year moving total of column 2 (3)	Twelve- month centered moving average (4)	Percent of twelve- month centered moving average (5)
	June	842		18,480	770.00	109.35
			9,316			
	July	834				
	Aug.	767				
	Sept.	590				
	Oct.	746				
	Nov.	794				
	Dec.	909				

Source of data: Department of Commerce, *Survey of Current Business.*

53 Computation of the twelve-month moving averages requires that the twelve-month moving totals first be determined. Thus the first twelve-month moving total listed in Table 15.3 signifies the total new-car registrations for the months _ _____, 1962, through _____, 1962.

January
December

54 Similarly, the second twelve-month moving total listed in Table 15.3 is for the period _____ (month, year), through _____ (month, year).

February, 1962
January, 1963

55 Suppose each twelve-month moving total were divided by 12. For the first total, since the period included is from January 1, 1962, through December 31, 1962, what date would be at the approximate center of this twelve-month period? _____ (month, day), 1962

July 1 (or June 30)

56 Because we want the moving average to be at the center of each month to correspond with the original posting of totals for each month, it is necessary to compute a two-year total to center the values before computing the averages. (*Note:* Some statisticians consider the uncentered averages to be close enough and do not go through this procedure of computing two-year totals.) Each two-year total is actually made up of two overlapping twelve-month periods. Thus the first two-year moving total posted in column 3 of Table 15.3 is a summation of the values for the months of _____, 1962, through _____, 1962, and _____, 1962, through _____, 1963.

January; December; February
January

57 Now we are ready to compute the twelve-month *centered* moving average, posted in column 4 of Table 15.3. This is accomplished simply by dividing each overlapping two-year total by _____ (number).

24

58 After computing the moving averages, the next step in the *ratio-to-moving-average* method is, as the name implies, to compute the ratio of each monthly value to the value of the moving average for that month. This ratio is then multiplied by 100, so that it is stated in percentage form, as posted in the final column of Table 15.3. According to our division, a percentage ratio of less than 100 indicates that the actual monthly value is (smaller / larger) than the moving average.

smaller

59 Before we proceed to the final step of computing the seasonal index for each month, note what the ratio to moving average tends to represent. Since each monthly value reflects the effect of the T, S, C, and I components, and each moving average reflects the effect of the T, C, and I components, then dividing the former group of symbols by the latter yields

$\dfrac{TSCI}{TCI} = S$ (a measure of the effect of the seasonal component on each monthly value)

Ratio to moving average $= \dfrac{\text{(symbols)}}{\text{(symbols)}}$

$= $ _____ (symbol)

60 The final step in computing the seasonal index for each month is to average the percentage ratios computed in Table 15.3 according to month of the year and to make certain adjustments to be described below. In order to carry out these computations, it is convenient to construct a table listing the percentage ratios according to the month of the year, as has been done in Table 15.4. Accordingly, for each of the months of the year Table 15.4 lists _____ (number) percentage ratios.

three

table 15.4 ▪ calculation of seasonal indexes using percent of twelve-month moving averages

Month	1962	1963	1964	1965	Median, by month	Adjusted seasonal index, med × 0.99860
Jan.	. . .	90.14	93.12	92.55	92.55	92.4
Feb.	. . .	80.47	83.39	86.42	83.39	83.3
Mar.	. . .	100.54	94.69	108.54	100.54	100.4
Apr.	. . .	121.72	119.93	120.95	120.95	120.8
May	. . .	114.36	116.31	111.53	114.36	114.2
June	. . .	110.16	112.50	109.35	110.16	110.0
July	105.82	111.46	107.36	. . .	107.36	107.2
Aug.	92.58	86.67	95.45	. . .	92.58	92.5
Sept.	63.86	63.04	81.88	. . .	63.86	63.8
Oct.	114.40	111.09	93.97	. . .	111.09	110.9
Nov.	106.12	98.74	79.86	. . .	98.74	98.6
Dec.	106.10	102.36	106.26	. . .	106.10	106.0
					1,201.68	1,200.1

Source of data: Table 15.3.

61 In computing the average percentage ratio for each month, one of three methods can be used, depending on the analyst's judgment. One method is to use the *median* of the percentage ratios reported, another is to use the *mean,* and the third frequently used method, particularly when a relatively large number of ratios is available, is to compute a modified mean. The latter is the arithmetic mean of the central items in the array (e.g., the "middle" five ratios), thus eliminating the effect of extreme and unusual observations on the mean. In Table 15.4 the average that is used is the

median

(median / mean / modified mean).

62 If the average seasonal index for all twelve months combined is to be equal to 100, by definition, the total of the seasonal indexes

1,200

for all twelve months of the year should be equal to _____ (value).

63 Whereas the total of the monthly indexes should be equal to 1,200, the actual total of the average ratios reported in Table 15.4 is 1,201.68. Therefore the final step in the computation of the seasonal indexes is to adjust each monthly average so that the total is approximately 1,200. This is accomplished by multiplying each monthly average by the ratio

$$\frac{\text{Desired total}}{\text{Actual total}}$$

$\dfrac{1{,}200}{1{,}201.68}\,(=0.99860)$ or, in this case, by ————— (fraction)

64 The final column of Table 15.4 lists the computed seasonal index value for each month, determined by making the adjustment described in Frame 63. In scanning these values, it is obvious that the seasonal peak in the number of new-car registrations occurs

April
September

in the month of _____ (at least this was true for the years 1962–1965), and the seasonal low occurs in the month of _____.

65 The occurrence of the seasonal peak in April probably did not surprise you, since the spring months are traditional car-buying months. What factor probably accounts for the other seasonal

the introduction of new-car models

peak in October? _____

summary   **66** To compute seasonal indexes by the ratio-to-moving-average method, first compute the twelve-month moving totals for the data, combine adjacent twelve-month totals, and divide by 24 to obtain the moving averages. This combination of adjacent twelve-month totals is necessitated by the desire to have the subsequent averages

center

located at the (beginning / center / end) of each month.

67 Second, compute the ratios to moving average by dividing the

moving average

actual value for each month by the _____

for each month and multiplying by 100 so that the ratio is in the form of a percentage.

68 Third, determine the average percentage ratio according to month by computing one of three kinds of averages: the _____, _____, or _____.

median; mean; modified mean

69 Finally, determine the seasonal indexes by multiplying each of the average ratios by a value such that the sum of all twelve monthly indexes is equal to approximately 1,200. Since this multiplier should be greater than 1 if the total of the averages before adjustment is less than 1,200, the multiplier is defined as (circle best choice):

(a) $\dfrac{\text{Actual total}}{1,200}$

(b) $\dfrac{1,200}{\text{Actual total}}$

b

15.d ▪ estimation of cyclical and irregular variations

Whereas the analysis of trend has direct practical value for long-term forecasting and the analysis of the seasonal component is of direct application in forecasting for the short run, the analysis of the cyclical and irregular components, taken by itself, is of dubious forecasting value for the managers of an organization. Like the seasonal component of the time series, the cyclical component also represents wavelike movements on the time-series graph, but the cyclical movements are longer in duration and less predictable than the seasonal movements. Economists have given extensive attention to the analysis of business cycles and their causes, but it is not our purpose here to consider the numerous theories addressed to this analysis. For the manager who has to make operating decisions, it appears more fruitful to base cyclical expectations on the particular factors that underlie cyclical fluctuations in his industry (e.g., inventory levels), rather than to anticipate cyclical fluctuations based on the assumed mathematical characteristics of the movements themselves. Because both the cyclical and irregular components of the time series are determined by the use of the *residual method,* described below, they are combined for discussion purposes in this section.

70 The essence of the classical approach to identifying the cyclical and irregular components of the time series is to eliminate (or average out) the effects of the trend and seasonal components from a time series, thus leaving the cyclical and irregular components. Because these components constitute that which remains after such adjustments, the method is referred to as the _____ method.

residual

71 The specific steps included in the residual method depend on whether we begin the analysis with monthly or annual time-series data; we shall illustrate both situations in the frames below. If we begin with monthly data, then the effects of both the trend and seasonal components have to be removed to identify those effects due to the cyclical and irregular components. If we begin with annual data, then the effects of the cyclical and long-term irregular components can be identified by removing only the effects of the _____ component from the data.

trend (since, by definition, there are no seasonal effects in annual data)

72 Though the use of annual data thus results in a simpler computational procedure, it does not make possible the identification of the short-term irregular variations, but only of those that are long-term and intertwined with the cyclical variations themselves. For this reason, when annual data are used as the basis for the decomposition, no attempt is usually made to separate the cyclical and irregular components that remain. Symbolically, then, the decomposition of the time series can in this case be represented as:

$$\frac{Y}{T} = \frac{TCI}{T} =$$

CI

73 In dividing through by trend, the first decision to be made is which basis for determining trend will be used. In our illustration we shall arbitrarily use the least-squares basis. Thus in Table 15.2 (page 303) the actual registrations for each year are posted in column 3, and the expected registrations based on the least-squares trend line are posted in column _____.

6

74 Of course, these expected values are based on the least-squares equation developed in Sec. 15.b. Thus, for example, the actual number of new-car registrations for 1960 was _____ million units, and the expected number based on the least-squares trend line was _____ million units.

6.577

6.774

75 In determining the relative effect of the cyclical component in each annual value, we accept the expected value as an accurate indication of trend and treat the discrepancy (residual) as being due to the cyclical component. Thus, as indicated in column 7 of Table 15.2, each *cyclical relative* is computed by dividing the actual registration for each year Y by the _____ (_____) and multiplying by 100 so that the ratio is in percentage form.

expected registration (Y_c)

76 In order to study the cyclical movements represented in column 7 of Table 15.2 over time, it is useful to portray them graphically, as has been done in Fig. 15.3. From this chart it would appear that the cyclical movements associated with new-car registrations (are / are not) of regular duration and relatively predictable.

are not

figure 15.3 ▪ cycle chart for annual new-car registrations, 1951 to 1965.

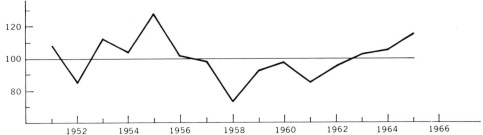

Cyclical relatives, %

77 Of course, though Fig. 15.3 is called a cycle chart, it actually reflects the effect of two influences on the time-series values: those associated with the cyclical component and the long-term _____ component. The separation of these two influences, if it were to be attempted, would be dependent on the analyst's judgment regarding the nature of the real cyclical influences.

> irregular

78 To the extent that Fig. 15.3 actually represents cyclical movements in new-car registrations, the data for 1955 represent the (bottom / peak) of a cyclical movement, and the data for 1958 represent a cyclical (bottom / peak).

> peak
> bottom

79 Turning now to the application of the residual method to monthly data, we shall illustrate the identification of the cyclical and irregular components by removing, in turn, the effect of both the _____ and _____ components. Actually, since we have monthly data for only four years of this time series, the time period covered may not be sufficient to attempt an identification of the (cyclical / irregular) component; therefore the procedure in the frames that follow is being presented for illustrative purposes only.

> trend; seasonal

> cyclical

80 First, if the original monthly values of the time series are divided by their corresponding seasonal indexes, the resulting data are said to be deseasonalized, or adjusted for seasonal variation. Since the resulting values still include the trend, cyclical, and irregular movements, the process of deseasonalizing data can be algebraically represented by

> TCI

$$\frac{Y}{S} = \frac{TSCI}{S} =$$

81 Table 15.5 lists the seasonally adjusted data for new-car registrations. These values were calculated by dividing the actual monthly values of Table 15.3 by the seasonal indexes of Table 15.4 and multiplying the result by 100. Because the effect of the seasonal component has been removed from these data, notice that in this table the number of new-car registrations for April of each year, a high registration month, (is / is not) markedly higher than for September, a low registration month.

Month	1962	1963	1964	1965
Jan.	547.6	599.6	662.3	721.9
Feb.	567.8	597.8	662.7	757.5
Mar.	589.6	621.5	634.5	795.8
Apr.	525.7	628.3	672.2	741.7
May	563.9	626.1	683.9	736.4
June	547.3	629.1	685.5	765.5
July	572.8	658.6	675.4	778.0
Aug.	583.8	597.8	701.6	829.2
Sept.	586.2	633.2	885.6	924.8
Oct.	611.4	644.7	593.3	672.7
Nov.	646.0	649.1	572.0	805.3
Dec.	607.5	671.7	714.2	857.5

Source of data: Tables 15.3 and 15.4.

82 Thus the data of Table 15.5 have had the effect of the seasonal component removed but still include the effects of the _____, _____, and _____ components.

83 After the data have been deseasonalized, they can be adjusted for trend, as was done with the annual data, by dividing the deseasonalized value for each month by the corresponding trend value. Note, however, that these need to be *monthly* trend values rather than the annual trend values that would be generated by use of the least-squares equation developed in Sec. 15.b. To change the scale of the equation from annual totals to monthly totals, we have

$$Y_c \text{ (monthly)} = \frac{a + bX}{12} = \frac{a}{12} + \frac{b}{12} X$$

Or, using the specific equation developed in Sec. 15.b, Frame 40,

$$Y_c \text{ (monthly)} = \frac{}{12} + \frac{}{12} X$$

for forecasting the monthly registrations in terms of millions of units.

84 For forecasting the monthly registration figures in terms of *thousands* of units instead of millions of units, which would be compatible with the format of the monthly data reported in Table 15.3, the final equation in Frame 83 would be modified to read Y_c (monthly) = _____.

$525.7 + 19.4X$

85 Of course, the X in the equation in Frame 84 still refers to units in terms of years, with the coded 0 year being centered at July 1, 1958 (per Table 15.2). We can step down the X value in this equation by dividing each coded year value by 12. Thus

$\frac{19.4X}{12} (= 1.6X)$ (with X = monthly units and $X = 0$ at July 1, 1958)

Y_c (monthly) = 525.7 + _____ (fraction)

86 Finally, in order to begin the series of months at January 15, 1958, instead of July 1, 1958, and thus making the monthly trend values compatible with the data of Table 15.3 (particularly in regard to the centering of values in each month), we need to subtract 5.5 (months) from each new X value. The final stepped-down trend equation thus becomes, in this case,

$525.7 + 1.6X - 8.8 = 516.9 + 1.6X$

$Y_c = 525.7 + 1.6(X - 5.5) =$ _____

January 15

with Y_c being expected monthly totals, X being months, and $X = 0$ located at _____ (month, day), 1958.

87 With this equation the monthly trend values posted in Table 15.6 were computed. Verify the trend value indicated for January, 1962, by using the final equation in Frame 86.

$516.9 + 1.6(48) = 516.9 + 76.8 = 593.7$ (in thousands) (January, 1962, is the forty-eighth month after January, 1958.)

Y_c (Jan., 1962) = 516.9 + 1.6X = _____

table 15.6 ■ monthly trend values: new-passenger-car registrations in the United States, 1962 to 1965 (in thousands of units)

Month	1962	1963	1964	1965
Jan.	593.7	612.9	632.1	651.3
Feb.	595.3	614.5	633.7	652.9
Mar.	596.9	616.1	635.3	654.5
Apr.	598.5	617.7	636.9	656.1
May	600.1	619.3	638.5	657.7
June	601.7	620.9	640.1	659.3
July	603.3	622.5	641.7	660.9
Aug.	604.9	624.1	643.3	662.5
Sept.	606.5	625.7	644.9	664.1
Oct.	608.1	627.3	646.5	665.7
Nov.	609.7	628.9	648.1	667.3
Dec.	611.3	630.5	649.7	668.9

Source of data: equation in Frame 86.

88 Now, if we divide each of the deseasonalized values of Table 15.5 by the corresponding monthly trend values of Table 15.6 and multiply by 100, the resulting percentages, reported in Table 15.7, have the effects of both the seasonal and trend components re-

moved from them, leaving the differential influences of the _____
_____ and _____ components in the monthly data.

table 15.7 ▪ new-passenger-car registrations by months, 1962 to 1965: seasonally adjusted data as percentage of trend (indicating cyclical and irregular components)

Month	1962	1963	1964	1965
Jan.	92.2	97.8	104.8	110.8
Feb.	95.4	97.3	104.6	116.0
Mar.	98.8	100.9	99.9	121.6
Apr.	87.8	101.7	105.5	113.0
May	94.0	101.1	107.1	112.0
June	91.0	101.3	107.1	116.1
July	94.9	105.8	105.3	117.7
Aug.	96.5	95.8	109.1	125.2
Sept.	96.7	101.2	137.3	139.3
Oct.	100.5	102.8	91.8	101.1
Nov.	106.0	103.2	88.3	120.7
Dec.	99.4	106.5	109.9	128.2

Source of data: Tables 15.5 and 15.6.

89 Unlike the application of the residual method to annual data, the method with these monthly data enables us also to separate computationally the apparent effects of the cyclical as contrasted to the short-term irregular components. In order to remove the effect of I, a moving average of a few months' duration is computed for the data already adjusted for seasonal and trend factors, thus smoothing the irregular variations. Therefore the five-month moving averages entered in Table 15.8 presumably reflect only the effect of the _____ component.

table 15.8 ▪ new-passenger-car registrations by months, 1962 to 1965: seasonally adjusted data as percentage of trend, five-month moving average (indicating cyclical component)

Month	1962	1963	1964	1965
Jan.	. . .	100.3	103.8	109.3
Feb.	. . .	99.4	104.3	114.3
Mar.	93.6	99.8	104.4	114.7
Apr.	93.4	100.5	104.8	115.7
May	93.3	102.2	105.0	116.1
June	92.8	101.1	106.8	116.8
July	94.6	101.0	113.2	122.1
Aug.	95.9	101.4	110.1	119.9
Sept.	98.9	101.8	106.4	120.8
Oct.	99.8	101.9	107.3	122.9
Nov.	100.1	103.7	107.6	
Dec.	100.2	104.4	103.4	

Source of data: Table 15.7.

90 If the residual variations of Table 15.8 indeed represent the cyclical effect in the time series, then it appears that throughout the 1962–1965 period the cycle was on the (downswing / upswing).

91 Finally, if we wish to attempt an identification of the short-term irregular component in the time series, this can be done by dividing each of the values already adjusted for the seasonal and trend factors (Table 15.7) by the values representing the effect of only the cyclical component (Table 15.8) and multiplying by 100. The resulting percentage indicates the relative contribution of the irregular component in the monthly values of the time series, as illustrated in Table 15.9. In terms of algebraic representation, what we have done in this final step in order to segregate the effect of the irregular component is to compute

$$\frac{CI}{C} \text{ (fraction)} = I$$

table 15.9 ▪ new-passenger-car registrations by months, 1962 to 1965: variations from trend attributable to the irregular component of the time series (where 100 indicates expected trend value)

Month	1962	1963	1964	1965
Jan.	. . .	97.5	101.0	101.4
Feb.	. . .	97.9	100.3	101.5
Mar.	105.6	101.1	95.7	106.0
Apr.	94.0	101.2	100.7	97.7
May	100.8	98.9	102.0	96.5
June	98.1	100.2	100.3	99.4
July	100.3	104.8	93.0	96.4
Aug.	100.6	94.5	99.1	104.4
Sept.	97.8	99.4	129.0	115.3
Oct.	100.7	100.9	85.6	82.3
Nov.	105.9	99.5	82.1	
Dec.	99.2	102.0	106.3	

Source of data: Tables 15.7 and 15.8.

92 The irregular variations in a time series, especially those that are sizable, can often be explained if we know of the factors that affect the time-series values. According to Table 15.9, an early introduction of new-car models in 1964 resulted in a positive variation in the month of _____, and that factor and a labor dispute in one of the auto companies resulted in variation in the negative direction in _____ and _____ of 1964.

September

October; November

15.e ▪ the use of time-series analysis in forecasting

In this unit we have been consistently cautious regarding the use of time-series analysis as the basis for forecasting, particularly in regard to the use of cyclical analysis. This caution does not suggest that time-series analysis is not of practical value, for indeed it is a widely used technique in economic analysis. However, the purely mechanical forecast based on a time-series analysis alone usually represents the beginning, rather than the culmination, of the analytical efforts associated with business and economic forecasting. In addition to the time-series analysis itself, improvement in forecasts can often be attained by two general approaches, both based on the analysis of information outside of the firm being studied. First, the study of general business conditions or of cyclical movements in other time series may provide clues to the timing of cyclical movements in the series being analyzed. Second, the study of relationships between specific environmental factors or managerial actions and changes in time-series values, carried out by correlation analysis, may provide direct indication of the "why" of time-series changes.

93 Of the four components of the time series, the one that has primary use for long-term forecasting is the _____ component.

trend

94 Similarly, the one that is useful for forecasts in the short run is the _____ component.

seasonal

95 The use of information about the trend of a time series and the seasonal variations related thereto in forecasting is predicated on the assumption that both influences (will / will not) operate in the future as they have in the past and that marked cyclical and irregular effects (will / will not) occur.

will

will not

96 Of the four classical components of the time series, the one that is of the least direct value in forecasting is the _____ component.

irregular

97 Finally, the component whose successful analysis would be extremely valuable in forecasting, but whose final analysis is rarely successfully achieved by the mechanical procedure of the time-series analysis alone, is the _____ component.

cyclical

98 As indicated in the introduction to this section, those concerned with business forecasting typically consider time-series analysis as the beginning, rather than the end, of forecasting efforts. As the next step, the greatest gains in forecasting effectiveness can be expected by obtaining more data from (within / outside of) the firm being studied.

outside of

99 For example, cyclical variations in the demand for a firm's products might be found to be related to general business conditions or cyclical fluctuations in other, though related, product fields. Since the classical analysis of cycles tends to be oriented toward the mathematical characteristics of the cyclical movements themselves, studies of business conditions and other series (do / do not) represent a basically new direction of analysis.

do

100 Also the study of specific relationships, such as that between the use of a variable price policy and its effects on seasonal levels of the time series, can add to the effectiveness of managerial

correlation (or regression)	forecasting. The statistical technique particularly useful for this purpose is that of _____ analysis.

review

trend seasonal; cyclical; irregular	**101** (Frames 1–15) The four principal sources of influence on time-series values have been identified as the _____, _____, _____, and _____ components.
$Y = TSCI$	**102** (Frames 16–25) Where Y represents the value of a time series at some particular point in time, the classical time-series model underlying all of the analyses in this unit can be represented by the equation _____.
line (not necessarily straight) freehand	**103** (Frames 26–27) Trend analysis always involves the identification of the location or algebraic formula for the best-fitting _____ _____. The method of trend analysis which is mathematically least sophisticated is the _____ method.
two straight	**104** (Frames 28–31) The method of semiaverages in trend analysis requires separating the data into _____ (number) parts and averaging the time-series values within each of these parts, resulting in the plotting of a trend line that is typically (straight / curvilinear).
curvilinear	**105** (Frames 32–36) The method of moving averages in trend analysis typically results in a trend line that is (straight / curvilinear).
least-squares	**106** (Frames 37–45) The final method of trend analysis which we discussed, and which may be used to determine the equation for the best-fitting straight line *or* curve, is the _____ _____ method.
index	**107** (Sec. 15.c, Introduction) Whereas the trend for a time series is defined in terms of a best-fitting line, or the algebraic equation representing the line, the seasonal component of the time series is represented by a(n) _____ number computed for each month (or quarter) of the year.
ratio moving-average	**108** (Frames 46–52) This index number is usually computed by comparing each monthly value to the moving average centered at that month, and hence the method is referred to as the _____-to-_____ method.
center	**109** (Frames 53–57) In computing the twelve-month moving averages, it is necessary not only to compute twelve-month moving totals but also to combine adjacent twelve-month totals so that the resulting averages will be located at the (beginning / center / end) of each month.

110 (Frames 58–59)   Next, the ratios to moving average are computed by dividing the actual value for each month by the _____ _____ for each month and multiplying by 100 so that the ratio is in percentage form.

| 110 | moving average |

111 (Frames 60–69)   Finally, the average percentage ratio by month (or quarter) is determined by using one of three types of averages: the _____, _____, or _____ _____, and these average ratios are adjusted so that the sum of all twelve monthly indexes is equal to approximately _____ (value).

| 111 | mean; median; modified mean |
| 111 | 1,200 |

112 (Frames 70–74)   Because both the cyclical and irregular components are identified by assuming that they are represented by the effects which remain after data have been adjusted for trend and seasonal factors, the general computational approach is referred to as the _____ method.

| 112 | residual |

113 (Frames 75–78)   In identifying the cyclical and long-term irregular components when annual data are used, the procedure of the time-series analysis can be algebraically represented by

$$CI =$$

| 113 | $\dfrac{TCI}{T}$ |

114 (Frames 79–82)   When monthly data are used in the residual method, the first step is typically that of seasonally adjusting the data. Algebraically, this step can be represented as

| 114 | $\dfrac{TSCI}{S} = TCI$ |

115 (Frames 83–88)   Next the deseasonalized data are adjusted for trend, which can be algebraically represented as

| 115 | $\dfrac{TCI}{T} = CI$ |

116 (Frames 89–92)   The apparent extent to which the cyclical component is represented in these combined CI influences can be determined by computing a _____ average, and then the influence of the irregular component can be residually identified, as represented algebraically:

| 116 | moving |
| 116 | $\dfrac{CI}{C} = I$ |

117 (Frames 93–100)   The two components of the time series that are most useful in business forecasting are the _____ and

| 117 | trend |

117 seasonal

117 additions to

_____ components. The study of general business conditions, cyclical changes in related product fields, and the correlation of specific types of events with changes in time-series values are (also part of / additions to) classical time-series analysis.

problems
(solutions given on page 367)

1 Indicate the component of the time series with which each of the following events would be associated by posting a T for trend, S for seasonal, C for cyclical, and I for irregular:

____ **(a)** an upturn in business activity
____ **(b)** inclement weather resulting in the postponement of consumer purchases
____ **(c)** a fire at the subcontractor's plant resulting in a delay in parts deliveries
____ **(d)** the annual January White Sale in a department store
____ **(e)** general increase in the demand for color television sets

2 The following data represent the annual sales volume, in millions of dollars, of the Acme Tool Company.

Year	Sales, in millions
1961	$1.5
1962	1.3
1963	1.1
1964	1.7
1965	1.9
1966	2.3

(a) Construct a line chart to portray these data graphically, including the year 1967 on the chart.
(b) Determine the location of the trend line by the method of semi-averages and enter this line on the line chart, labeling it SA.
(c) Determine the location of the trend line by computing a three-year moving average and enter this line on the chart, labeling it $3M$.
(d) Determine the equation for the trend line by the least-squares method, coding 1963 as 0. Enter this line on the graph, labeling it LS. To what does the a in this least-squares trend equation refer?

3 For the annual data in Prob. 2:

(a) Determine the cyclical component by the residual method, using the least-squares regression line as the best estimate of the trend component of the time series.
(b) Construct a cycle chart and interpret it.

4 The following data represent the quarterly sales volume, in hundreds of thousands of dollars, for the Acme Tool Company.

Year	Quarter	Sales in thousands
1961	1	$500
	2	350
	3	250
	4	400
1962	1	450
	2	350
	3	200
	4	300
1963	1	350
	2	200
	3	150
	4	400
1964	1	550
	2	350
	3	250
	4	550
1965	1	550
	2	400
	3	350
	4	600
1966	1	750
	2	500
	3	400
	4	650

(a) Compute the four-quarter moving averages and moving totals.
(b) Compute the four-quarter centered moving average.
(c) Determine the adjusted seasonal indexes by quarter, using the modified mean of the ratios representing percents of moving average.

5 For the data of Prob. 4:

(a) Compute the seasonally adjusted value for each quarter by the use of the seasonal indexes determined in Prob. 4c.
(b) Change the scale of the least-squares equation determined in Prob. 2d so that it can be applied for the purpose of determining quarterly trend values in hundreds of thousands of dollars, with $X = 0$ located at the midpoint of the first quarter of 1963.
(c) Remove the effects of the trend component from the deseasonalized values in Prob. 5a, leaving the effects of the cyclical and irregular components in the data.
(d) Remove the effects due to the irregular component by computing a three-quarter moving average for the data of Prob. 5c.

(e) Adjust the data of Prob. 5c for the effects of the cyclical components, identified in Prob. 5d, thus identifying the effect of the irregular component by the residual method.

additional problems   **6**   Indicate the component of the time series with which each of the following events would be associated by posting a T for trend, S for seasonal, C for cyclical, and I for irregular:

____   **(a)** the pre-Christmas period in retail sales
____   **(b)** diminished need for kerosene lanterns
____   **(c)** increased demand for housing in a small community as a result of the location of a new manufacturing plant there
____   **(d)** a recession
____   **(e)** sales of fireworks

7   The following data represent the monthly sales volume, in thousands of dollars, of a toy-manufacturing firm established July 1, 1963.

monthly sales, in thousands of dollars

| | | | Year | | |
Month	1963	1964	1965	1966	1967
Jan.	...	2.7	2.9	4.3	4.8
Feb.	...	2.8	3.6	4.2	5.4
Mar.	...	3.4	4.1	4.8	6.0
Apr.	...	3.6	4.5	5.7	6.7
May	...	3.8	4.9	6.1	7.0
June	...	4.0	5.0	6.2	6.9
July	3.5	4.3	5.2	6.6	
Aug.	3.4	4.5	5.1	6.8	
Sept.	4.5	5.7	6.0	8.5	
Oct.	5.5	7.0	8.2	10.1	
Nov.	6.0	6.9	7.9	10.3	
Dec.	4.8	5.0	6.0	7.4	

(a) Construct a line chart to portray graphically the annual sales totals, using the fiscal year of July 1 through June 30 as the basis for the totals, rather than the calendar year.
(b) Using July-through-June annual totals, determine the location of the trend line by the method of semiaverages and enter this line on the chart, labeling it SA.
(c) Determine the location of the trend line by computing a two-year moving average and enter this line on the line chart, labeling it $2M$.
(d) Determine the location of the trend line by using the least-squares method with the July-through-June annual totals, coding the 1965–1966 fiscal year as 0. Enter this line on the graph, labeling it LS. To what does the b in this trend equation refer?

(e) Comment on the observed similarity or dissimilarity of the several trend lines posted on the line chart.

8 For the July-through-June annual totals in Prob. 7, determine the cyclical component by the residual method, using the least-squares regression line as the best indicator of the trend component of the time series. Interpret your results.

9 Determine the seasonal indexes for the sales values of Prob. 7, using the mean of the monthly ratios representing percents of moving average.

10 Deseasonalize the data presented in Prob. 7.

11 Presuming negligible cyclical effects in these data, identify the effects due to the irregular component by using the residual method with the monthly data and the least-squares equation determined in Prob. 7d as the best indicator of trend.

unit 16 · index numbers

An index number is a statistical value designed to measure changes in a variable, such as price or quantity, with respect to time. The study of index numbers represents the second of the two main categories of techniques specifically directed toward analyzing data classified over time, the other being time-series analysis, discussed in Unit 15. In this unit we shall discuss the basic types of index numbers used in business and economic analysis and their construction, and we shall consider the characteristics of three widely used index numbers published by agencies of the Federal government: the Consumer Price Index, the Wholesale Price Index, and the Industrial Production Index.

16.a · introduction

An index number always indicates a comparison between a present measurement and a measurement at some previous point or interval of time that has been chosen as the base. For example, we could use 1951 as the base period for a study of unit sales of automobiles and report sales for later years as percentages of the 1951 value. Thus an index of 150 in this case would signify a sales volume 50 percent above the 1951 level. This index number would be referred to as a simple quantity index. In the frames below we shall differentiate a simple index from a composite index and discuss the nature of price and value indexes as well as quantity indexes.

1 Suppose that a time series representing the volume of automobile sales between 1951 and 1966 is available. Could a series of quantity index numbers, with 1951 as the base, be constructed using the data in this single time series? (yes / no)

> yes

2 The indexes computed in Frame 1 would be referred to as *simple* index numbers. Thus the essential characteristic of a simple index number is that it generally relates to (a particular commodity / a number of commodities).

> a particular commodity

3 On the other hand, a *composite* index number refers to a change in quantity, price, or value for (a particular commodity / a number of commodities).

> a number of commodities

4 The type of index number that could be constructed when a single time series is known is the _____ index number; the type that could be constructed when time series for several related commodities are available is the _____ index number.

> simple
>
> composite

5 The Consumer Price Index, which represents the price movement for a combination of commodities rather than for a single commodity, is an example of a (simple / composite) index number.

> composite

6 Before considering some important problems related to the construction of composite index numbers, let us briefly consider the kinds of measurements that can be represented by index numbers. In passing, we have already indicated that index numbers can represent changes in *quantity, price,* or *value.* Thus both the Consumer Price Index and the Wholesale Price Index are examples of _____ indexes.

price (They are also composite indexes.)

7 The Industrial Production Index reflects changes in physical volume of output in manufacturing, mining, and utilities. It is thus a (quantity / price / value) index.

quantity

8 Finally, an index number might relate to the total value of an output or commodity, without regard to whether the change was due to a change in price, quantity, or both. The Federal Reserve Board Index of Department Store Sales, which does not separate price and quantity as such, is thus a _____ index.

value

9 In this introduction we have indicated that an index number can be simple or _____ and that it can represent changes in quantity, _____, or _____.

composite
price; value

10 If a composite index number is to be constructed—and all of the important indexes are of this type—then decisions have to be made regarding the particular commodities to be included in the index and the statistical weight to be used with each commodity. For example, would you expect an index of retail prices to include consideration of all commodities that could possibly be purchased? (yes / no)

no (The list of items would be virtually inexhaustible.)

11 Thus the universe of commodities to be described by a composite index must first be identified, and then a sample of these commodities must be chosen for use in calculation of the index number. Because of the necessity of using a sample of items that is considered representative as well as comparable from period to period, the commodities to be included in the sample are chosen on the basis of their evaluated importance in the total universe of commodities. Therefore the sampling method used in the construction of a composite index number results in the collection of a (convenience / judgment / probability) sample.

judgment (See Unit 7, Frames 17–27, for a review of these concepts.)

12 Since the commodities to be included in a composite index are selected on the basis of judgment, the methods of statistical inference described in the previous units (can / cannot) be used in evaluating such index numbers.

cannot

13 Having chosen the commodities to be used as the sample items for a composite index, we then have to decide how each item should be weighted in the composite. For a composite price index, if we were to accumulate the price of one unit of each com-

does not

modity to obtain the composite, the price of each item in the index would, in effect, be its weight in the composite index. Thus an unweighted composite index in fact (does / does not) exist.

14 A so-called unweighted composite index would not be very useful because the effective weights would be arbitrary and thus would not generally reflect the importance of each item in the index. For example, if men's shoes and butter were to be included in a retail price index, including the average price of *one* pair of shoes and *one* pound of butter would have the result that greater weight in the composite index is being given to (shoes / butter / neither), since one unit of each commodity is included in the index.

shoes (since their prices are being accumulated)

15 Thus, when constructing a composite index number, we have not only a sampling problem but a weighting problem as well. If we want our retail price index to weight each commodity according to its extent of purchase, and if the average person consumes $1\frac{1}{2}$ pounds of butter per month and purchases three pairs of shoes per year, then a *monthly* index would weight (or multiply) the price of butter by a factor of _____ (number) and the price of a pair of shoes by _____ (number).

$1\frac{1}{2}$

$\frac{1}{4}$ (since, on the average, $\frac{1}{4}$ pair of shoes is purchased per month)

16 For composite index numbers to have a comparable meaning from period to period, it is desirable that the same base period be used throughout the analysis, that the same sample of commodities be included in each period, and that the _____ assigned to each commodity be identical from period to period.

weight

17 But in constructing a retail price index, we might discover that the pattern of things being purchased is shifting over time. For example, if the selection of commodities and their relative weights is based on purchasing patterns in the year 1910, then in terms of actual purchasing patterns in 1967 kerosene is likely to be (under- / over-) represented in the index and power tools are likely to be (under- / over-) represented.

over-

under-

18 The processes of linking and chaining, to be described in Sec. 16.c, make it possible to change the commodities and/or the weights used in constructing a series of composite index numbers, thus making comparison of index numbers constructed over extensive time periods (more / less) difficult.

less

16.b ▪ construction of index numbers

In Sec. 16.a we observed that index numbers can be simple or composite and that they can represent comparisons of quantity, price, or value. Like our study of time-series analysis, this section on computation is introductory in nature, and hence we shall describe several of the most widely used index numbers, but we shall not consider the variations or combinations of the techniques that are sometimes used, even though these other techniques may be statistically interesting. Accordingly, we shall describe the computation of simple indexes, Laspeyres' index, Paasche's index, and the weighted average of relatives.

19 The computation of simple indexes is relatively straight-forward compared to the variety of computational techniques available for constructing composite index numbers. If p_0 indicates the price of a commodity in a base period and p_1 indicates its price in a later given period, then a simple price index, or price relative, can be computed by using the formula (choose one):

(a) $\dfrac{p_0}{p_1} \times 100$

b   **(b)** $\dfrac{p_1}{p_0} \times 100$

20 For example, if the average price of butter was 90 cents per pound in 1950, used as the base, and its average price in 1966 was 72 cents per pound, as indicated in Table 16.1, then the simple price relative for 1966 is

$\dfrac{0.72}{0.90} \times 100 = 80$ $\dfrac{p_1}{p_0} \times 100 =$

table 16.1 ▪ prices and consumption of specified commodities in a geographic area, 1950 and 1966

Commodity	Unit quotation	Average price 1950, p_0	1966, p_1	Per capita consumption 1950, q_0	1966, q_1
Butter	pound	$ 0.90	$ 0.72	12	18
Coffee	pound	0.55	0.60	12	14
Shoes	pair	10.00	12.00	3	3

21 Since a simple price index is concerned only with measuring the relative change in the price of a single commodity, there is no need for weighting. Thus the weighting problems discussed at the end of Sec. 16.a apply only to _____ indexes.

composite

22 Similarly, where q_0 represents the quantity of a commodity during the base period and q_1 represents the quantity during the given period, the quantity relative is designated by the formula

$\dfrac{q_1}{q_0}$ ──── $\times 100$.

23 Thus, if 12 pounds of butter per person was consumed in a particular geographic area in 1950, used as the base, and 18 pounds was consumed in 1966, then the quantity relative is equal to

$18/12 \times 100 = 150$ $\dfrac{q_1}{q_0} \times 100 =$

24 The third type of simple index number is the value relative. According to the data for butter price and consumption in Table 16.1, the value relative for 1966 with the 1950 base-year value being set equal to 100 is

$$\frac{p_1 q_1}{p_0 q_0} \times 100 = \frac{12.96}{\underline{\hspace{1cm}}} \times 100 =$$

$\dfrac{12.96}{10.80} \times 100 = 120$

25 Since most of the index numbers in use are composite rather than simple, the remainder of this section will be devoted to the construction of composite index numbers. Further, since composite *price* relatives are particularly important, we shall direct our discussion to this type of composite index. The essential difference between a simple and a composite price relative is that the prices of several commodities, rather than just one commodity, are included in the _____ price relative.

composite

26 We return now to the problem of weighting the respective prices of the commodities included in a composite price index. The general basis used for this weighting is the quantity of each item purchased during a defined period, and these quantities are applied as the weights for the accumulation of both the base-year prices and given-year prices. Thus, if we were to use *base-year* quantities as the weighting factor, the computational formula for the composite price index would be indicated by the formula (enter missing subscripts):

$$\text{Price index} = \frac{\Sigma p_1 q}{\Sigma p_0 q} \times 100$$

$\dfrac{\Sigma p_1 q_0}{\Sigma p_0 q_0} \times 100$

27 Note that the use of the formula in Frame 26 results in the computation of a composite *price index* that involves a weighting factor for each commodity price. The index produced is *not* a value index, for a value index requires multiplication of unit prices during a period by quantities in the *same* period. Thus, for computing a composite *value* index, the formula to be used is (enter missing subscripts):

$$\text{Value index} = \frac{\Sigma p_1 q}{\Sigma p_0 q} \times 100$$

$\dfrac{\Sigma p_1 q_1}{\Sigma p_0 q_0} \times 100$

28 Getting back to the composite price indexes, when both the base-year and given-year prices are weighted by base-year quantities, the resulting index, called *Laspeyres' index,* uses the market basket of commodities of the base year for price-comparison purposes. Again, Laspeyres' index is defined by the formula (enter subscripts):

$$\text{Laspeyres' index} = \frac{\Sigma p \quad q}{\Sigma p \quad q} \times 100$$

$\dfrac{\Sigma p_1 q_0}{\Sigma p_0 q_0} \times 100$

29 For the data of Table 16.1, compute Laspeyres' weighted aggregate price index by first completing the table below.

Commodity	$p_0 q_0$	$p_1 q_0$
Butter	$10.80	$ 8.64
Coffee	6.60	7.20
Shoes		
	$\Sigma p_0 q_0 = \$47.40$	$\Sigma p_1 q_0 = \$51.84$

$$L = \frac{\Sigma p_1 q_0}{\Sigma p_0 q_0} \times 100 = \text{———} \times 100 = 109$$

30 Based on extent of use, the Laspeyres' index is the most important of the composite price indexes. Expressed as a relative (i.e., relative to base-year prices), it can be described as being a weighted aggregate, with prices weighted by the quantities associated with the (base / given) year.

31 Instead of using the base-year quantities to define the weights to be applied in determining the composite price index, we could obviously use the given-year quantities instead and then sum the weighted prices. The computational formula in this case would be expressed as (enter subscripts):

$$\text{Price index} = \frac{\Sigma p \quad q}{\Sigma p \quad q} \times 100$$

32 Such a weighted aggregate using given-year weights is sometimes used; it is referred to as *Paasche's index*. Compute Paasche's index for the data of Table 16.1 by first completing the table below:

Commodity	$p_0 q_1$	$p_1 q_1$
Butter	$16.20	$12.96
Coffee		
Shoes	30.00	36.00
	$\Sigma p_0 q_1 = \$53.90$	$\Sigma p_1 q_1 = \$57.36$

$$P = \frac{\Sigma p_1 q_1}{\Sigma p_0 q_1} \times 100 = \text{———} \times 100 = 106$$

33 Though the weighted aggregate of price relatives determined by the Laspeyres and Paasche formulas may not differ substantially from one another in any particular instance, they do represent two distinct approaches to the weighting problems in constructing composite price indexes. According to Frames 29 and 32, for the data of Table 16.1 the numerically larger composite price relative for 1966 resulted from the use of (Laspeyres' / Paasche's) index.

Paasche's (since the prices are weighted on the basis of given-period quantities)

34 Of course, the two indexes address themselves to different questions, and so we would expect their values to differ. The index which compares the total value of the package of commodities of the given period with what the same package would have cost in the base period is (Laspeyres' / Paasche's) index.

base

35 On the other hand, Laspeyres' index uses the quantities of commodities purchased in the (base / given) period as the basis for computing the value of each package.

36 Thus the computational formula for Laspeyres' index is

$$\frac{\Sigma p_1 q_0}{\Sigma p_0 q_0} \times 100$$

$L =$

37 And the computational formula for Paasche's index is

$$\frac{\Sigma p_1 q_1}{\Sigma p_0 q_1} \times 100$$

$P =$

38 But which index is really the "best" index as an indicator of price levels and cost of living is a question outside of the realm of statistical analysis as such. With changing consumption patterns, the use of the market basket of the base period, and thus use of

Laspeyres'

(Laspeyres' / Paasche's) index, becomes less meaningful.

39 Yet, to the extent that a lowered price of some commodity over time has resulted in a relatively high consumption of it in the given

Paasche's

period, the use of given-year quantities in (Laspeyres' / Paasche's) index becomes less meaningful.

40 As we previously indicated, in practice Laspeyres' index has been much more frequently used than Paasche's index. The index which would require an annual survey of expenditure patterns to

Paasche (And this is one factor affecting its use.)

determine the necessary weighting factors is the _____ index.

41 Both the Laspeyres and Paasche approaches to the construction of a composite price relative can be described as being *weighted-aggregate* methods, the difference being that for the Laspeyres the basis for weighting the prices is provided by the

base

given

_____-period quantities whereas for the Paasche the _____-period quantities provide this basis.

42 An alternative to the weighted-aggregate-of-prices approach is the weighted-average-of-price-relatives approach. As suggested by the name of the latter method, instead of summing weighted price figures, the computation of the weighted average of price relatives requires that the weighted values of _____

price relatives

_____ be combined.

43 Furthermore, if the average of the weighted price relatives is to be determined, then the type of average to be used must be specified. Though geometric and harmonic means are sometimes used in this connection, the most frequently used average is the (arithmetic) mean _____ itself.

44 In terms of our discussion of simple price relatives at the beginning of this section, each price relative to be weighted is determined by the formula (enter subscripts):

$\frac{p_1}{p_0} \times 100$

$$\frac{p}{p} \times 100$$

45 The next step in the weighted-average-of-relatives method is to weight each relative by a *value* figure pq, and, again, we have the choice of using either base-year (p_0q_0) or given-year ($p \quad q \quad$) figures (enter subscripts for the latter value).

p_1q_1

46 Since the *base-year values* are commonly used as the weighting factor in the weighted-average-of-price-relatives method, the price-index formula is:

$$I_p = \frac{\Sigma(p_0q_0)(p_1/p_0 \times 100)}{\Sigma p_0q_0}$$

As would be true for any mean of a series of weighted values, the denominator of this fraction represents the (number of commodities / sum of the weights used).

sum of the weights used

47 The price relatives posted in Table 16.2 were computed on the basis of the data supplied in Table 16.1. Using the figures of Table 16.2, make the appropriate substitutions in the formula for the weighted average of price relatives:

$\frac{5{,}183.40}{47.40}$

$$I_p = \frac{\Sigma(p_0q_0)(p_1/p_0 \times 100)}{\Sigma p_0q_0} = \frac{}{} = 109$$

table 16.2 ■ **data for the computation of the weighted average of price relatives**

Commodity	Price relative $p_1/p_0 \times 100$	Value weight p_0q_0	Weighted relative $p_0q_0(p_1/p_0 \times 100)$
Butter	80	$10.80	864.00
Coffee	109	6.60	719.40
Shoes	120	30.00	3,600.00
Total		$47.40	5,183.40

48 If the value of the composite price relative in Frame 47 appears familiar to you, it is more than coincidental. The formula for the weighted average of price relatives can be arithmetically simplified, so that

$$I_p = \frac{\Sigma(p_0 q_0)(p_1/p_0 \times 100)}{\Sigma p_0 q_0} = \frac{\Sigma p_1 q_0}{\Sigma p_0 q_0} \times 100$$

Notice that this now becomes the same formula as for one of the weighted-aggregate methods, namely, the (Laspeyres / Paasche) index.

Laspeyres

49 Since the computational result of using the weighted average of price relatives is the same as for Laspeyres' index, it can be interpreted in the same way, i.e., as an indication of what the package of commodities associated with the base period would cost in a given period. Of these two indexes, the one that would typically be computed when we are interested in identifying the simple price relative associated with each commodity as well as computing the composite price index is the _____.

weighted average of price relatives
(Simple price relatives are not computed when using the Laspeyres index.)

summary

50 In this unit it has not been our intention to discuss the statistical criteria that might be used to evaluate the "goodness" of an index or to describe the indexes that are statistically interesting because of the way they are computed. Rather, we have directed our attention at the major types of indexes in actual use. Of the three types of *simple* relatives, the price relative is computed by using the formula _____, the quantity relative by the formula _____, and the value relative by the formula _____.

$\dfrac{p_1}{p_0} \times 100$

$\dfrac{q_1}{q_0} \times 100$

$\dfrac{p_1 q_1}{p_0 q_0} \times 100$

51 In the area of composite indexes two of the composite price indexes we have discussed involve a summation, or aggregate, of the weighted prices themselves as the basis for computing the composite relative. The index in which the base- and given-year prices are weighted by the base-year quantities is _____ index; the one in which the prices are weighted by the given-year quantities is _____ index.

Laspeyres'

Paasche's

52 Thus the appropriate formulas used in constructing Laspeyres' and Paasche's indexes are:

$$L = \frac{\rule{1.5cm}{0.4pt}}{} \times 100$$

$$P = \frac{\rule{1.5cm}{0.4pt}}{} \times 100$$

$\dfrac{\Sigma p_1 q_0}{\Sigma p_0 q_0}$

$\dfrac{\Sigma p_1 q_1}{\Sigma p_0 q_1}$

53 Though the computational result is the same as for Laspeyres' formula, if simple price relatives are computed first ($p_1/p_0 \times 100$), then each of these price relatives can be weighted by the value of the commodity associated with the base year ($p_0 q_0$), and the arithmetic mean of these weighted price relatives can then be determined. Referred to as the weighted average of price relatives, this index is computed by using the formula

$$I_p = \frac{\Sigma(p_0 q_0)(p_1/p_0 \times 100)}{\Sigma p_0 q_0}$$

16.c ▪ link and chain relatives

When a composite index number has been periodically computed over an extended period of years, it may be desirable to change the sample of commodities included in the index, or their weighting, in order to reflect current prices, quantities, or values more meaningfully. Were we not to make such changes, established commodities would have too much of a representation in the composite index and new commodities would have no representation at all. The processes of linking and chaining make it possible to make such changes while maintaining a basis for the long-run comparability of composite indexes. The use of these methods does not solve the problem generated by changes in consumption patterns, for this problem has no real solution. However, these procedures do make it computationally possible to maintain a sense of comparability in the given index over time. The actual application of linking and chaining in index-number construction can lead to considerable complexity in computations. Therefore in this section we shall present an example involving the use of only simple index numbers, rather than composite indexes, in order to highlight the essential characteristics of linking and chaining as such.

54 Linking involves the use of a constantly shifting base period, rather than a fixed base period. For example, the 1967 price relative would use 1966 as the base, the 1966 relative would use 1965 as the base, and so forth. Would a price relative so computed be directly comparable with, say, a price relative for a period five years earlier? (yes / no)

no

55 Table 16.3 reports hypothetical sales data for the Acme Tool Company between 1961 and 1966. Since each link relative uses the previous year as the base, the link relative of 111.8 for 1965 indicates that the sales level for 1965 was 11.8 percent higher than the sales level reported for the year _____.

1964

table 16.3 ▪ Acme Tool Company sales, link relatives, and chain indexes, 1961 to 1966

Year	Sales, in millions	Link relative	Chain index, 1963 = 100
1961	$1.5	. . .	136.3
1962	1.3	86.7	118.2
1963	1.1	84.6	100.0
1964	1.7	154.5	154.5
1965	1.9	111.8	172.7
1966	2.3	121.1	209.1

56 However, direct comparisons over a number of years cannot be made by using link relatives alone. For example, the link relatives of 154.5 for 1964 and 121.1 for 1966 (do / do not) directly indicate which relative represents a higher sales volume.

do not (In this case, the lower-valued relative represents the higher volume.)

57 In terms of the single-commodity data reported in Table 16.3, the relationship between using link relatives and changing the sample of commodities in a composite index may not be immediately obvious. Suppose we wish to add a new commodity to a composite index for 1966. We would first compute the index exactly as it had been determined in 1965, so that comparison in respect to that base year could be made. Then we would add the new item to the 1966 composite and use this revised package of commodities as the base for the _____ (year) index.

1967

58 Thus, even though direct comparability of indexes computed for several years is not achieved, changes in the package of commodities used for a composite index can be made by using the process of _____.

linking

59 Though link relatives cannot themselves be directly compared, their conversion into *chain indexes* does allow this kind of comparison to be made. This suggests, then, that the conversion from link to chain relatives involves a recomputation of relatives in terms of (a single / several) base year(s).

a single

60 For the year, or period, chosen as the base, the value of the chain index is automatically set at 100. Thus in Table 16.3 the year that has been chosen as the base is _____ (year).

1963

61 The chain indexes for the years following 1963 were determined by multiplying the link relative for each year by the chain index of the preceding year. Thus, where n refers to the given year in the series,

$$C_n = \frac{L_n C_{n-1}}{100}$$

With the substitution of the appropriate values from Table 16.3 in this formula, the chain relative for 1965 is

$$\frac{111.8 \times 154.5}{100} = 172.7$$

$$C_{1965} = \frac{L_{1965} C_{1964}}{100} =$$

62 To go backward in time from a base period, the algebraic equation has to be solved for C_{n-1} instead of for C_n. Accordingly, the chain index for 1961 was computed by substituting the following values in the equation:

$$C_{n-1} = \frac{C_n}{L_n} \times 100$$

$$\frac{118.2}{86.7} \times 100 = 136.3$$

Therefore $C_{1961} = \dfrac{C_{1962}}{L_{1962}} \times 100 =$

63 Given the chain-index values of 136.3 and 154.5 for 1961 and 1964, respectively, can we say that the second relative is indicative of a higher sales figure than the first relative? (yes / no)

yes

64 Thus the terms "linking" and "chaining" are aptly descriptive of what is accomplished by these processes. A change of commodity mix with direct comparison restricted to adjoining periods is made possible by the process of _____.

linking

65 Conversion of link relatives so that their values are all stated in respect to a common base period is accomplished by the process of _____.

chaining

66 As indicated in the introduction to this section, however, the use of linking and chaining makes it possible to achieve numerical comparability in indexes, but it does not solve the problem of changes in consumption patterns. When outmoded commodities are continuously replaced by new ones, the meaning of the chain index becomes increasingly vague. For example, suppose that over a span of years all of the commodities in a price index have been changed. Would the value of the chain relative indicate the current relative cost of the original market basket? (yes / no) Would it indicate the comparative cost of the present market basket of goods? (yes / no)

no (The original market basket is not represented in current weighted prices.)

no (The present market basket is not represented in the base-period weighted prices.)

16.d ▪ some leading published indexes

In this section we shall briefly discuss the characteristics of three indexes published by agencies of the Federal government: the Consumer Price Index, the Wholesale Price Index, and the Industrial Production Index. Because of its widespread use as an indicator of cost of living, the Consumer Price Index, published by the Bureau of Labor Statistics, is probably the most important of the indexes now being published. The Wholesale Price Index, also published by the Bureau of Labor Statistics, is somewhat misleading in its name in that the index measures price movements in primary markets, i.e., the markets involving first commercial transactions with commodities, rather than wholesale or jobber prices as such. The Industrial Production Index is issued by the Federal Reserve Board; it reflects changes in the physical volume of activities in manufacturing, mining, and utilities and, as such, is widely used as an indicator of general business conditions.

67 In terms of the brief introduction given above, it is obvious that the Consumer Price Index, Wholesale Price Index, and Industrial Production Index are all (simple / composite) indexes.

composite

68 Furthermore this group of three composite indexes includes _____ (number) price index(es) and _____ (number) quantity index(es).

69 *The Consumer Price Index* is often considered the most important of the published indexes because of its use as an indicator of _____.

70 Published by the Bureau of Labor Statistics, the Consumer Price Index indicates the average change in a fixed market basket of goods and services purchased by families of urban wage earners and clerical workers. Thus the cost of living of high-income and low-income families as such (is / is not) represented by the index.

71 In addition to the overall Consumer Price Index, other indexes are published both for a selected list of cities and for specific groups of commodities and services. Thus, if the overall Consumer Price Index shows a rise, the product or service groups contributing most to this rise (can / cannot) be identified by the reader.

72 The Consumer Price Index is of course a composite price index, as we have already indicated. In terms of its computation, it is essentially a weighted average of price relatives. According to our earlier discussion in this unit, the Consumer Price Index can therefore also be described as a (Laspeyres / Paasche) type of index.

73 The index is actually a modification of Laspeyres' index in that the quantities used in weighting the prices are not base-period quantities but quantities associated with a somewhat later period. For the indexes published in May, 1966, for example, the base period for price comparison (p_0) was the 1957–1959 period; the period whose quantities were used for the weights (q_a) was 1960–1961. If p_1 designates the prices in the given period under study, then the modified Laspeyres formula used for the Consumer Price Index can be represented by (enter subscripts):

$$\frac{\Sigma p \quad q}{\Sigma p \quad q} \times 100$$

74 Though not indicated in the formula in Frame 73, over the years the particular commodities included in the Consumer Price Index and their relative weights have been modified to reflect changing patterns of consumer expenditure. These changes, then, have necessitated the application of the processes of _____ and _____ in the construction of this index.

75 Though we think of many of the published indexes as being useful because they serve to summarize that which has already happened, their use can also affect future economic activity. For example, cost-of-living clauses in many wage contracts are tied to movements of the _____ Index.

Consumer Price

---

76 Within the limits of the assumptions included in the computation of a price index, the reciprocal of such an index can be used as an indicator of the purchasing power of the dollar in comparison with the base period of the index. Thus, if the value of the Consumer Price Index is 125, then the current purchasing power of the dollar in comparison with the base period can be identified as _____.

$\$0.80 \left(= \dfrac{1}{125} \times 100 \right)$

---

77 In February, 1967, the overall Consumer Price Index was 114.8, on the 1957–1959 base. The purchasing power of the dollar in February, in comparison with the 1957–1959 average, was thus _____ (nearest cent), based on the market basket included in the Consumer Price Index.

$\$0.87$

---

78 Or, interpreting the February, 1967, Consumer Price Index in a somewhat different way, the market basket of commodities which cost $10 in the 1957–1959 period cost _____ in February, 1967.

$\$11.48$

---

79 The *Wholesale Price Index* is also published by the Bureau of Labor Statistics. As indicated in the introduction to this section, it (is / is not) essentially a "wholesale price" index.

---

is not

---

80 Since the Wholesale Price Index reflects primary market prices of a large number of major product groups, subgroups, and product classes, it is particularly useful for the (general consumer / businessman).

---

businessman

---

81 The computation of the Wholesale Price Index is similar to that of the Consumer Price Index. Thus the Wholesale Price Index can also be described as a (Laspeyres / Paasche) Index.

Laspeyres (The actual computational procedure is the weighted average of price relatives, which simplifies the computation of additional indexes by product group.)

---

82 Because the pattern of commodity transactions in the primary markets has shifted over time, the Wholesale Price Index has also been updated through the application of the processes of _____ and _____.

---

linking

chaining

---

83 Thus the two composite price indexes of importance to the general consumer and to the businessman which we have discussed are the _____ Index and the _____ Index.

Consumer Price

Wholesale Price

---

84 Finally, the *Industrial Production Index,* issued by the Federal Reserve Board, reflects the amount of physical output in manufacturing, mining, and the utilities and includes indexes for major industrial groups and subgroups, as well as an overall index. In terms of this description, it is a (simple / composite) index involving the comparison of (quantity / price / value).

composite
quantity

85 Since the Industrial Production Index is a quantity index, its method of calculation is not a direct modification of Laspeyres' and Paasche's indexes as such, which are composite price indexes. However, like the Consumer and Wholesale Price Indexes, the method of calculation follows the weighted _____ of relatives.

average (In this case, quantity rather than price relatives are averaged.)

86 Comparability of the Industrial Production Index over the long run has been enhanced by use of linking and chaining and for the short run by making adjustments for seasonal variations, thus making it useful as a continuing indicator of _____ _____.

general business conditions; general production level; state of the economy

review

87 (Sec. 16.a, Introduction; Frames 1–5) If an index number represents a comparison of the measurements of one commodity at two points in time, it is a _____ index. If it represents a comparison for a package of commodities, it is a _____ index.

simple
composite

88 (Frames 6–9) In terms of the kinds of measurements represented by index numbers, they are referred to as being _____, _____, or _____ indexes.

price
quantity; value

89 (Frames 10–12) One of the first problems encountered in the construction of a composite index number is the decision as to what commodities should be directly included in the index. The sampling method generally used results in what can be described as a _____ sample.

judgment

90 (Frames 13–18) Once the commodities to be included in a composite index are decided on, the other principal problem has to do with how these commodities should be _____.

weighted (or combined)

91 (Frames 19–25) The simple price, quantity, and value relatives can be computed by the respective formulas (enter subscripts):

$\dfrac{p_1}{p_0}$; $\dfrac{q_1}{q_0}$; $\dfrac{p_1 q_1}{p_0 q_0}$

$$\frac{p}{p} \times 100 \qquad \frac{q}{q} \times 100 \qquad \frac{p}{p}\ \frac{q}{q} \times 100$$

92 (Frames 26–30) Laspeyres' composite price index weights the prices being accumulated for comparison by the base-year

$$\frac{\Sigma p_1 q_0}{\Sigma p_0 q_0} \times 100$$

quantities of the commodities; this is algebraically represented by

$$L =$$

93 (Frames 31–32) On the other hand, Paasche's index applies the quantities of the given year as the weights and is therefore represented by the formula

$$\frac{\Sigma p_1 q_1}{\Sigma p_0 q_1} \times 100$$

$$P =$$

Paasche

94 (Frames 33–41) Whether we use the Laspeyres or Paasche approach to computing the weighted aggregate depends on whether we wish to gauge the overall impact of price movements on the basis of the purchasing pattern of the base or given year. If the current purchasing pattern is considered the most significant and meaningful factor, then the _____ index should be used.

95 (Frames 42–47) Remember that the computation of the weighted average of price relatives involves weighting each simple price relative ($p_1/p_0 \times 100$) by base-year values ($p_0 q_0$) and then determining the arithmetic mean of the sum of these weighted values. The computational procedure can be represented by the formula

$$\frac{\Sigma (p_0 q_0)(p_1/p_0 \times 100)}{\Sigma p_0 q_0}$$

$$I_p =$$

96 (Frames 48–53) The weighted average of price relatives would usually be the composite index computed when we wish to identify the simple price relatives associated with each of the commodities that make up the composite. As a composite price index, the computational result is identical to that of (Laspeyres' / Paasche's) index.

Laspeyres'

97 (Frames 54–58) The process whereby the commodities and weights of a composite index can be changed, resulting in the construction of a series of composite indexes each of which takes the preceding period as its base, is called _____.

linking

98 (Frames 59–65) The process by which link relatives are converted to a common base, so that long-run comparisons of index numbers can be made, is referred to as _____.

chaining

99 (Sec. 16.c, Introduction; Frame 66) When the market basket of commodities has substantially changed over time, using the processes of linking and chaining (does / does not) solve the problem of making cost-of-living comparisons.

does not

100 (Frames 67–78) The weighted average of price relatives published by the Bureau of Labor Statistics and widely used as an

Consumer Price

indicator of cost of living is the _____ Index.

101 (Frames 79–83) The composite index published by the Bureau of Labor Statistics to indicate changes in primary market prices of product groups, subgroups, and product classes is the

Wholesale Price

_____ Index.

102 (Frames 84–86) The composite quantity index published by the Federal Reserve Board to reflect output in manufacturing, mining, and the utilities is the _____

Industrial Production

Index.

problems
(solutions given
on page 372)

average wholesale prices
(1957–1959 = 100)

1 The following wholesale prices are taken from the *Survey of Current Business,* published by the Department of Commerce.

	1962	*1963*	*1964*	*1965*
Household appliances	94.0	91.8	91.3	89.2
Household furniture	103.8	104.6	105.3	106.2

(a) What was the percentage decline in the wholesale price of household appliances between 1962 and 1965, based on 1962 prices? What was the percentage increase in wholesale-furniture prices during the same time period?

(b) If the average wholesale price of an appliance was $150 in the period 1957–1959, what is the estimate of its average price in 1965?

(c) If the average wholesale price of an item of furniture was $150 in 1963, what is the estimate of its average wholesale price in 1965?

(d) Identify two important errors in the statement: "The figures given above indicate that the average consumer spends 7 percent more of his dollar on household furniture than he does on household appliances."

2 The following data reporting yearly production of butter and cheese and average wholesale prices are also taken from the *Survey of Current Business.*

	1962	*1963*	*1964*	*1965*
Factory butter production, millions of pounds	1,537.2	1,419.6	1,442.4	1,337.1
Wholesale price, per pound	$0.594	$0.590	$0.599	$0.610
Factory cheese production, millions of pounds	1,585.2	1,630.8	1,726.5	1,743.2
Wholesale price, per pound	$0.400	$0.426	$0.434	$0.450

(a) Compute the simple price relatives for butter for these four years, using 1962 as the base.

(b) Compute the price relatives for cheese for these four years, also using 1962 as the base.

(c) What can we say about the percentage changes in the whole-sale prices of butter and cheese during this four-year period?

(d) Compute the quantity relatives for both butter and cheese for 1965, using 1962 as the base, and interpret in terms of percentage change.

(e) Compute the total dollar value of butter and cheese production in 1962 and 1965.

(f) Using the figures from Prob. 2e, compute the value relatives for butter and cheese for 1965, using 1962 as the base. Interpret these indexes.

3 The following simplified data represent average prices and monthly quantities of some of the supplies used in a business office.

Item	Unit quotation	Average price 1965, p_0	1966, p_1	Monthly consumption 1965, q_0	1966, q_1
Paper, white bond	ream	$1.80	$2.00	2.2	2.8
Paper, onionskin	ream	0.68	0.72	5.0	8.0
Paper clips	package of 100	0.10	0.10	2.0	2.0
Typewriter ribbons	each	1.20	1.00	4.0	5.0

(a) Compute the simple price and quantity relatives for the bond paper, using 1965 as the base.

(b) Compute the simple value relatives for the bond and onionskin paper and compare them.

(c) Compute Laspeyres' index and interpret its meaning.

(d) Compute Paasche's index and interpret it.

(e) Compute the weighted average of price relatives and compare its value to that of the Laspeyres and Paasche indexes.

4 The following data are taken from the 1965 *Annual Report* of the General Electric Company.

Year	Net earnings, in millions
1961	$238.4
1962	256.5
1963	272.2
1964	219.6
1965	355.1

(a) Compute earnings indexes for the years indicated, using 1962 as the base.

(b) Compute link relatives for the net-earnings data. What is the base year in this case?

(c) Convert the link relatives to chain indexes, setting 1962 = 100. Compare your results with those of Prob. 4a. Under what circumstances is it necessary to use chaining?

additional problems　　**5**　Given the following indexes taken from the *Survey of Current Business:*

average wholesale prices
(1957–1959 = 100)

	1962	1963	1964	1965
Radio receivers and phonographs	86.1	82.8	81.5	80.1
Television receivers	94.2	92.3	90.9	88.5

(a) What kind of indexes are reported in the table?

(b) In terms of the 1957–1959 wholesale prices, what was the percentage decline in prices between 1962 and 1965? What was the percentage decline based on 1962 prices?

(c) Given a radio whose average wholesale price during 1957–1959 was $24, estimate its price in 1965.

(d) Given a radio whose wholesale price in 1962 was $24, estimate its price in 1965.

(e) Given a radio whose wholesale price in 1965 was $24, estimate its price in 1962.

6　The following data were also taken from the *Survey of Current Business:*

	1962	1963	1964	1965
Wheat production, millions of bushels	1,094	1,138	1,291	1,327
Wholesale price, per bushel	$ 2.41	$ 2.33	$ 1.92	$ 1.70
Rice production, millions of 100-pound bags	66.0	70.1	73.1	76.9
Wholesale price, per pound	$0.094	$0.093	$0.086	$0.083

(a) Compute the simple price and quantity relatives for wheat for these four years, using 1962 as the base. Interpret these indexes.

(b) Similarly, compute the simple price and quantity relatives for rice, using 1962 as the base, and interpret.

(c) Compute the value relative for 1965 for each commodity, using 1962 as the base. Interpret your results.

7 Given the following simplified data regarding average retail price and the weekly patterns of consumption for a selected family of four:

Commodity	Unit quotation	Average price 1963, p_0	Average price 1966, p_1	Weekly consumption 1963, q_0	Weekly consumption 1966, q_1
Bread	1-pound loaf	$0.19	$0.24	4.5	4.5
Milk	½ gallon	0.45	0.41	4.0	6.0

(a) Compute the simple price and quantity relatives for the two commodities, using 1963 as the base.

(b) Compute Laspeyres' index and interpret its meaning.

(c) Compute Paasche's index and interpret it.

(d) Compare the two composite indexes. Which do you think is more meaningful? Why?

(e) Compute the weighted average of price relatives, using the price relatives determined in Prob. 7a. Compare this index to the other two composite indexes you have computed.

8 The following data are taken from the 1965 *Annual Report* of Texaco, Inc.:

Year	Total net income, in millions
1961	$433.6
1962	481.7
1963	547.6
1964	577.4
1965	636.7

(a) Compute the link relatives for these income data, using appropriate base years. Interpret the meanings of the link relatives in percentage terms.

(b) Convert the link relatives into chain indexes, using 1961 as the base.

selected bibliography of texts on business statistics

Bryant, Edward C.: *Statistical Analysis,* 2d ed., McGraw-Hill, New York, 1966.

Croxton, Frederick E., and Dudley J. Cowden: *Practical Business Statistics,* 3d ed., Prentice-Hall, Englewood Cliffs, N.J., 1960.

Ekeblad, Frederick A.: *The Statistical Method in Business,* Wiley, New York, 1962.

Freund, John E., and Frank J. Williams: *Modern Business Statistics* Prentice-Hall, Englewood Cliffs, N.J., 1958.

Freund, John E., and Frank J. Williams: *Elementary Business Statistics: The Modern Approach,* Prentice-Hall, Englewood Cliffs, N.J., 1964.

Kurnow, Ernest, Gerald J. Glasser, and Frederick R. Ottman: *Statistics for Business Decisions,* Irwin, Homewood, Ill., 1959.

Neter, John, and William Wasserman: *Fundamental Statistics for Business and Economics,* 3d ed., Allyn and Bacon, Boston, 1966.

Richmond, Samuel B.: *Statistical Analysis,* 2d ed., Ronald, New York, 1964.

Schlaifer, Robert: *Introduction to Statistics for Business Decisions,* McGraw-Hill, New York, 1961.

Spurr, William A., Lester S. Kellogg, and John H. Smith: *Business and Economic Statistics,* 2d ed., Irwin, Homewood, Ill., 1961.

Stockton, John R.: *Introduction to Business and Economic Statistics,* 3d ed., South-Western Publishing Company, Cincinnati, 1966.

Yamane, Taro: *Statistics, An Introductory Analysis,* 2d ed. Harper & Row, New York, 1967.

solutions

1(a) *S*—since it is on the basis of sample data that inferences concerning the population are made.

(b) *P*—Only when the general characteristics of an entire population are known can deductions regarding the characteristics of specific elements be made.

(c) *P*—By definition, this is a descriptive measurement of a population.

(d) *S*—used in the process of statistical inference.

(e) *P*—enumeration, or measurement, of an entire population.

2 Data whose possible values can be only integers (whole numbers). Typically generated by the process of counting.

3(a) *D* or *C*
(b) *C*
(c) *C*
(d) *D* or *C*
(e) *C*
(f) *D* or *C*

4(a) $333.00 + 22 = 355.00 = 355$
(b) $333.00 + 22$ (discrete) $= 355.00$
(c) $333.00 - 22 = 311.00 = 311$
(d) $333.00 - 22$ (discrete) $= 311.00$
(e) $333.00 \times 22 = 7326.00 = 7,300$ (2 sig. dig.)
(f) 333.00×22 (discrete) $= 7,326.0$
(g) $333.00 \div 22 = 15.1364 = 15$
(h) $333.00 \div 22$ (discrete) $= 15.1364 = 15.136$

5(a) 7 sig. dig.; 613
(b) 7 sig. dig.; 612
(c) 4 sig. dig.; .0612 (or 0.0612)
(d) 4 sig. dig.; 0.0612 (or .0612)
(e) 7 sig. dig.; .0601 (or 0.0601)
(f) 6 sig. dig.; .614 (or 0.614)

1(a)

Class boundaries	f
2.5–5.5	1
5.5–8.5	2
8.5–11.5	2
11.5–14.5	5
14.5–17.5	4

(b) Class interval $i = B_U - B_L = 5.5 - 2.5 = 3$
(Or any of the other methods for determining i may be used.)

(c) f

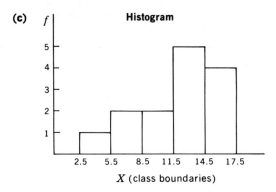

Histogram

(d) f

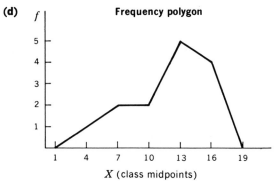

Frequency polygon

(e) negatively skewed

(f)

Class boundaries	f	cf
2.5–5.5	1	1
5.5–8.5	2	3
8.5–11.5	2	5
11.5–14.5	5	10
14.5–17.5	4	14

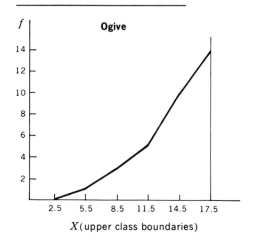

Ogive

Column chart

Sales, $1,000's

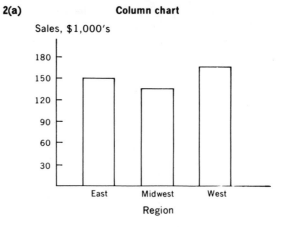

Region

(b)

Component bar chart

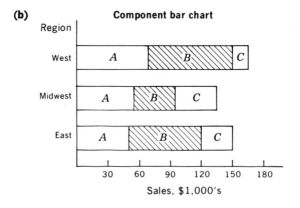

Sales, $1,000's

(c)

Pie chart

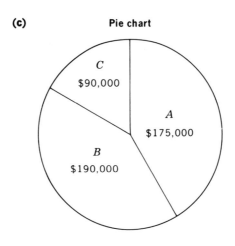

3(a)

Line chart

Sales, $1,000's

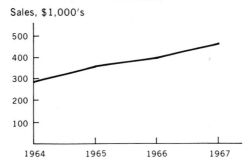

(b)

Stratum chart

Sales, $1,000's

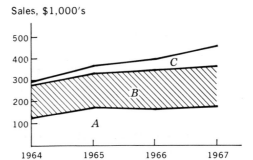

unit 3 • measures of central tendency

1(a) $\bar{X} = \dfrac{\Sigma X}{n} = \dfrac{34}{10} = 3.4$

(b) Array: [0, 1, 1, 1, 2, 3, 5, 5, 7, 9]
Med $= X_{n/2+\frac{1}{2}} = X_{5.5} = 2.5$ (which is midway between the fifth and sixth measurements in array)

(c) Mode $= 1$ (most frequent)

(d) $Q_1 = X_{n/4+\frac{1}{2}} = X_3 = 1$ (the third measurement in the array)
$Q_2 = X_{n/2+\frac{1}{2}} = X_{5.5} = 2.5$
$Q_3 = X_{3n/4+\frac{1}{2}} = X_8 = 5$

2 With the mean being larger than the median, the distribution can be described as being positively skewed.

3

Class boundaries	f	X_c	fX	cf
0.95–1.45	0	1.2	. . .	0
1.45–1.95	2	1.7	3.4	2
1.95–2.45	10	2.2	22.0	12
2.45–2.95	9	2.7	24.3	21
2.95–3.45	6	3.2	19.2	27
3.45–3.95	3	3.7	11.1	30
	$\Sigma f = 30$		$\Sigma fX = 80.0$	

(a) $\bar{X} = \dfrac{\Sigma fX}{\Sigma f} = \dfrac{80}{30} = 2.67 = 2.7$

(b) $\text{Med} = B_L + \dfrac{n/2 - cf_B}{f_c} i = 2.45 + \left(\dfrac{15 - 12}{9}\right) 0.5$

$$= 2.45 + \left(\dfrac{1}{3}\right) 0.5 = 2.45 + 0.17 = 2.62 = 2.6$$

(c) $\text{Mode} = B_L + \dfrac{D_1}{D_1 + D_2} i = 1.95 + \left(\dfrac{8}{8+1}\right) 0.5$

$$= 1.95 + 0.44 = 2.39 = 2.4$$

(d) $Q_1 = B_L + \dfrac{n/4 - cf_B}{f_c} i = 1.95 + \left(\dfrac{7.5 - 2}{10}\right) 0.5$

$= 1.95 + 0.275 = 2.225 = 2.2$ (25 percent of the measurements in the distribution are located below this value.)

$Q_3 = B_L + \dfrac{3n/4 - cf_B}{f_c} i = 2.95 + \left(\dfrac{22.5 - 21}{6}\right) 0.5$

$$= 2.95 + \left(\dfrac{1.5}{6}\right) 0.5 = 2.95 + 0.125$$

$= 3.075 = 3.1$ (75 percent of the measurements in the distribution are located below this point.)

(e) With the mean being larger than the median, the distribution is positively skewed.

unit 4 ▪ measuring dispersion   **1**   *Number of days absent*

(X)	$|x|*$	X^2
5	1.6	25
0	3.4	0
1	2.4	1
7	3.6	49
1	2.4	1
2	1.4	4
9	5.6	81
5	1.6	25
1	2.4	1
3	0.4	9
$\Sigma X = 34$	$\Sigma|x| = 24.8$	$\Sigma X^2 = 196$

$*\bar{X} = \Sigma X / n = {}^{34}/_{10} = 3.4$

(a) $R = H - L = 9 - 0 = 9$

(b) $Q_1 = 1$ and $Q_3 = 5$ (from the solution of Prob. 1, Unit 3)

$$QD = \dfrac{Q_3 - Q_1}{2} = \dfrac{5 - 1}{2} = 2.0$$

(c) $MD = \dfrac{\Sigma|x|}{n} = \dfrac{24.8}{10} = 2.5$

(d) $s = \sqrt{\dfrac{\Sigma X^2}{n} - \left(\dfrac{\Sigma X}{n}\right)^2} = \sqrt{\dfrac{196}{10} - \left(\dfrac{34}{10}\right)^2}$

$$= \sqrt{19.60 - 11.55} = \sqrt{8.05} = 2.8$$

(e) $V = \dfrac{s}{\bar{X}} = \dfrac{2.8}{3.4} = 0.8$

2

Class boundaries	f	X_c	$|x|$*	$f|x|$	fX	X^2	fX^2	cf
0.95–1.45	0	1.2	1.5	...	...	1.44	...	0
1.45–1.95	2	1.7	1.0	2.0	3.4	2.89	5.78	2
1.95–2.45	10	2.2	0.5	5.0	22.0	4.84	48.40	12
2.45–2.95	9	2.7	0	...	24.3	7.29	65.61	21
2.95–3.45	6	3.2	0.5	3.0	19.2	10.24	61.44	27
3.45–3.95	3	3.7	1.0	3.0	11.1	13.69	41.07	30
				$\Sigma f|x| = 13.0$	$\Sigma fX = 80.0$		$\Sigma fX^2 = 222.30$	

*$\bar{X} = \Sigma fX/\Sigma f = {}^{80}\!/_{30} = 2.7$

(a) $R = B_U \text{ (highest class)} - B_L \text{ (lowest class)}$
$$= 3.95 - 1.45 = 2.50 = 2.5$$

(b) $Q_1 = 2.2 \text{ and } Q_3 = 3.1$ (from the solution of Prob. 3, Unit 3)

$$QD = \dfrac{Q_3 - Q_1}{2} = \dfrac{3.1 - 2.2}{2} = \dfrac{0.9}{2} = 0.45 = 0.4$$

(c) $MD = \dfrac{\Sigma f|x|}{\Sigma f} = \dfrac{13.0}{30} = 0.43 = 0.4$

(d) $s = \sqrt{\dfrac{\Sigma fX^2}{\Sigma f} - \left(\dfrac{\Sigma fX}{\Sigma f}\right)^2} = \sqrt{\dfrac{222.30}{30} - \left(\dfrac{80}{30}\right)^2} = \sqrt{7.41 - 7.11}$

$$= \sqrt{0.30} = 0.54 = 0.5$$

(e) $V = \dfrac{s}{\bar{X}} = \dfrac{0.5}{2.7} = 0.19 = 0.2$

3

X	x*	x^2	x^3	x^4
2	−4	16	−64	256
2	−4	16	−64	256
4	−2	4	−8	16
6	0	0	0	0
6	0	0	0	0
8	2	4	8	16
10	4	16	64	256
10	4	16	64	256
$\Sigma X = 48$		$\Sigma x^2 = 72$	$\Sigma x^3 = 0$	$\Sigma x^4 = 1{,}056$

*$\bar{X} = \Sigma X/n = {}^{48}\!/_8 = 6$

$$s = \sqrt{\dfrac{\Sigma x^2}{n}} = \sqrt{\dfrac{72}{8}} = \sqrt{9} = 3$$

$$a_3 = \frac{\Sigma x^3/n}{s^3} = \frac{0}{27} = 0 \qquad \text{(Therefore the distribution is symmetrical.)}$$

$$a_4 = \frac{\Sigma x^4/n}{s^4} = \frac{1,056/8}{81} = \frac{132}{81} = 1.6 \qquad \text{(Therefore the distribution is platykurtic.)}$$

unit 5 • probability

1(a) $P(400\text{–}499) = 0.10$
$P(\geq 500) = 0.05$
$P(400\text{–}499)$ or $(\geq 500) = P(400\text{–}499) + P(\geq 500)$
$$= 0.10 + 0.05 = 0.15$$

(b) $P(200\text{–}299) = 0.30$
$P(300\text{–}399) = 0.30$
$P(200\text{–}299)$ or $(300\text{–}399) = P(200\text{–}299) + P(300\text{–}399)$
$$= 0.30 + 0.30 = 0.60$$

2 $P(G \text{ or } W) = P(G) + P(W) - P(G,W)$
$$= 0.30 + 0.70 - 0.20 = 0.80$$
$$\text{No. } = 0.80(300) = 240$$

3

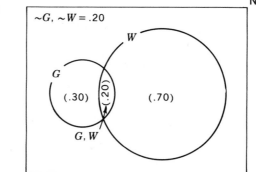

4(a)

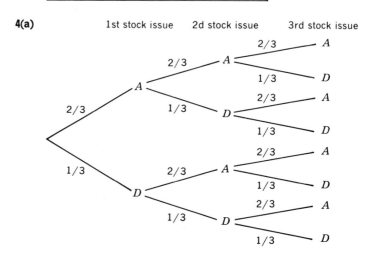

(b) $P(D,D,D) = P(D)P(D)P(D) = \frac{1}{3} \times \frac{1}{3} \times \frac{1}{3} = \frac{1}{27}$
(c) P (at least one D) $= 1 - P(A,A,A)$
$$= 1 - (\frac{2}{3} \times \frac{2}{3} \times \frac{2}{3}) = 1 - \frac{8}{27} = \frac{19}{27}$$

5(a)

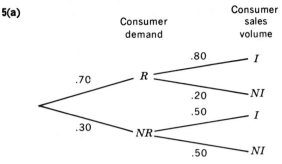

(b) $P(R,I) = P(R)P(I|R) = (0.70)(0.80) = 0.56$
(c) $P(NR,I) = P(NR)P(I|NR) = (0.30)(0.50) = 0.15$

unit 6 ▪ probability distributions **1(a)**

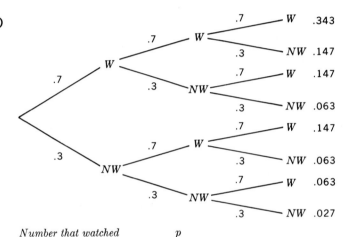

Number that watched	p
0	0.027
1	0.189 (= 3 × 0.063)
2	0.441 (= 3 × 0.147)
3	0.343

(b) $p = 0.70$
$q = 0.30$
$n = 3$
$(q + p)^3 = q^3 + 3q^2p + 3qp^2 + p^3$
$= (0.30)^3 + 3(0.30)^2(0.70) + 3(0.30)(0.70)^2 + (0.70)^3$
$= 0.027 + 0.189 + 0.441 + 0.343$

Number that watched	p
0	0.027
1	0.189
2	0.441
3	0.343

(c)

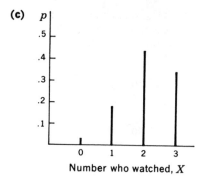

Number who watched, X

(d)   0.027   (from the table in either solution 1a or 1b)

$q^3 = (0.70)^3 = 0.343$ when $p = 0.30$, $q = 0.70$

2(a) $\mu = 500$

$\sigma = 100$

Area 300 to μ = area -2σ to μ =   0.4772

$+$Area μ to 700 = area μ to $+2\sigma$ = $+0.4772$

Total area = $\overline{0.9544}$ = 95.44%

(b)   Area below μ =   0.5000

$-$Area 225 to μ = area -2.75σ to μ = -0.4970

Proportion < 225 = $\overline{0.0030}$

Expected number = 0.0030(10,000) =   30

Area above μ =   0.5000

$-$Area μ to 675 = area μ to 1.75σ = -0.4599

Proportion ≥ 675 = $\overline{0.0401}$

Expected number = 0.0401(10,000) = 401

(c)   Since proportion in upper tail = 0.10, proportion between μ and $Z = 0.40$. Closest value to 0.40 in the body of Table A.1 is 0.3997, for $Z = 1.28$. Thus we now simply solve for X in the following formula in order to determine the test score equivalent to the Z value of 1.28.

$$Z = \frac{X - \mu}{\sigma}$$

$$1.28 = \frac{X - 500}{100}$$

$$X - 500 = 128$$

$$X = 628$$

unit 7 ▪ sampling and sampling distributions

1(a)   For a simple random sample the names can be chosen from the list by some random process for the purpose of individual contact. If each person's name is assigned a unique number, a table of random numbers can be used for sample selection.

(b)   For a systematic sample every nth (such as fifth) person on the list can be contacted.

(c)   For a stratified sample we might classify the population of owners according to sex and then choose a simple random or systematic sample from each stratum.

(d) For a cluster sample, since we have the addresses of the car owners, we might choose to interview all owners living on randomly selected blocks in the test area. Having a geographic basis, this type of cluster sampling can also be called area sampling.

2

X	x	x^2
3	-4	16
6	-1	1
9	2	4
10	3	9
$\Sigma X = 28$		$\Sigma x^2 = 30$

(a) $\mu = \dfrac{\Sigma X}{N} = \dfrac{28}{4} = 7.0$

(b) $\sigma = \sqrt{\dfrac{\Sigma x^2}{N}} = \sqrt{\dfrac{30}{4}} = \sqrt{7.5} = 2.74$

(c)

Sample	$\bar{X}$	$\bar{X}^2$
3, 6	4.5	20.25
3, 9	6.0	36.00
3, 10	6.5	42.25
6, 9	7.5	56.25
6, 10	8.0	64.00
9, 10	9.5	90.25
	$\Sigma\bar{X} = 42.0$	$\Sigma\bar{X}^2 = 309.00$

(d) $\mu_{\bar{X}} = \dfrac{\Sigma\bar{X}}{N_s} = \dfrac{42.0}{6} = 7.0$ (which equals μ computed in solution 2a)

(e) $\sigma_{\bar{X}} = \sqrt{\dfrac{\Sigma\bar{X}^2}{N_s} - \left(\dfrac{\Sigma\bar{X}}{N_s}\right)^2}$ (computational formula)

$= \sqrt{309\% - 7^2} = \sqrt{51.5 - 49.0} = \sqrt{2.5} = 1.58$

(f) $\sigma_{\bar{X}} = \dfrac{\sigma}{\sqrt{n}}\sqrt{\dfrac{N - n}{N - 1}}$ (formula when σ is known and population is finite)

$= \dfrac{2.74}{\sqrt{2}}\sqrt{\dfrac{4 - 2}{4 - 1}} = \dfrac{2.74}{\sqrt{2}} \times \dfrac{\sqrt{2}}{\sqrt{3}} = \dfrac{2.74}{\sqrt{3}} = \dfrac{2.74}{1.73} = 1.58$

3(a) $E(\bar{X}) = \mu = 10,000$ hours

(b) $\sigma_{\bar{X}} = \dfrac{\sigma}{\sqrt{n}} = \dfrac{500}{\sqrt{25}} = \dfrac{500}{5} = 100$

4 $s_{\bar{X}} = \dfrac{s}{\sqrt{n - 1}} = \dfrac{400}{\sqrt{10 - 1}} = \dfrac{400}{3} = 133.3$

5(a) $E(\mu) = \bar{X} = \$3$

(b) $s_{\bar{X}} = \dfrac{s}{\sqrt{n-1}} \sqrt{\dfrac{N-n}{N-1}}$ (formula when s is known and population is finite)

$$= \dfrac{0.50}{\sqrt{26-1}} \sqrt{\dfrac{257-26}{256}} = \dfrac{0.50}{5} \sqrt{\dfrac{231}{256}} = 0.1\left(\dfrac{15.2}{16}\right) = 0.095$$

unit 8 · estimating population values

1 $s_{\bar{X}} = \dfrac{s}{\sqrt{n-1}} = \dfrac{14.00}{\sqrt{50-1}} = \dfrac{14.00}{7} = 2.00$

(a) $\bar{X} \pm 1.64 s_{\bar{X}} = 53.00 \pm 1.64(2.00) = 53.00 \pm 3.28 = \$49.72$ to $\$56.28$

(b) $\bar{X} \pm 1.96 s_{\bar{X}} = 53.00 \pm 1.96(2.00) = 53.00 \pm 3.92 = \$49.08$ to $\$56.92$

(c) $\bar{X} \pm 2.58 s_{\bar{X}} = 53.00 \pm 2.58(2.00) = 53.00 \pm 5.16 = \$47.84$ to $\$58.16$

(d)   Which of the confidence intervals is most useful depends on the objectives of the decision maker. Though the 90 percent confidence interval involves the greatest degree of risk of not including the actual mean of all accounts, it is the most precise of the three estimates. At the other extreme the 99 percent confidence interval involves least risk of an estimation error, but it is the widest of the three estimation intervals.

2(a) $N(\bar{X} \pm 1.64 s_{\bar{X}}) = 3,000(\$49.72$ to $\$56.28) = \$149,160$ to $\$168,840$

(b) $N(\bar{X} \pm 1.96 s_{\bar{X}}) = 3,000(\$49.08$ to $\$56.92) = \$147,240$ to $\$170,760$

(c) $N(\bar{X} \pm 2.58 s_{\bar{X}}) = 3,000(\$47.84$ to $\$58.16) = \$143,520$ to $\$174,480$

3 $s_{\bar{X}_1 - \bar{X}_2} = \sqrt{s_{\bar{X}_1}{}^2 + s_{\bar{X}_2}{}^2} = \sqrt{(2.00)^2 + (3.00)^2} = \sqrt{13.00} = \$3.61$

Diff $= \bar{X}_1 - \bar{X}_2 \pm 1.96 s_{\bar{X}_1 - \bar{X}_2} = 54.00 - 45.00 \pm 1.96(3.61)$
$= 9.00 \pm 7.08 = \$1.92$ to $\$16.08$

4 $s_p = \sqrt{\dfrac{p(1-p)}{n}} = \sqrt{\dfrac{0.60(0.40)}{100}} = \sqrt{0.0024} = 0.049$

(a) $p \pm 1.64 s_p = 0.60 \pm 1.64(0.049) = 0.60 \pm 0.08$
$= 0.52$ to $0.68 = 52\%$ to 68%

(b) $p \pm 1.96 s_p = 0.60 \pm 1.96(0.049) = 0.60 \pm 0.10$
$= 0.50$ to $0.70 = 50\%$ to 70%

(c) $p \pm 2.58 s_p = 0.60 \pm 2.58(0.049) = 0.60 \pm 0.13$
$= 0.47$ to $0.73 = 47\%$ to 73%

5 $N(p \pm 1.96 s_p) = 2,000(0.50$ to $0.70) = 1,000$ to $1,400$

6 $s_{p_1} = \sqrt{\dfrac{p_1(1-p_1)}{n_1}} = \sqrt{\dfrac{(0.60(0.40)}{100}} = \sqrt{0.0024} = 0.049$

$s_{p_2} = \sqrt{\dfrac{p_2(1-p_2)}{n_2}} = \sqrt{\dfrac{(0.50)(0.50)}{100}} = \sqrt{0.0025} = 0.050$

$s_{p_1 - p_2} = \sqrt{s_{p_1}{}^2 + s_{p_2}{}^2} = \sqrt{0.0024 + 0.0025} = \sqrt{0.0049} = 0.07$

Diff $= p_1 - p_2 \pm 1.96 s_{p_1 - p_2} = (0.60 - 0.50) \pm 1.96(0.07)$
$= 0.10 \pm 0.14 = -0.04$ to $0.24 = -4\%$ to 24%

The -4% signifies that the percentage of voters in the second district who are in favor of the proposal may actually exceed the percentage in the first district by as much as 4 percent. On the other hand, the percentage in favor of the proposal in the first district may exceed the second district percentage by as much as 24 percent at the 95 percent degree of confidence.

unit 9 ▪ hypothesis testing

1

$$s_{\bar{X}} = \frac{s}{\sqrt{n-1}} = \frac{600}{\sqrt{37-1}} = \frac{600}{6} = 100$$

$$Z_{CR} = \frac{\bar{X} - \mu_H}{s_{\bar{X}}} = \frac{2{,}325 - 2{,}500}{100} = \frac{-175}{100} = -1.75$$

The critical values of Z for the two-tailed test at the 5 percent level are ± 1.96. Since $|-1.75| < |\pm 1.96|$, the obtained Z value is in the region of acceptance of the null hypothesis, and hence the manufacturer's claim is not rejected.

2

The critical value of Z for the one-tailed test at the 5 percent level is -1.64. Since $-1.75 < -1.64$, the null hypothesis is rejected, and the alternative hypothesis that the bulbs are inferior in respect to the claim is accepted.

3

$$s_{\bar{X}_1} = \frac{s_1}{\sqrt{n_1 - 1}} = \frac{0.02}{\sqrt{65-1}} = \frac{0.02}{8} = 0.0025$$

$$s_{\bar{X}_2} = \frac{s_2}{\sqrt{n_2 - 1}} = \frac{0.04}{\sqrt{65-1}} = \frac{0.04}{8} = 0.005$$

$$s_{\bar{X}_1 - \bar{X}_2} = \sqrt{s_{\bar{X}_1}{}^2 + s_{\bar{X}_2}{}^2} = \sqrt{(0.0025)^2 + (0.005)^2}$$
$$= \sqrt{0.00000625 + 0.000025} = \sqrt{0.00003125} = 0.0056$$

$$Z_{CR} = \frac{\bar{X}_1 - \bar{X}_2}{s_{\bar{X}_1 - \bar{X}_2}} = \frac{0.24 - 0.25}{0.0056} = \frac{-0.01}{0.0056} = -1.79$$

The critical values of Z for the two-tailed test at the 5 percent level are ± 1.96. Since $|-1.79| < |\pm 1.96|$, the hypothesis of no difference cannot be rejected at the 5 percent level.

4

The critical value of Z for this one-tailed test at the 5 percent level is -1.64. Since $-1.79 < -1.64$, the null hypothesis is rejected, and we would conclude that the machine is out of adjustment.

5

We can determine the probability of obtaining just one order and no orders out of 10 attempts by solving for the values of the following two terms from the binomial expansion, with $n = 10$ and assuming that $p = 0.3$:

$$p \text{ (1 order)} = 10pq^9 = 10(0.3)(0.7)^9 = 0.1211$$
$$+ p \text{ (0 orders)} = q^{10} = (0.7)^{10} = \underline{0.0282}$$
$$p \text{ (0 orders or 1 order)} = 0.1493$$

Since $0.1493 > 0.05$, the two extreme outcomes described would happen by chance more than five times out of 100, given the accuracy of the claim that p (actually, π) $= 0.3$. Therefore the salesman's claim cannot be rejected on the basis of this sample evidence.

6 $$\sigma_p = \sqrt{\frac{\pi_H(1 - \pi_H)}{n}} = \sqrt{\frac{0.30(0.70)}{100}} = \sqrt{\frac{0.2100}{100}} = \sqrt{0.0021} = 0.046$$

(Note that it is appropriate to compute σ_p rather than s_p when π_H is specified.)

$$Z_{CR} = \frac{p - \pi_H}{\sigma_p} = \frac{0.20 - 0.30}{0.046} = \frac{-0.10}{0.046} = -2.17$$

(a) The critical value of Z for this one-tailed test at the 5 percent level is -1.64. Since $-2.17 < -1.64$, his claim would be rejected at this level of significance.

(b) The critical value of Z for this one-tailed test at the 1 percent level is -2.33. Since $-2.17 > -2.33$, the Z value is in the region of acceptance, and the claim cannot be rejected at the 1 percent level of significance.

unit 10 ▪ the use of Student's t distribution

1

X	x	x^2
11.8	-0.1	0.01
11.7	-0.2	0.04
12.1	$+0.2$	0.04
11.9	0	
12.0	$+0.1$	0.01
12.0	$+0.1$	0.01
11.7	-0.2	0.04
12.0	$+0.1$	0.01
11.8	-0.1	0.01
12.0	$+0.1$	0.01
$\Sigma X = 119.0$		$\Sigma x^2 = 0.18$

(a) $\bar{X} = \dfrac{\Sigma X}{n} = \dfrac{119.0}{10} = 11.90$

(b) $s = \sqrt{\dfrac{\Sigma x^2}{n}} = \sqrt{\dfrac{0.18}{10}} = \sqrt{0.018} = 0.134$ (Since the deviations from the mean are so small, this formula for the standard deviation is easier to use in this instance than the computational formula.)

(c) $s_{\bar{X}} = \dfrac{s}{\sqrt{n - 1}} = \dfrac{0.134}{\sqrt{10 - 1}} = \dfrac{0.134}{3} = 0.045$

(d) $\bar{X} \pm t s_{\bar{X}} = 11.90 \pm 2.262(0.045) = 11.90 \pm 0.102$
$= 11.9 \pm 0.1 = 11.8$ to 12.0 ounces

2 $$t_{CR} = \frac{\bar{X} - \mu}{s_{\bar{X}}} = \frac{11.9 - 12.0}{0.045} = \frac{-0.1}{0.045} = -2.2$$

With df = 9, the critical value of t for the 5 percent level, one-tailed, is -1.833. Since $-2.2 < -1.833$, the obtained t is in the region of rejection of the null hypothesis, and we thus reject the hypothesis that the average minimum content requirement is being satisfied.

3(a) $\quad s_{\bar{X}} = \dfrac{s}{\sqrt{n-1}} \sqrt{\dfrac{N-n}{N-1}} = \dfrac{0.25}{\sqrt{25-1}} \sqrt{\dfrac{100-25}{100-1}} = \dfrac{0.25}{\sqrt{24}} \sqrt{\dfrac{75}{99}}$

$\quad = \dfrac{0.25}{4.899}\left(\dfrac{8.660}{9.950}\right) = \dfrac{2.165}{48.646} = 0.045$

$\quad \bar{X} \pm t s_{\bar{X}} = \$1.75 \pm 2.064(0.045) = \$1.75 \pm 0.09 = \$1.66$ to $\$1.84$

(b) $\quad t_{\mathrm{CR}} = \dfrac{1.75 - 1.85}{0.045} = \dfrac{-0.10}{0.045} = -2.2$

With df = 24, the critical value of t for the 5 percent level, one-tailed, is -1.711. Since $-2.2 < -1.711$, the obtained t is in the region of rejection, and the $1.75 per hour average is considered significantly lower than $1.85.

4(a) $\quad s_{\bar{X}_1} = \dfrac{s_1}{\sqrt{n_1-1}} = \dfrac{500}{\sqrt{15-1}} = \dfrac{500}{3.7417} = 133.6$

$\quad s_{\bar{X}_2} = \dfrac{s_2}{\sqrt{n_2-1}} = \dfrac{600}{\sqrt{10-1}} = \dfrac{600}{3} = 200.0$

$\quad s_{\bar{X}_1-\bar{X}_2} = \sqrt{s_{\bar{X}_1}{}^2 + s_{\bar{X}_2}{}^2} = \sqrt{(133.6)^2 + (200.0)^2}$

$\quad\quad\quad = \sqrt{17,848.96 + 40,000.00} = \sqrt{57,848.96} = 240.5$

$\quad t_{\mathrm{CR}} = \dfrac{\bar{X}_1 - \bar{X}_2}{s_{\bar{X}_1-\bar{X}_2}} = \dfrac{3,000 - 2,600}{240.5} = \dfrac{400}{240.5} = +1.67$

With df = $n_1 + n_2 - 2 = 23$, the critical values of t for the 5 percent level, two-tailed, is ± 2.069. Since $|+1.67| < |\pm 2.069|$, the difference is not significant.

(b) With df = 23, the critical value of t for the 5 percent level, one-tailed, is $+1.714$. Since $+1.67 < +1.714$, it also cannot be concluded that the performance in territory A is significantly superior to that in territory B. In order to carry out the test as a one-tailed test, the direction of difference would have to be specified before sample results were seen.

unit 11 ▪ the chi-square test

1(a)

	Marketing area				
	A	B	C	D	Total
Sales, prior month	75	45	30	150	300
Proportion, prior month, p	0.25	0.15	0.10	0.50	1.0
Sales, present month	115	75	40	170	400
Expected sales, present month, Np	100	60	40	200	400

(b) $\chi^2 = \sum \dfrac{(f_o - f_e)^2}{f_e} = \dfrac{(15)^2}{100} + \dfrac{(15)^2}{60} + \dfrac{(0)^2}{40} + \dfrac{(-30)^2}{200}$

$= \dfrac{225}{100} + \dfrac{225}{60} + \dfrac{0}{40} + \dfrac{900}{200} = 2.25 + 3.75 + 0 + 4.5 = 10.5$

(c) With df $= 4 - 1 = 3$, the critical value of χ^2 for significance at the 5 percent level is 7.82. Since $10.5 > 7.82$, the difference is significant.

(d) With df $= 3$, the critical value of χ^2 for significance at the 1 percent level is 11.35. Since $10.5 < 11.35$, the difference is not significant at this level.

2(a) Expected frequencies:

Additional feature desired

Respondents	Disk brakes	Collapsible steering wheel	Automatic door locks	Speed warning buzzer	Total
Men	10	20	12.5	7.5	50
Women	10	20	12.5	7.5	50
Total	20	40	25.0	15.0	100

Computation of above cell entries was carried out by the use of the marginal totals, as follows:

$f_e \text{ (row 1, col. 1)} = \dfrac{\Sigma r \Sigma k}{\Sigma f} = \dfrac{(50)(20)}{100} = \dfrac{1,000}{100} = 10$

$f_e \text{ (row 1, col. 2)} = \dfrac{(50)(40)}{100} = \dfrac{2,000}{100} = 20$

$f_e \text{ (row 1, col. 3)} = \dfrac{(50)(25)}{100} = \dfrac{1,250}{100} = 12.5$

(Other values can be similarly computed or determined by subtraction from marginal totals.)

(b) $\chi^2 = \sum \dfrac{(f_o - f_e)^2}{f_e} = \dfrac{(5)^2}{10} + \dfrac{(5)^2}{20} + \dfrac{(-7.5)^2}{12.5} + \dfrac{(-2.5)^2}{7.5} + \dfrac{(-5)^2}{10}$

$+ \dfrac{(-5)^2}{20} + \dfrac{(7.5)^2}{12.5} + \dfrac{(2.5)^2}{7.5} = 2.5 + 1.25 + 4.5 + 0.83$

$+ 2.5 + 1.25 + 4.5 + 0.83 = 18.16$

(c) With df $= (r - 1)(k - 1) = (1)(3) = 3$, the critical value of χ^2 for significance at the 1 percent level is 11.35. Since $18.16 > 11.35$ the difference is significant.

(d) A significant χ^2 value indicates that the two bases for classification are not independent. In this case it indicates that there is an interaction between the sex of the respondent and the safety feature most desired.

3 For this problem only the column totals are tested for goodness of fit.

	Disk brakes	Collapsible steering wheel	Automatic door locks	Speed warning buzzer	Total
$f_o =$	20	40	25	15	100
$f_e =$	25	25	25	25	100

$$\chi^2 = \sum \frac{(f_o - f_e)^2}{f_e} = \frac{(-5)^2}{25} + \frac{(15)^2}{25} + \frac{(0)^2}{25} + \frac{(-10)^2}{25}$$
$$= 1.0 + 9.0 + 0 + 4.0 = 14.0$$

With df $= 4 - 1 = 3$, the critical value of χ^2 for significance at the 1 percent level is 11.35. Since $14.0 > 11.35$, the difference is significant.

4(a) Expected frequencies:

Present status of loan	Status at time of loan Employed	Unemployed	Total
In default	12.6	5.4	18
Not in default	57.4	24.6	82
Total	70.0	30.0	100

$$f_e \text{ (row 1, col. 1)} = \frac{\Sigma r \Sigma k}{\Sigma f} = \frac{(18)(70)}{100} = \frac{1,260}{100} = 12.6$$

(Others are determined by subtraction from column totals.)

$$\chi^2 = \sum \frac{(f_o - f_e)^2}{f_e} = \frac{(-2.6)^2}{12.6} + \frac{(2.6)^2}{5.4} + \frac{(2.6)^2}{57.4} + \frac{(-2.6)^2}{24.6}$$
$$= 0.54 + 1.25 + 0.12 + 0.27 = 2.18$$

(b) $$\chi^2 = \frac{n(ad - bc)^2}{(a + b)(c + d)(a + c)(b + d)} = \frac{100(220 - 480)^2}{(18)(82)(70)(30)}$$
$$= \frac{6,760,000}{3,099,600} = 2.18$$

(c) With df $= (r - 1)(k - 1) = (1)(1) = 1$, the critical value of χ^2 for significance at the 5 percent level is 3.84. Since $2.18 < 3.84$, the difference between observed and expected frequencies is not significant.

5(a) Expected frequencies:

Present status of loan	Status at time of loan Employed	Unemployed	Total
In default	6.3	2.7	9
Not in default	63.7	27.3	81
Total	70.0	30.0	100

$$f_e \text{ (row 1, col. 1)} = \frac{\Sigma r \Sigma k}{\Sigma f} = \frac{(9)(70)}{100} = \frac{630}{100} = 6.3$$

(Others are determined by subtraction from column totals.)

(b) $x^2 = \sum \frac{(|f_o - f_e| - 0.5)^2}{f_e} = \frac{(0.8)^2}{6.3} + \frac{(0.8)^2}{2.7} + \frac{(0.8)^2}{6.37} + \frac{(0.8)^2}{27.3}$
$= 0.10 + 0.24 + 0.01 + 0.02 = 0.37$

(c) With df $= 1$, critical value of x^2 for the 5 percent level is 3.84. Since $0.37 < 3.84$, the difference is not significant.

---

unit 12 • Bayesian inference and decision theory

1(a)

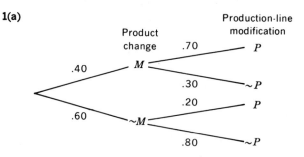

Product change   Production-line modification

(b) $P(\sim P|\sim M) = 0.80$ (from the tree diagram above)

(c) $P(P) = P(M)P(P|M) + P(\sim M)P(P|\sim M) = (0.40)(0.70)$
$+ (0.60)(0.20) = 0.28 + 0.12 = 0.40$

(d) $P(M) = 0.40$ (from the tree diagram above)

(e) $P(M|P) = \dfrac{P(M)P(P|M)}{P(M)P(P|M) + P(\sim M)P(P|\sim M)}$
$= \dfrac{(0.40)(0.70)}{(0.40)(0.70) + (0.60)(0.20)} = \dfrac{0.28}{0.40} = 0.70$

(f) $P(M|\sim P) = \dfrac{P(M)P(\sim P|M)}{P(M)P(\sim P|M) + P(\sim M)P(\sim P|\sim M)}$
$= \dfrac{(0.40)(0.30)}{(0.40)(0.30) + (0.60)(0.80)} = \dfrac{0.12}{0.60} = 0.20 \cdot$

2(a)

Sets stocked	Sets demanded 0	1	2	3
0	$ 0	$ 0	$ 0	$ 0
1	−120	90	90	90
2	−240	−30	180	180
3	−360	−150	60	270

(b) Expected payoff for stocking one set:

Sets demanded	Payoff X	Probability P(X)	XP(X)
0	$-120	0.10	$-12
1	90	0.40	36
2	90	0.30	27
3	90	0.20	18
		$\Sigma XP(X) =$	$ 69

Expected payoff for stocking two sets:

Sets demanded	Payoff X	Probability P(X)	XP(X)
0	$-240	0.10	$-24
1	-30	0.40	-12
2	180	0.30	54
3	180	0.20	36
		$\Sigma XP(X) =$	$ 54

Expected payoff for stocking three sets:

Sets demanded	Payoff X	Probability P(X)	XP(X)
0	$-360	0.10	$-36
1	-150	0.40	-60
2	60	0.30	18
3	270	0.20	54
		$\Sigma XP(X) =$	$-24

Thus the decision that maximizes the expected payoff is that of stocking one stereo set.

3(a) According to the payoff table in solution 2a, the decision which maximizes the maximum possible payoff (of $270) is that of stocking three sets.

(b) According to the payoff table in solution 2a, the decision which maximizes the minimum possible payoff (of $0) is that of stocking no sets. All other decision acts involve the possibility of a loss.

(c) Opportunity losses:

Sets stocked	0	1	2	3	Maximum regret
0	$ 0	$ 90	$180	$270	$270
1	120	0	90	180	180
2	240	120	0	90	240
3	360	240	120	0	360

Thus the decision which minimizes the maximum possible regret (of $180) is that of stocking one set.

(d) The answer depends on the firm's philosophy regarding uncertainty. In this problem, however, the decision to stock no sets when the maximin criterion is used appears to be overly conservative, given that the retailer's function is supposed to be that of offering merchandise for sale.

4(a) Payoffs to A:

Player A	Player B Act 1	Player B Act 2	Row minima
Act 1	40	−10	−10
Act 2	90	−20	−20
Column maxima	90	−10	

Since the maximum of the row minima is equal to the minimum of the column maxima, a saddle point exists.

(b) Player A is likely to choose act 1, thus minimizing his maximum possible loss. As long as player B uses the maximin criterion, any other action on A's part would lead to greater loss (−20 instead of −10).

(c) Player B is likely to choose act 2, thus maximizing his minimum possible gain. The other action would lead to a loss on his part as long as player A uses the maximin criterion (really minimax for A in this case, which is equivalent to the maximin).

(d) The game is not equitable in that the best that player A can do is to minimize his maximum loss, whereas B is in the position of being able to maximize his minimum gain. At the saddle point the payoff to A is −10.

unit 13 ▪ linear-regression analysis

1

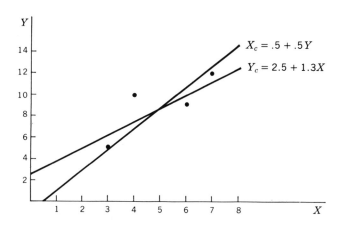

$X_c = .5 + .5Y$

$Y_c = 2.5 + 1.3X$

2

X	Y	XY	X²	Y²
3	5	15	9	25
4	10	40	16	100
6	9	54	36	81
7	12	84	49	144
$\Sigma X = 20$	$\Sigma Y = 36$	$\Sigma XY = 193$	$\Sigma X^2 = 110$	$\Sigma Y^2 = 350$

$$b = \frac{\Sigma XY - n\bar{X}\bar{Y}}{\Sigma X^2 - n\bar{X}^2} = \frac{193 - 4(5)(9)}{110 - 4(25)} = \frac{193 - 180}{110 - 100} = \frac{13}{10} = 1.3$$

$a = \bar{Y} - b\bar{X} = 9 - 1.3(5) = 9 - 6.5 = 2.5$

Therefore $Y_c = a + bX = 2.5 + 1.3X$

3

$$b' = \frac{\Sigma XY - n\bar{X}\bar{Y}}{\Sigma Y^2 - n\bar{Y}^2} = \frac{193 - 4(5)(9)}{350 - 4(81)} = \frac{193 - 180}{350 - 324} = \frac{13}{26} = 0.5$$

$a' = \bar{X} - b'\bar{Y} = 5 - 0.5(9) = 5 - 4.5 = 0.5$

Therefore $X_c = a' + b'Y = 0.5 + 0.5Y$

The two regression lines both satisfy the least-squares criterion with respect to different axes, or variables. Specifically, the equation in Prob. 2 minimizes the sum of squares of the differences between actual and estimated values on the Y variable, whereas use of the equation developed in this problem minimizes the sum of the squares of the differences between actual and estimated values on the X variable.

4

X	Y	Y_c	$Y - Y_c$	$(Y - Y_c)^2$
3	5	6.4	−1.4	1.96
4	10	7.7	2.3	5.29
6	9	10.3	−1.3	1.69
7	12	11.6	0.4	0.16
				$\Sigma(Y - Y_c)^2 = 9.10$

$$\hat{s}_{Y.X} = \sqrt{\frac{\Sigma(Y - Y_c)^2}{n - 2}} = \sqrt{\frac{9.1}{4 - 2}} = \sqrt{4.55} = 2.13$$

5

$Y_c = 2.5 + 1.3X = 2.5 + 1.3(8) = 2.5 + 10.4 = 12.9$

6

$Y_c \pm t\hat{s}_{Y.X} = 12.9 \pm 4.303(2.13) = 12.9 \pm 9.2 = 3.7$ to 22.1

(The relatively wide confidence interval is reflective of both the high value of t associated with the low df of 2 and the relatively high standard error which, again, is to some extent influenced by the small sample size.)

1

X	Y	XY	X²	Y²
3	5	15	9	25
4	10	40	16	100
6	9	54	36	81
7	12	84	49	144
$\Sigma X = 20$	$\Sigma Y = 36$	$\Sigma XY = 193$	$\Sigma X^2 = 110$	$\Sigma Y^2 = 350$

$$r = \frac{n\Sigma XY - \Sigma X \Sigma Y}{\sqrt{n\Sigma X^2 - (\Sigma X)^2}\ \sqrt{n\Sigma Y^2 - (\Sigma Y)^2}}$$

$$= \frac{4(193) - (20)(36)}{\sqrt{4(110) - (20)^2}\ \sqrt{4(350) - (36)^2}}$$

$$= \frac{772 - 720}{\sqrt{440 - 400}\ \sqrt{1{,}400 - 1{,}296}} = \frac{52}{\sqrt{(40)(104)}}$$

$$= \frac{52}{\sqrt{4{,}160}} = \frac{52}{64.5} = .806$$

With df $= n - 2 = 2$, a correlation value of .950 is required for significance at the 5 percent level. Since $.806 < .950$, the difference is not significant (indicating the price paid for collecting such a small sample).

2 $r^2 = (.806)^2 = .650$

This value indicates that a proportion of .65 of the variance in the dependent variable is statistically explained, or accounted for, by knowledge of the independent variable.

3

X (rank)	Y (rank)	D	D²
4	4	0	0
3	2	1	1
2	3	−1	1
1	1	0	0
		$\Sigma D^2 = 2$	

$$r_{\text{rank}} = 1 - \frac{6\Sigma D^2}{n(n^2 - 1)} = 1 - \frac{6(2)}{4(16 - 1)} = 1 - \frac{12}{60} = 1 - .20 = .80$$

(In this case, the value of r_{rank} is unusually close to the value of r, of which it is essentially an estimate.)

4 $Y_c = \left(\bar{Y} - r\frac{s_Y}{s_X}\bar{X} \right) + \left(r\frac{s_Y}{s_X} \right) X$

$$s_X = \sqrt{\frac{\Sigma X^2}{n} - \left(\frac{\Sigma X}{n} \right)^2} = \sqrt{\frac{110}{4} - (5)^2} = \sqrt{27.5 - 25}$$

$$= \sqrt{2.5} = 1.58$$

$$s_Y = \sqrt{\frac{\Sigma Y^2}{n} - \left(\frac{\Sigma Y}{n}\right)^2} = \sqrt{\frac{350}{4} - (9)^2} = \sqrt{87.5 - 81}$$

$$= \sqrt{6.5} = 2.55$$

$$Y_c = \left[9 - (.806)\left(\frac{2.55}{1.58}\right)(5)\right] + .806\left(\frac{2.55}{1.58}\right)X$$

$$= [9 - (.806)(1.61)(5)] + .806(1.61)X$$

$$= (9 - 6.5) + 1.3X = 2.5 + 1.3X$$

This regression equation is identical to the one developed in Prob. 2, Unit 13.

5      $$\hat{s}_{Y.X} = s_Y \sqrt{1 - r^2} \sqrt{\frac{n}{n-2}} = 2.55 \sqrt{1 - .650} \sqrt{\frac{4}{2}}$$

$$= 2.55 \sqrt{.35} \sqrt{2} = 2.55(.592)(1.414) = 2.13$$

Again, this standard error of estimate is identical to the one developed in Prob. 4, Unit 13.

unit 15 ▪ time-series   **1(a)** C
analysis   **(b)** I

      (c) I

      (d) S

      (e) T

2(a)   **Line chart**

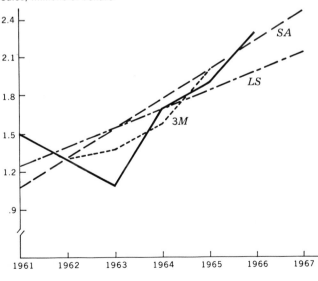

Sales, millions of dollars

(b) Mean for 1961–1963 = $(1.5 + 1.3 + 1.1)/3 = 3.9/3 = 1.30$
(entered over 1962 on chart)
Mean for 1964–1966 = $(1.7 + 1.9 + 2.3)/3 + 5.9/3 = 1.97$
(entered over 1965 on chart)

(c)

Year	Sales, in millions	Three-year moving total	Three-year moving average
1961	$1.5		
1962	1.3	3.9	1.30
1963	1.1	4.1	1.37
1964	1.7	4.7	1.57
1965	1.9	5.9	1.97
1966	2.3		

(d)

Year	Year, coded, X	Sales, in millions, Y	XY	X^2
1961	-2	$1.5	-3.0	4
1962	-1	1.3	-1.3	1
1963	0	1.1	...	0
1964	$+1$	1.7	1.7	1
1965	$+2$	1.9	3.8	4
1966	$+3$	2.3	6.9	9
	$\Sigma X = 3$	$\Sigma Y = 9.8$	$\Sigma XY = 8.1$	$\Sigma X^2 = 19$

For the equation $Y_c = a + bX$,

$$b = \frac{\Sigma XY - n\bar{X}\bar{Y}}{\Sigma X^2 - n\bar{X}^2} = \frac{8.1 - 6(0.5)(1.63)}{19 - 6(0.5)^2} = \frac{8.1 - 4.89}{19 - 1.50} = \frac{3.21}{17.5} = 0.183$$

$a = \bar{Y} - b\bar{X} = 1.633 - 0.183(0.5) = 1.633 - 0.092 = 1.541$
Thus $Y_c = 1.541 + 0.183X$

The value of a in this equation refers to the expected dollar sales volume, in millions, for 1963. This is so since $X_{1963} = 0$.

3(a)

Year	Sales, in millions, Y	Expected sales,* Y_c	Cyclical relative, $100Y/Y_c$
1961	$1.5	$1.18	127.1
1962	1.3	1.36	95.6
1963	1.1	1.54	71.4
1964	1.7	1.72	98.8
1965	1.9	1.91	99.5
1966	2.3	2.09	110.0

* For 1961: $Y_c = 1.541 + 0.183X = 1.541 + 0.183(-2) = 1.541 - 0.366 = 1.175$
$= 1.18$ (and similarly for the other years of this time series).

(b) **Cycle chart**

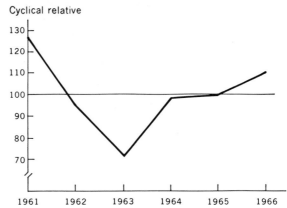

The chart indicates a cyclical dip completed in 1963 and a rise in each of the succeeding years, relative to trend. The trend line is represented at 100 on this chart.

4(a) and (b)

Year	Quarter	Sales, in thousands of dollars	Four-quarter moving total	Two-year moving total	Four-quarter centered moving average	Percent of four-quarter centered moving average
1961	1	5.0				
	2	3.5				
			15.0			
	3	2.5		29.5	3.69	67.8
			14.5			
	4	4.0		29.0	3.62	110.5
			14.5			
1962	1	4.5		28.5	3.56	126.4
			14.0			
	2	3.5		27.0	3.38	103.6
			13.0			
	3	2.0		25.0	3.12	64.1
			12.0			
	4	3.0		22.5	2.81	106.8
			10.5			
1963	1	3.5		20.5	2.56	136.7
			10.0			
	2	2.0		21.0	2.62	76.3
			11.0			
	3	1.5		24.0	3.00	50.0
			13.0			
	4	4.0		27.5	3.44	116.3
			14.5			

Year	Quarter	Sales, in thousands of dollars	Four-quarter moving total	Two-year moving total	Four-quarter centered moving average	Percent of four-quarter centered moving average
1964	1	5.5		30.0	3.75	146.7
			15.5			
	2	3.5		32.5	4.06	86.2
			17.0			
	3	2.5		34.0	4.25	58.8
			17.0			
	4	5.5		34.5	4.31	127.6
			17.5			
1965	1	5.5		36.0	4.50	122.2
			18.5			
	2	4.0		37.5	4.69	85.3
			19.0			
	3	3.5		40.0	5.00	70.0
			21.0			
	4	6.0		43.0	5.38	111.5
			22.0			
1966	1	7.5		44.5	5.56	134.9
			22.5			
	2	5.0		45.5	5.69	87.9
			23.0			
	3	4.0				
	4	6.5				

(c)

Quarter	1961	Percent of moving average 1962	1963	1964	1965	1966	Modified mean*	Adjusted seasonal index, mean × 1.0111†
1	...	126.4	136.7	146.7	122.2	134.9	132.7	134.2
2	...	103.6	76.3	86.2	85.3	87.9	86.5	87.5
3	67.8	64.1	50.0	58.8	70.0	...	63.6	64.3
4	110.5	106.8	116.3	127.6	111.5	...	112.8	114.1
							395.6	400.1

* Highest and lowest values left out; e.g., for first quarter, modified mean =
(126.4 + 136.7 + 134.9)/3 = 398.0/3 = 132.7.

† Adjustment = $\dfrac{\text{desired total}}{\text{actual total}} = \dfrac{400}{395.6} = 1.0111$

5(a) Seasonally adjusted values:*

Quarter	1961	1962	1963	1964	1965	1966
1	3.7	3.4	2.6	4.1	4.1	5.6
2	4.0	4.0	2.3	4.0	4.6	5.7
3	3.9	3.1	2.3	3.9	5.4	6.2
4	3.5	2.6	3.5	4.8	5.3	5.7

* Determined by dividing each of the quarterly sales figures listed in Prob. 4a by the appropriate seasonal index and multiplying by 100 for appropriate decimal location. For example, the seasonally adjusted value for the first quarter of 1961 = $(5.0/134.2) - 100 = 3.725 = 3.7$.

(b) To change the a and b so that they are applicable for quarterly data:

$$Y_c = \frac{a}{4} + \frac{b}{4}X = \frac{1.541}{4} + \frac{0.183}{4}X = 0.385 + 0.046X$$

To modify the scale so that sales are being estimated in hundreds of thousands instead of millions of dollars:

$$Y_c = 10(0.385 + 0.046X) = 3.85 + 0.46X$$

To change X to quarterly units rather than yearly units:

$$Y_c = 3.85 + \frac{0.46X}{4} = 3.85 + 0.115X$$

Finally, to begin the quarterly code numbers with the first quarter of 1963:

$$Y_c = 3.85 + 0.115(X - 1.5) = 3.85 + 0.115X - 0.172$$
$$Y_c = 3.678 + 0.115X = 3.7 + 0.1X$$

(c) Quarterly trend values:*

Quarter	1961	1962	1963	1964	1965	1966
1	2.9	3.3	3.7	4.1	4.5	4.9
2	3.0	3.4	3.8	4.2	4.6	5.0
3	3.1	3.5	3.9	4.3	4.7	5.1
4	3.2	3.6	4.0	4.4	4.8	5.2

* Computed by use of the regression equation determined in solution 5b. For example, for the first quarter of 1961, $Y_c = 3.7 + 0.1X = 3.7 + 0.1(-8) = 3.7 - 0.8 = 2.9$.

Seasonally adjusted data as percentage of trend (indicates cyclical and irregular components):*

Quarter	1961	1962	1963	1964	1965	1966
1	127.6	103.0	70.3	100.0	91.1˙	114.3
2	133.3	117.6	60.5	95.2	100.0	114.0
3	125.8	88.6	59.0	90.7	114.9	121.6
4	109.4	72.2	87.5	109.1	110.4	109.6

* Determined by dividing the seasonally adjusted values in solution 5a by the trend values of solution 5c and multiplying by 100. Symbolically, $TCI/T = CI$. Thus, for the first quarter of 1961, (3.7/2.9) $\times$ 100 = 127.586 = 127.6.

(d) Three-quarter moving average (this residual presumably includes only cyclical effects):*

Quarter	1961	1962	1963	1964	1965	1966
1	. . .	110.0	67.7	94.2	100.1	112.9
2	128.9	103.1	63.3	95.3	102.0	116.6
3	122.8	92.8	69.0	98.3	108.4	115.1
4	112.7	77.0	82.2	97.0	113.2	

* For example, the moving average for the second quarter of 1961 is (127.6 + 133.3 + 125.8)/3 = 386.7/3 = 128.9.

(e) Variations from trend attributable to the irregular component:*

Quarter	1961	1962	1963	1964	1965	1966
1	. . .	93.7	103.8	106.2	91.0	101.2
2	103.4	114.1	95.6	99.9	98.0	97.8
3	102.4	95.5	85.5	92.3	106.0	105.6
4	97.1	93.8	106.4	112.5	97.5	

* Determined by dividing the seasonally adjusted data as percentage of trend in solution 5c by the moving averages in solution 5d. Symbolically, $CI/C = I$. For the second quarter of 1961 the value is (133.3/128.9) $\times$ 100 = 103.4.

unit 16 ▪ index numbers

1(a) Percentage decline for appliance prices:

$$\frac{1962\ price - 1965\ price}{1962\ price} \times 100 = \frac{94.0 - 89.2}{94.0} \times 100 = 5.1\%$$

Percentage increase for furniture prices:

$$\frac{1965\ price - 1962\ price}{1962\ price} \times 100 = \frac{106.2 - 103.8}{103.8} \times 100 = 2.3\%$$

(b) Of course, the wholesale price indexes are averages and thus may not apply to any one commodity. As an estimate, however,

Estimated 1965 price = 89.2 $\times$ 1957–1959 price
= 89.2($150) = $133.80

(c) $\dfrac{\text{Estimated 1965 price}}{\text{1963 price}} = \dfrac{\text{1965 price index}}{\text{1963 price index}}$

$\text{Estimated 1965 price} = \dfrac{\text{1965 price index}}{\text{1963 price index}} \times \text{1963 price}$

$\text{Estimated 1965 price} = \dfrac{106.2}{104.6} \times \$150 = \$152.29$

(d) The prices reported are wholesale, not retail. More importantly, they indicate nothing regarding total value or comparative value of sales of the two categories of commodities. In order to address ourselves to this kind of question, quantity data in addition to price data would be needed.

2(a) Simple price relatives for butter:

$\dfrac{p_{1962}}{p_{1962}} \times 100 = \dfrac{0.594}{0.594} \times 100 = 100.0$

$\dfrac{p_{1963}}{p_{1962}} \times 100 = \dfrac{0.590}{0.594} \times 100 = 99.3$

$\dfrac{p_{1964}}{p_{1962}} \times 100 = \dfrac{0.599}{0.594} \times 100 = 100.8$

$\dfrac{p_{1965}}{p_{1962}} \times 100 = \dfrac{0.610}{0.594} \times 100 = 102.7$

(b) Simple price relatives for cheese:

$\dfrac{p_{1962}}{p_{1962}} \times 100 = \dfrac{0.400}{0.400} \times 100 = 100.0$

$\dfrac{p_{1963}}{p_{1962}} \times 100 = \dfrac{0.426}{0.400} \times 100 = 106.5$

$\dfrac{p_{1964}}{p_{1962}} \times 100 = \dfrac{0.434}{0.400} \times 100 = 108.5$

$\dfrac{p_{1965}}{p_{1962}} \times 100 = \dfrac{0.450}{0.400} \times 100 = 112.5$

(c) Whereas butter increased in wholesale price by 2.7 percent during this period, cheese increased by 12.5 percent.

(d) Simple quantity relatives, 1965:

$\text{Butter} = \dfrac{q_{1965}}{q_{1962}} \times 100 = \dfrac{1{,}337.1}{1{,}537.2} \times 100 = 87.0$

$\text{Cheese} = \dfrac{q_{1965}}{q_{1962}} \times 100 = \dfrac{1{,}743.2}{1{,}585.2} \times 100 = 110.0$

Thus the production of butter declined by 13 percent, and the production of cheese increased by 10 percent.

(e) Total dollar values of production:

Butter (1962) $= p_{1962}q_{1962} = \$.594(1{,}537{,}200{,}000) = \$913{,}096{,}800$
Butter (1965) $= p_{1965}q_{1965} = \$.610(1{,}337{,}100{,}000) = \$815{,}631{,}000$
Cheese (1962) $= p_{1962}q_{1962} = \$.400(1{,}585{,}200{,}000) = \$634{,}080{,}000$
Cheese (1965) $= p_{1965}q_{1965} = \$.450(1{,}743{,}200{,}000) = \$784{,}440{,}000$

(f)   Value relatives:

$$\text{Butter} = \frac{p_{1965}q_{1965}}{p_{1962}q_{1962}} \times 100 = \frac{815,631,000}{913,096,800} \times 100 = 89.3$$

$$\text{Cheese} = \frac{p_{1965}q_{1965}}{p_{1962}q_{1962}} \times 100 = \frac{784,440,000}{634,080,000} \times 100 = 123.7$$

Thus the wholesale value of butter production decreased by 10.7 percent between 1962 and 1965, and the wholesale value of cheese production increased by 23.7 percent. Since the per-pound wholesale price of butter increased slightly during this period, as shown in solution 5e, the decrease in total value of butter production is entirely attributable to the decrease in quantity produced. For cheese both price and quantity increased.

3(a) $\dfrac{p_1}{p_0} \times 100 = \dfrac{2.00}{1.80} \times 100 = 111.1$

$\dfrac{q_1}{q_0} \times 100 = \dfrac{2.8}{2.2} \times 100 = 127.3$

(b)   Value relatives:

$$\text{Bond paper} = \frac{p_1 q_1}{p_0 q_0} \times 100 = \frac{(2.00)(2.8)}{(1.80)(2.2)} \times 100 = \frac{5.60}{3.96} \times 100 = 141.4$$

$$\text{Onionskin} = \frac{p_1 q_1}{p_0 q_0} \times 100 = \frac{(0.72)(8.0)}{(0.68)(5.0)} \times 100 = \frac{5.76}{3.40} \times 100 = 169.4$$

There has thus been a 41.4 percent increase in expenditure for bond paper and a 69.4 percent increase in the expenditure for onionskin paper.

(c)

Item	$p_0 q_0$	$p_1 q_0$
Paper, white bond	3.96	4.40
Paper, onionskin	3.40	3.60
Paper clips	0.20	0.20
Typewriter ribbons	4.80	4.00
	$\Sigma p_0 q_0 = 12.36$	$\Sigma p_1 q_0 = 12.20$

$$L = \frac{\Sigma p_1 q_0}{\Sigma p_0 q_0} \times 100 = \frac{12.20}{12.36} \times 100 = 98.7$$

For the quantities (market basket) of the base period, the composite cost in 1966 is 98.7 percent of that in 1965.

(d)

Item	$p_0 q_1$	$p_1 q_1$
Paper, white bond	5.04	5.60
Paper, onionskin	5.44	5.76
Paper clips	0.20	0.20
Typewriter ribbons	6.00	5.00
	$\Sigma p_0 q_1 = 16.68$	$\Sigma p_1 q_1 = 16.56$

$$P = \frac{\Sigma p_1 q_1}{\Sigma p_0 q_1} \times 100 = \frac{16.56}{16.68} \times 100 = 99.3$$

This index indicates the relative cost of the market basket of goods associated with the given period (1966, in this case).

(e)

Item	Price relative, $p_1/p_0 \times 100$	Value weight, $p_0 q_0$	Weighted relative, $p_0 q_0 (p_1/p_0 \times 100)$
Paper, white bond	111.1	$ 3.96	439.96
Paper, onionskin	105.9	3.40	360.06
Paper clips	100.0	0.20	20.00
Typewriter ribbons	83.3	4.80	399.84
		($12.36)	(1,219.86)

$$\text{Weighted average of price relatives} = \frac{\Sigma (p_0 q_0)(p_1/p_0 \times 100)}{\Sigma p_0 q_0}$$

$$= \frac{1,219.86}{12.36} = 98.7$$

As expected, the index is the same as that obtained by the Laspeyres formula.

4

Year (1)	Net earnings, in millions (2)	Index, 1962 = 100 (3)	Link relative (4)	Chain index, 1962 = 100 (5)
1961	$238.4	92.9	. . .	92.9
1962	256.5	100.0	107.6	100.0
1963	272.2	106.1	106.1	106.1
1964	219.6	85.6	80.7	85.6
1965	355.1	138.4	161.7	138.4

(a) The earnings indexes, using 1962 as the base, are posted in column 3 above. For 1961, for example, the index

$$\frac{e_{1961}}{e_{1962}} \times 100 = \frac{238.4}{256.5} \times 100 = 92.9$$

(b) By definition, the base year for a link relative is the preceding year's figure. Thus the link relative for 1965 posted in column 4 above is

$$\frac{\text{earnings (1965)}}{\text{earnings (1964)}} \times 100 = \frac{355.1}{219.6} \times 100 = 161.7$$

(c) With 1962 = 100, for the chain indexes after 1962, $C_n = L_n C_{n-1}/100$. For example,

$$C_{1963} = \frac{L_{1963} C_{1962}}{100} = \frac{(106.1)(100.0)}{100} = 106.1$$

For the chain indexes before 1962, $C_{n-1} = C_n/L_n \times 100$. For example,

$$C_{1961} = \frac{C_{1962}}{L_{1962}} \times 100 = \frac{100.0}{107.6} \times 100 = 92.9$$

The results are identical to those of Prob. 4a, since in both cases 1962 = 100. Chaining as a technique in index-number construction is associated with changes in commodities included in a composite price index, rather than in the kind of simple index-number example presented here in order to highlight the computational method.

appendix

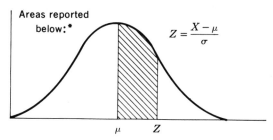

Areas reported below:*

$$Z = \frac{X - \mu}{\sigma}$$

table A.1 ■ table of areas under the normal curve

Z	.00	.01	.02	.03	.04	.05	.06	.07	.08	.09
0.0	.0000	.0040	.0080	.0120	.0160	.0199	.0239	.0279	.0319	.0359
0.1	.0398	.0438	.0478	.0517	.0557	.0596	.0636	.0675	.0714	.0753
0.2	.0793	.0832	.0871	.0910	.0948	.0987	.1026	.1064	.1103	.1141
0.3	.1179	.1217	.1255	.1293	.1331	.1368	.1406	.1443	.1480	.1517
0.4	.1554	.1591	.1628	.1664	.1700	.1736	.1772	.1808	.1844	.1879
0.5	.1915	.1950	.1985	.2019	.2054	.2088	.2123	.2157	.2190	.2224
0.6	.2257	.2291	.2324	.2357	.2389	.2422	.2454	.2486	.2518	.2549
0.7	.2580	.2612	.2642	.2673	.2704	.2734	.2764	.2794	.2823	.2852
0.8	.2881	.2910	.2939	.2967	.2995	.3023	.3051	.3078	.3106	.3133
0.9	.3159	.3186	.3212	.3238	.3264	.3289	.3315	.3340	.3365	.3389
1.0	.3413	.3438	.3461	.3485	.3508	.3531	.3554	.3577	.3599	.3621
1.1	.3643	.3665	.3686	.3708	.3729	.3749	.3770	.3790	.3810	.3830
1.2	.3849	.3869	.3888	.3907	.3925	.3944	.3962	.3980	.3997	.4015
1.3	.4032	.4049	.4066	.4082	.4099	.4115	.4131	.4147	.4162	.4177
1.4	.4192	.4207	.4222	.4236	.4251	.4265	.4279	.4292	.4306	.4319
1.5	.4332	.4345	.4357	.4370	.4382	.4394	.4406	.4418	.4429	.4441
1.6	.4452	.4463	.4474	.4484	.4495	.4505	.4515	.4525	.4535	.4545
1.7	.4554	.4564	.4573	.4582	.4591	.4599	.4608	.4616	.4625	.4633
1.8	.4641	.4649	.4656	.4664	.4671	.4678	.4686	.4693	.4699	.4706
1.9	.4713	.4719	.4726	.4732	.4738	.4744	.4750	.4756	.4761	.4767
2.0	.4772	.4778	.4783	.4788	.4793	.4798	.4803	.4808	.4812	.4817
2.1	.4821	.4826	.4830	.4834	.4838	.4842	.4846	.4850	.4854	.4857
2.2	.4861	.4864	.4868	.4871	.4875	.4878	.4881	.4884	.4887	.4890
2.3	.4893	.4896	.4898	.4901	.4904	.4906	.4909	.4911	.4913	.4916
2.4	.4918	.4920	.4922	.4925	.4927	.4929	.4931	.4932	.4934	.4936
2.5	.4938	.4940	.4941	.4943	.4945	.4946	.4948	.4949	.4951	.4952
2.6	.4953	.4955	.4956	.4957	.4959	.4960	.4961	.4962	.4963	.4964
2.7	.4965	.4966	.4967	.4968	.4969	.4970	.4971	.4972	.4973	.4974
2.8	.4974	.4975	.4976	.4977	.4977	.4978	.4979	.4979	.4980	.4981
2.9	.4981	.4982	.4983	.4983	.4984	.4984	.4985	.4985	.4986	.4986
3.0	.4986									
3.5	.4997									
4.0	.4999									

* Example: For Z = 1.96, shaded area is 0.4750 out of the total area of 1.0.

table A.2 ▪ table of coefficients for the binomial distribution For the Expansion of $(q + p)^n$*

n	Coefficient of the terms in which the exponent of p is:										
	0	1	2	3	4	5	6	7	8	9	10
1	1	1									
2	1	2	1								
3	1	3	3	1							
4	1	4	6	4	1						
5	1	5	10	10	5	1					
6	1	6	15	20	15	6	1				
7	1	7	21	35	35	21	7	1			
8	1	8	28	56	70	56	28	8	1		
9	1	9	36	84	126	126	84	36	9	1	
10	1	10	45	120	210	252	210	120	45	10	1

* Example: $(q + p)^4 = q^4 + 4q^3p + 6q^2p^2 + 4qp^3 + p^4$

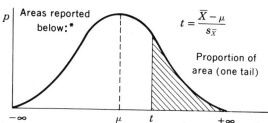

$$t = \frac{\overline{X} - \mu}{s_{\overline{X}}}$$

p | Areas reported below: *

Proportion of area (one tail)

$-\infty$ μ t $+\infty$

used for a one-tailed test.

table A.3 ■ **table of areas for t distributions**

2-tailed

df	0.10	0.05	0.025	0.01	0.005
	.20	.10	.05	.02	.01
1	3.078	6.314	12.706	31.821	63.657
2	1.886	2.920	4.303	6.965	9.925
3	1.638	2.353	3.182	4.541	5.841
4	1.533	2.132	2.776	3.747	4.604
5	1.476	2.015	2.571	3.365	4.032
6	1.440	1.943	2.447	3.143	3.707
7	1.415	1.895	2.365	2.998	3.499
8	1.397	1.860	2.306	2.896	3.355
9	1.383	1.833	2.262	2.821	3.250
10	1.372	1.812	2.228	2.764	3.169
11	1.363	1.796	2.201	2.718	3.106
12	1.356	1.782	2.179	2.681	3.055
13	1.350	1.771	2.160	2.650	3.012
14	1.345	1.761	2.145	2.624	2.977
15	1.341	1.753	2.131	2.602	2.947
16	1.337	1.746	2.120	2.583	2.921
17	1.333	1.740	2.110	2.567	2.898
18	1.330	1.734	2.101	2.552	2.878
19	1.328	1.729	2.093	2.539	2.861
20	1.325	1.725	2.086	2.528	2.845
21	1.323	1.721	2.080	2.518	2.831
22	1.321	1.717	2.074	2.508	2.819
23	1.319	1.714	2.069	2.500	2.807
24	1.318	1.711	2.064	2.492	2.797
25	1.316	1.708	2.060	2.485	2.787
26	1.315	1.706	2.056	2.479	2.779
27	1.314	1.703	2.052	2.473	2.771
28	1.313	1.701	2.048	2.467	2.763
29	1.311	1.699	2.045	2.462	2.756
30	1.310	1.697	2.042	2.457	2.750
40	1.303	1.684	2.021	2.423	2.704
60	1.296	1.671	2.000	2.390	2.660
120	1.289	1.658	1.980	2.358	2.617
∞	1.282	1.645	1.960	2.326	2.576

* Example: For shaded area to represent 0.05 of the total area of 1.0, value of t with 10 degrees of freedom is 1.812.

Source: Abridged from Table IV of R. A. Fisher, *Statistical Methods for Research Workers*, by Oliver & Boyd Ltd., Edinburgh and London, 13th ed., Rev., 1958, by permission of the author's literary executor and publishers.

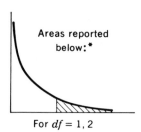

Areas reported
below:*

For *df* = 1, 2

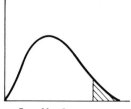

For *df* = 3 or more

table A.4 ▪ **values of** χ^2

Degrees of freedom, df	Levels of significance	
	0.05	*0.01*
1	3.84	6.63
2	5.99	9.21
3	7.81	11.35
4	9.49	13.28
5	11.07	15.09
6	12.59	16.81
7	14.07	18.48
8	15.51	20.09
9	16.92	21.67
10	18.31	23.21
11	19.68	24.73
12	21.03	26.22

* Example: For shaded area to represent 0.05 of the total area of 1.0, value of χ^2 with two degrees of freedom is 5.99.

Source: Abridged from Table III of R. A. Fisher, *Statistical Methods for Research Workers*, Oliver & Boyd Ltd., Edinburgh and London, 13th ed., Rev., 1958 by permission of the author's literary executor and publishers.

table A.5 ■ values of the simple linear correlation coefficient needed for significance	df, $(n - 2)$	0.05	0.01
	1	.996917	.9998766
	2	.95000	.990000
	3	.8783	.95873
different from zero.	4	.8114	.91720
	5	.7545	.8745
	6	.7067	.8343
	7	.6664	.7977
	8	.6319	.7646
	9	.6021	.7348
	10	.5760	.7079
	11	.5529	.6835
	12	.5324	.6614
	13	.5139	.6411
	14	.4973	.6226
	15	.4821	.6055
	16	.4683	.5897
	17	.4555	.5751
	18	.4438	.5614
	19	.4329	.5487
	20	.4227	.5368
	25	.3809	.4869
	30	.3494	.4487
	35	.3246	.4182
	40	.3044	.3932
	45	.2875	.3721
	50	.2732	.3541
	60	.2500	.3248
	70	.2319	.3017
	80	.2172	.2830
	90	.2050	.2673
	100	.1946	.2540

* Example: With 20 degrees of freedom, correlation coefficient of ±.4227 is needed for significance at the 0.05 level.

Source: Abridged from Table V-A of R. A. Fisher, *Statistical Methods for Research Workers*, Oliver & Boyd Ltd., Edinburgh and London, 13th ed., Rev., 1958 by permission of the author's literary executor and publishers.

table A.6 ■ table
of squares and
square roots

N	N^2	$\sqrt{N}$	N	N^2	$\sqrt{N}$	N	N^2	$\sqrt{N}$
			45	2 025	6.708204	90	8 100	9.486833
1	1	1.000000	46	2 116	6.782330	91	8 281	9.539392
2	4	1.414214	47	2 209	6.855655	92	8 464	9.591663
3	9	1.732051	48	2 304	6.928203	93	8 649	9.643651
4	16	2.000000	49	2 401	7.000000	94	8 836	9.695360
5	25	2.236068	50	2 500	7.071068	95	9 025	9.746794
6	36	2.449490	51	2 601	7.141428	96	9 216	9.797959
7	49	2.645751	52	2 704	7.211103	97	9 409	9.848858
8	64	2.828427	53	2 809	7.280110	98	9 604	9.899495
9	81	3.000000	54	2 916	7.348469	99	9 801	9.949874
10	100	3.162278	55	3 025	7.416198	100	10 000	10.00000
11	121	3.316625	56	3 136	7.483315	101	10 201	10.04988
12	144	3.464102	57	3 249	7.549834	102	10 404	10.09950
13	169	3.605551	58	3 364	7.615773	103	10 609	10.14889
14	196	3.741657	59	3 481	7.681146	104	10 816	10.19804
15	225	3.873983	60	3 600	7.745967	105	11 025	10.24695
16	256	4.000000	61	3 721	7.810250	106	11 236	10.29563
17	289	4.123106	62	3 844	7.874008	107	11 449	10.34408
18	324	4.242641	63	3 969	7.937254	108	11 664	10.39230
19	361	4.358899	64	4 096	8.000000	109	11 881	10.44031
20	400	4.472136	65	4 225	8.062258	110	12 100	10.48809
21	441	4.582576	66	4 356	8.124038	111	12 321	10.53565
22	484	4.690416	67	4 489	8.185353	112	12 544	10.58301
23	529	4.795832	68	4 624	8.246211	113	12 769	10.63015
24	576	4.899979	69	4 761	8.306624	114	12 996	10.67708
25	625	5.000000	70	4 900	8.366600	115	13 225	10.72381
26	676	5.099020	71	5 041	8.426150	116	13 456	10.77033
27	729	5.196152	72	5 184	8.485281	117	13 689	10.81665
28	784	5.291503	73	5 329	8.544004	118	13 924	10.86278
29	841	5.385165	74	5 476	8.602325	119	14 161	10.90871
30	900	5.477226	75	5 625	8.660254	120	14 400	10.95445
31	961	5.567874	76	5 776	8.717798	121	14 641	11.00000
32	1 024	5.656854	77	5 929	8.774964	122	14 884	11.04536
33	1 089	5.744563	78	6 084	8.831761	123	15 129	11.09054
34	1 156	5.830952	79	6 241	8.888194	124	15 376	11.13553
35	1 225	5.916080	80	6 400	8.944272	125	15 625	11.18034
36	1 296	6.000000	81	6 561	9.000000	126	15 876	11.22497
37	1 369	6.082763	82	6 724	9.055385	127	16 129	11.26943
38	1 444	6.164414	83	6 889	9.110434	128	16 384	11.31371
39	1 521	6.245998	84	7 056	9.165151	129	16 641	11.35782
40	1 600	6.324555	85	7 225	9.219544	130	16 900	11.40175
41	1 681	6.403124	86	7 396	9.273618	131	17 161	11.44552
42	1 764	6.480741	87	7 569	9.327379	132	17 424	11.48913
43	1 849	6.557439	88	7 744	9.380832	133	17 689	11.53256
44	1 936	6.633250	89	7 921	9.434981	134	17 956	11.57584

N	N^2	$\sqrt{N}$	N	N^2	$\sqrt{N}$	N	N^2	$\sqrt{N}$
135	18 225	11.61895	180	32 400	13.41641	225	50 625	15.00000
136	18 496	11.66190	181	32 761	13.45362	226	51 076	15.03330
137	18 769	11.70470	182	33 124	13.49074	227	51 529	15.06652
138	19 044	11.74734	183	33 489	13.52775	228	51 984	15.09967
139	19 321	11.78983	184	33 856	13.56466	229	52 441	15.13275
140	19 600	11.83216	185	34 225	13.60147	230	52 900	15.16575
141	19 881	11.87434	186	34 596	13.63818	231	53 361	15.19868
142	20 164	11.91638	187	34 969	13.67479	232	53 824	15.23155
143	20 449	11.95826	188	35 344	13.71131	233	54 289	15.26434
144	20 736	12.00000	189	35 721	13.74773	234	54 756	15.29706
145	21 025	12.04159	190	36 100	13.78405	235	55 225	15.32971
146	21 316	12.08305	191	36 481	13.82027	236	55 696	15.36229
147	21 609	12.12436	192	36 864	13.85641	237	56 169	15.39480
148	21 904	12.16553	193	37 249	13.89244	238	56 644	15.42725
149	22 201	12.20656	194	37 636	13.92839	239	57 121	15.45962
150	22 500	12.24745	195	38 025	13.96424	240	57 600	15.49193
151	22 801	12.28821	196	38 416	14.00000	241	58 081	15.52417
152	23 104	12.32883	197	38 809	14.03567	242	58 564	15.55635
153	23 409	12.36932	198	39 204	14.07125	243	59 049	15.58846
154	23 716	12.40967	199	39 601	14.10674	244	59 536	15.62050
155	24 025	12.44990	200	40 000	14.14214	245	60 025	15.65248
156	24 336	12.49000	201	40 401	14.17745	246	60 516	15.68439
157	24 649	12.52996	202	40 804	14.21267	247	61 009	15.71623
158	24 964	12.56981	203	41 209	14.24781	248	61 504	15.74802
159	25 281	12.60952	204	41 616	14.28286	249	62 001	15.77973
160	25 600	12.64911	205	42 025	14.31782	250	62 500	15.81139
161	25 921	12.68858	206	42 436	14.35270	251	63 001	15.84298
162	26 244	12.72792	207	42 849	14.38749	252	63 504	15.87451
163	26 569	12.76715	208	43 264	14.42221	253	64 009	15.90597
164	26 896	12.80625	209	43 681	14.45683	254	64 516	15.93738
165	27 225	12.84523	210	44 100	14.49138	255	65 025	15.96872
166	27 556	12.88410	211	44 521	14.52584	256	65 536	16.00000
167	27 889	12.92285	212	44 944	14.56022	257	66 049	16.03122
168	28 224	12.96148	213	45 369	14.59452	258	66 564	16.06238
169	28 561	13.00000	214	45 796	14.62874	259	67 081	16.09348
170	28 900	13.03840	215	46 225	14.66288	260	67 600	16.12452
171	29 241	13.07670	216	46 656	14.69694	261	68 121	16.15549
172	29 584	13.11488	217	47 089	14.73092	262	68 644	16.18641
173	29 929	13.15295	218	47 524	14.76482	263	69 169	16.21727
174	30 276	13.19091	219	47 961	14.79865	264	69 696	16.24808
175	30 625	13.22876	220	48 400	14.83240	265	70 225	16.27882
176	30 976	13.26650	221	48 841	14.86607	266	70 756	16.30951
177	31 329	13.30413	222	49 284	14.89966	267	71 289	16.34013
178	31 684	13.34166	223	49 729	14.93318	268	71 824	16.37071
179	32 041	13.37909	224	50 176	14.96663	269	72 361	16.40122

N	N^2	$\sqrt{N}$	N	N^2	$\sqrt{N}$	N	N^2	$\sqrt{N}$
270	72 900	16.43168	315	99 225	17.74824	360	129 600	18.97367
271	73 441	16.46208	316	99 856	17.77639	361	130 321	19.00000
272	73 984	16.49242	317	100 489	17.80449	362	131 044	19.02630
273	74 529	16.52271	318	101 124	17.83255	363	131 769	19.05256
274	75 076	16.55295	319	101 761	17.86057	364	132 496	19.07878
275	75 625	16.58312	320	102 400	17.88854	365	133 225	19.10497
276	76 176	16.61325	321	103 041	17.91647	366	133 956	19.13113
277	76 729	16.64332	322	103 684	17.94436	367	134 689	19.15724
278	77 284	16.67333	323	104 329	17.97220	368	135 424	19.18333
279	77 841	16.70329	324	104 976	18.00000	369	136 161	19.20937
280	78 400	16.73320	325	105 625	18.02776	370	136 900	19.23538
281	78 961	16.76305	326	106 276	18.05547	371	137 641	19.26136
282	79 524	16.79286	327	106 929	18.08314	372	138 384	19.28730
283	80 089	16.82260	328	107 584	18.11077	373	139 129	19.31321
284	80 656	16.85230	329	108 241	18.13836	374	139 876	19.33908
285	81 225	16.88194	330	108 900	18.16590	375	140 625	19.36492
286	81 796	16.91153	331	109 561	18.19341	376	141 376	19.39072
287	82 369	16.94107	332	110 224	18.22087	377	142 129	19.41649
288	82 944	16.97056	333	110 889	18.24829	378	142 884	19.44222
289	83 521	17.00000	334	111 556	18.27567	379	143 641	19.46792
290	84 100	17.02939	335	112 225	18.30301	380	144 400	19.49359
291	84 681	17.05872	336	112 896	18.33030	381	145 161	19.51922
292	85 264	17.08801	337	113 569	18.35756	382	145 924	19.54483
293	85 849	17.11724	338	114 244	18.38478	383	146 689	19.57039
294	86 436	17.14643	339	114 921	18.41195	384	147 456	19.59592
295	87 025	17.17556	340	115 600	18.43909	385	148 225	19.62142
296	87 616	17.20465	341	116 281	18.46619	386	148 996	19.64688
297	88 209	17.23369	342	116 964	18.49324	387	149 769	19.67232
298	88 804	17.26268	343	117 649	18.52026	388	150 544	19.69772
299	89 401	17.29162	344	118 336	18.54724	389	151 321	19.72308
300	90 000	17.32051	345	119 025	18.57418	390	152 100	19.74842
301	90 601	17.34935	346	119 716	18.60108	391	152 881	19.77372
302	91 204	17.37815	347	120 409	18.62794	392	153 664	19.79899
303	91 809	17.40690	348	121 104	18.65476	393	154 449	19.82423
304	92 416	17.43560	349	121 801	18.68154	394	155 236	19.84934
305	93 025	17.46425	350	122 500	18.70829	395	156 025	19.87461
306	93 636	17.49286	351	123 201	18.73499	396	156 816	19.89975
307	94 249	17.52142	352	123 904	18.76166	397	157 609	19.92486
308	94 864	17.54993	353	124 609	18.78829	398	158 404	19.94994
309	95 481	17.57840	354	125 316	18.81489	399	159 201	19.97498
310	96 100	17.60682	355	126 025	18.84144	400	160 000	20.00000
311	96 721	17.63519	356	126 736	18.86796	401	160 801	20.02498
312	97 344	17.66352	357	127 449	18.89444	402	161 604	20.04994
313	97 969	17.69181	358	128 164	18.92089	403	162 409	20.07486
314	98 596	17.72005	359	128 881	18.94730	404	163 216	20.09975

N	N^2	$\sqrt{N}$	N	N^2	$\sqrt{N}$	N	N^2	$\sqrt{N}$
405	164 025	20.12461	450	202 500	21.21320	495	245 025	22.24860
406	164 836	20.14944	451	203 401	21.23676	496	246 016	22.27106
407	165 649	20.17424	452	204 304	21.26029	497	247 009	22.29350
408	166 464	20.19901	453	205 209	21.28380	498	248 004	22.31591
409	167 281	20.22375	454	206 116	21.30728	499	249 001	22.33831
410	168 100	20.24846	455	207 025	21.33073	500	250 000	22.36068
411	168 921	20.27313	456	207 936	21.35416	501	251 001	22.38303
412	169 744	20.29778	457	208 849	21.37756	502	252 004	22.40536
413	170 569	20.32240	458	209 764	21.40093	503	253 009	22.42766
414	171 396	20.34699	459	210 681	21.42429	504	254 016	22.44994
415	172 225	20.37155	460	211 600	21.44761	505	255 025	22.47221
416	173 056	20.39608	461	212 521	21.47091	506	256 036	22.49444
417	173 889	20.42058	462	213 444	21.49419	507	257 049	22.51666
418	174 724	20.44505	463	214 369	21.51743	508	258 064	22.53886
419	175 561	20.46949	464	215 296	21.54066	509	259 081	22.56103
420	176 400	20.49390	465	216 225	21.56386	510	260 100	22.58318
421	177 241	20.51828	466	217 156	21.58703	511	261 121	22.60531
422	178 084	20.54264	467	218 089	21.61018	512	262 144	22.62742
423	178 929	20.56696	468	219 024	21.63331	513	263 169	22.64950
424	179 776	20.59126	469	219 961	21.65641	514	264 196	22.67157
425	180 625	20.61553	470	220 900	21.67948	515	265 225	22.69361
426	181 476	20.63977	471	221 841	21.70253	516	266 256	22.71563
427	182 329	20.66398	472	222 784	21.72556	517	267 289	22.73763
428	183 184	20.68816	473	223 729	21.74856	518	268 324	22.75961
429	184 041	20.71232	474	224 676	21.77154	519	269 361	22.78157
430	184 900	20.73644	475	225 625	21.79449	520	270 400	22.80351
431	185 761	20.76054	476	226 576	21.81742	521	271 441	22.82542
432	186 624	20.78461	477	227 529	21.84033	522	272 484	22.84732
433	187 489	20.80865	478	228 484	21.86321	523	273 529	22.86919
434	188 356	20.83267	479	229 441	21.88607	524	274 576	22.89105
435	189 225	20.85665	480	230 400	21.90890	525	275 625	22.91288
436	190 096	20.88061	481	231 361	21.93171	526	276 676	22.93469
437	190 969	20.90454	482	232 324	21.95450	527	277 729	22.95648
438	191 844	20.92845	483	233 289	21.97726	528	278 784	22.97825
439	192 721	20.95233	484	234 256	22.00000	529	279 841	23.00000
440	193 600	20.97618	485	235 225	22.02272	530	280 900	23.02173
441	194 481	21.00000	486	236 196	22.04541	531	281 961	23.04344
442	195 364	21.02380	487	237 169	22.06808	532	283 024	23.06513
443	196 249	21.04757	488	238 144	22.09072	533	284 089	23.08679
444	197 136	21.07131	489	239 121	22.11334	534	285 156	23.10844
445	198 025	21.09502	490	240 100	22.13594	535	286 225	23.13007
446	198 916	21.11871	491	241 081	22.15852	536	287 296	23.15167
447	199 809	21.14237	492	242 064	22.18107	537	288 369	23.17326
448	200 704	21.16601	493	243 049	22.20360	538	289 444	23.19483
449	201 601	21.18962	494	244 036	22.22611	539	290 521	23.21637

table A.6 ▪ table
of squares and
square roots
(continued)

N	N^2	$\sqrt{N}$	N	N^2	$\sqrt{N}$	N	N^2	$\sqrt{N}$
540	291 690	23.23790	585	342 225	24.18677	630	396 900	25.09980
541	292 681	23.25941	586	343 396	24.20744	631	398 161	25.11971
542	293 764	23.28089	587	344 569	24.22808	632	399 424	25.13961
543	294 849	23.30236	588	345 744	24.24871	633	400 689	25.15949
544	295 936	23.32381	589	346 921	24.26932	634	401 956	25.17936
545	297 025	23.34524	590	348 100	24.28992	635	403 225	25.19921
546	298 116	23.36664	591	349 281	24.31049	636	404 496	25.21904
547	299 209	23.38803	592	350 464	24.33105	637	405 769	25.23886
548	300 304	23.40940	593	351 649	24.35159	638	407 044	25.25866
549	301 401	23.43075	594	352 836	24.37212	639	408 321	25.27845
550	302 500	23.45208	595	354 025	24.39262	640	409 600	25.29822
551	303 601	23.47339	596	355 216	24.41311	641	410 881	25.31798
552	304 704	23.49468	597	356 409	24.43358	642	412 164	25.33772
553	305 809	23.51595	598	357 604	24.45404	643	413 449	25.35744
554	306 916	23.53720	599	358 801	24.47448	644	414 736	25.37716
555	308 025	23.55844	600	360 000	24.49490	645	416 025	25.39685
556	309 136	23.57965	601	361 201	24.51530	646	417 316	25.41653
557	310 249	23.60085	602	362 404	24.53569	647	418 609	25.43619
558	311 364	23.62202	603	363 609	24.55606	648	419 904	25.45584
559	312 481	23.64318	604	364 816	24.57641	649	421 201	25.47548
560	313 600	23.66432	605	366 025	24.59675	650	422 500	25.49510
561	314 721	23.68544	606	367 236	24.61707	651	423 801	25.51470
562	315 844	23.70654	607	368 449	24.63737	652	425 104	25.53429
563	316 969	23.72762	608	369 664	24.65766	653	426 409	25.55386
564	318 096	23.74868	609	370 881	24.67793	654	427 716	25.57342
565	319 225	23.76973	610	372 100	24.69818	655	429 025	25.59297
566	320 356	23.79075	611	373 321	24.71841	656	430 336	25.61250
567	321 489	23.81176	612	374 544	24.73863	657	431 649	25.63201
568	322 624	23.83275	613	375 769	24.75884	658	432 964	25.65151
569	323 761	23.85372	614	376 996	24.77902	659	434 281	25.67100
570	324 900	23.87467	615	378 225	24.79919	660	435 600	25.69047
571	326 041	23.89561	616	379 456	24.81935	661	436 921	25.70992
572	327 184	23.91652	617	380 689	24.83948	662	438 244	25.72936
573	328 329	23.93742	618	381 924	24.85961	663	439 569	25.74879
574	329 476	23.95830	619	383 161	24.87971	664	440 896	25.76820
575	330 625	23.97916	620	384 400	24.89980	665	442 225	25.78759
576	331 776	24.00000	621	385 641	24.91987	666	443 556	25.80698
577	332 929	24.02082	622	386 884	24.93993	667	444 889	25.82634
578	334 084	24.04163	623	388 129	24.95997	668	446 224	25.84570
579	335 241	24.06242	624	389 376	24.97999	669	447 561	25.86503
580	336 400	24.08319	625	390 625	25.00000	670	448 900	25.88436
581	337 561	24.10394	626	391 876	25.01999	671	450 241	25.90367
582	338 724	24.12468	627	393 129	25.03997	672	451 584	25.92296
583	339 889	24.14539	628	394 384	25.05593	673	452 929	25.94224
584	341 056	24.16609	629	395 641	25.07987	674	454 276	25.96151

N	N²	√N	N	N²	√N	N	N²	√N
675	455 625	25.98076	720	518 400	26.83282	765	585 225	27.65863
676	456 976	26.00000	721	519 841	26.85144	766	586 756	27.67671
677	458 329	26.01922	722	521 284	26.87006	767	588 289	27.69476
678	459 684	26.03843	723	522 729	26.88866	768	589 824	27.71281
679	461 041	26.05763	724	624 176	26.90725	769	591 361	27.73085
680	462 400	26.07681	725	525 625	26.92582	770	592 900	27.74887
681	463 761	26.09598	726	527 076	26.94439	771	594 441	27.76689
682	465 124	26.11513	727	528 529	26.96294	772	595 984	27.78489
683	466 489	26.13427	728	529 984	26.98148	773	597 529	27.80288
684	467 856	26.15339	729	531 441	27.00000	774	599 076	27.82086
685	469 225	26.17250	730	532 900	27.01851	775	600 625	27.83882
686	470 596	26.19160	731	534 361	27.03701	776	602 176	27.85678
687	471 969	26.21068	732	535 824	27.05550	777	603 729	27.87472
688	473 344	26.22975	733	537 289	27.07397	778	605 284	27.89265
689	474 721	26.24881	734	538 756	27.09243	779	606 841	27.91057
690	476 100	26.26785	735	540 225	27.11088	780	608 400	27.92848
691	477 481	26.28688	736	541 696	27.12932	781	609 961	27.94638
692	478 864	26.30589	737	543 169	27.14774	782	611 524	27.96426
693	480 249	26.32489	738	544 644	27.16616	783	613 089	27.98214
694	481 636	26.34388	739	546 121	27.18455	784	614 656	28.00000
695	483 025	26.36285	740	547 600	27.20294	785	616 225	28.01785
696	484 416	26.38181	741	549 081	27.22132	786	617 796	28.03569
697	485 809	26.40076	742	550 564	27.23968	787	619 369	28.05352
698	487 204	26.41969	743	552 049	27.25803	788	620 944	28.07134
699	488 601	26.43861	744	553 536	27.27636	789	622 521	28.08914
700	490 000	26.45751	745	555 025	27.29469	790	624 100	28.10694
701	491 401	26.47640	746	556 516	27.31300	791	625 681	28.12472
702	492 804	26.49528	747	558 009	27.33130	792	627 264	28.14249
703	494 209	26.51415	748	559 504	27.34959	793	528 849	28.16026
704	495 616	26.53300	749	561 001	27.36786	794	630 436	28.17801
705	497 025	26.55184	750	562 500	27.38613	795	632 025	28.19574
706	498 436	26.57066	751	564 001	27.40438	796	633 616	28.21347
707	499 849	26.58947	752	565 504	27.42262	797	635 209	28.23119
708	501 264	26.60827	753	567 009	27.44085	798	636 804	28.24889
709	502 681	26.62705	754	568 516	27.45906	799	638 401	28.26659
710	504 100	26.64583	755	570 025	27.47726	800	640 000	28.28427
711	505 521	26.66458	756	571 536	27.49545	801	641 601	28.30194
712	506 944	26.68333	757	573 049	27.51363	802	643 204	28.31960
713	508 369	26.70206	758	574 564	27.53180	803	644 809	28.33725
714	509 796	26.72078	759	576 081	27.54995	804	646 416	28.35489
715	511 225	26.73948	760	577 600	27.56810	805	648 025	28.37252
716	512 656	26.75818	761	579 121	27.58623	806	649 636	28.39014
717	514 089	26.77686	762	580 644	27.60435	807	651 249	28.40775
718	515 524	26.79552	763	582 169	27.62245	808	652 864	28.42534
719	516 961	26.81418	764	583 696	27.64055	809	654 481	28.44293

table A.6 ■ table	N	N²	√N	N	N²	√N	N	N²	√N
of squares and									
square roots	810	656 100	28.46050	855	731 025	29.24038	900	810 000	30.00000
(continued)	811	657 721	28.47806	856	732 736	29.25748	901	811 801	30.01666
	812	659 344	28.49561	857	734 449	29.27456	902	813 604	30.03331
	813	660 969	28.51315	858	736 164	29.29164	903	815 409	30.04996
	814	662 596	28.53069	859	737 881	29.30870	904	817 216	30.06659
	815	664 225	28.54820	860	739 600	29.32576	905	819 025	30.08322
	816	665 856	28.56571	861	741 321	29.34280	906	820 836	30.09983
	817	667 489	28.58321	862	743 044	29.35984	907	822 649	30.11644
	818	669 124	28.60070	863	744 769	29.37686	908	824 464	30.13304
	819	670 761	28.61818	864	746 496	29.39388	909	826 281	30.14963
	820	672 400	28.63564	865	748 225	29.41088	910	828 100	30.16621
	821	674 041	28.65310	866	749 956	29.42788	911	829 921	30.18278
	822	675 684	28.67054	867	751 689	29.44486	912	831 744	30.19934
	823	677 329	28.68798	868	753 424	29.46184	913	833 569	30.21589
	824	678 976	28.70540	869	755 161	29.47881	914	835 396	30.23243
	825	680 625	28.72281	870	756 900	29.49576	915	837 225	30.24897
	826	682 276	28.74022	871	758 641	29.51271	916	839 056	30.26549
	827	683 929	28.75761	872	760 384	29.52965	917	840 889	30.28201
	828	685 584	28.77499	873	762 129	29.54657	918	842 724	30.29851
	829	687 241	28.79236	874	763 876	29.56349	919	844 561	30.31501
	830	688 900	28.80972	875	765 625	29.58040	920	846 400	30.33150
	831	690 561	28.82707	876	767 376	29.59730	921	848 241	30.34798
	832	692 224	28.84441	877	769 129	29.61419	922	850 084	30.36445
	833	693 889	28.86174	878	770 884	29.63106	923	851 929	30.38092
	834	695 556	28.87906	879	772 641	29.64793	924	853 776	30.39737
	835	697 225	28.89637	880	774 400	29.66479	925	855 625	30.41381
	836	698 896	28.91366	881	776 161	29.68164	926	857 476	30.43025
	837	700 569	28.93095	882	777 924	29.69848	927	859 329	30.44667
	838	702 244	28.94823	883	779 689	29.71532	928	861 184	30.46309
	839	703 921	28.96550	884	781 456	29.73214	929	863 041	30.47950
	840	705 600	28.98275	885	783 225	29.74895	930	864 900	30.49590
	841	707 281	29.00000	886	784 996	29.76575	931	866 761	30.51229
	842	708 964	29.01724	887	786 769	29.78255	932	868 624	30.52868
	843	710 649	29.03446	888	788 544	29.79933	933	870 489	30.54505
	844	712 336	29.05168	889	790 321	29.81610	934	872 356	30.56141
	845	714 025	29.06888	890	792 100	29.83287	935	874 225	30.57777
	846	715 716	29.08608	891	793 881	29.84962	936	876 096	30.59412
	847	717 409	29.10326	892	795 664	29.86637	937	877 969	30.61046
	848	719 104	29.12044	893	797 449	29.88311	938	879 844	30.62679
	849	720 801	29.13760	894	799 236	29.89983	939	881 721	30.64311
	850	722 500	29.15476	895	801 025	29.91655	940	883 600	30.65942
	851	724 201	29.17190	896	802 816	29.93326	941	885 481	30.67572
	852	725 904	29.18904	897	804 609	29.94996	942	887 364	30.69202
	853	727 609	29.20616	898	806 404	29.96665	943	889 249	30.70831
	854	729 316	29.22328	899	808 201	29.98333	944	891 136	30.72458

N	N^2	$\sqrt{N}$	N	N^2	$\sqrt{N}$	N	N^2	$\sqrt{N}$
945	893 025	30.74085	965	931 225	31.06445	985	970 225	31.38471
946	894 916	30.75711	966	933 156	31.08054	986	972 196	31.40064
947	896 809	30.77337	967	935 089	31.09662	987	974 169	31.41656
948	898 704	30.78961	968	937 024	31.11270	988	976 144	31.43247
949	900 601	30.80584	969	938 961	31.12876	989	978 121	31.44837
950	902 500	30.82207	970	940 900	31.14482	990	980 100	31.46427
951	904 401	30.83829	971	942 841	31.16087	991	982 081	31.48015
952	906 304	30.85450	972	944 784	31.17691	992	984 064	31.49603
953	908 209	30.87070	973	946 729	31.19295	993	986 049	31.51190
954	910 116	30.88689	974	948 676	31.20897	994	988 036	31.52777
955	912 025	30.90307	975	950 625	31.22499	995	990 025	31.54362
956	913 936	30.91925	976	952 576	31.24100	996	992 016	31.55947
957	915 849	30.93542	977	954 529	31.25700	997	994 009	31.57531
958	917 764	30.95158	978	956 484	31.27299	998	996 004	31.59114
959	919 681	30.96773	979	958 441	31.28898	999	998 001	31.60696
960	921 600	30.98387	980	960 400	31.30495	1,000	1 000 000	31.62278
961	923 521	31.00000	981	962 361	31.32092			
962	925 444	31.01612	982	964 324	31.33688			
963	927 369	31.03224	983	966 289	31.35283			
964	929 296	31.04835	984	968 256	31.36877			

85017	84532	13618	23157	86952	02438
16719	82789	69041	05545	44109	05403
65842	27672	82186	14871	22115	86529
76875	20684	39187	38976	94324	43204
93640	39160	41453	97312	41548	93137
99478	70086	71265	11742	18226	29004
65119	26486	47353	43361	99436	42753
70322	21592	48233	93806	32584	21828
58113	41278	11679	49540	61777	67954
44655	81225	31133	36768	60452	38537
02295	13487	98662	07092	44673	61303
85035	54881	35587	43310	48897	48493
01197	86935	28021	61570	23350	65710
97907	19078	40646	31352	48625	44369
63268	96905	28797	57048	46359	74294
52841	59684	67411	09243	56092	84369
53722	71399	10916	07959	21225	13018
11434	51908	62171	93732	26958	02400
62375	99292	21177	72621	66995	07289
28337	20923	87929	61020	62841	31374
38631	79430	62421	97959	67422	69992
49172	16332	44670	35089	17691	89246
89232	57327	34679	62235	79655	81336
02844	15026	32439	58537	48274	81330
40387	65406	37929	08709	60623	22237
80240	44177	51171	08723	39323	05798
44910	99321	72173	56239	04595	10835
33663	86347	00926	44915	34823	51770
86430	19102	37420	41876	76569	24358
31379	68588	81675	15694	43438	36879

glossary of formulas

This glossary lists all of the general formulas presented in the book. As contrasted to the units themselves, which were designed as teaching instruments, this glossary is particularly useful as a reference when working on problems involving statistical analysis. All formulas are presented in the order of their occurrence in this book; in order to facilitate review, the unit and frame number in which each formula was introduced is indicated with each entry. Thus (2–27) indicates that the formula was introduced in Frame 27 of Unit 2.

(2–27) $i = B_U - B_L$

Determining the class interval by the use of the upper and lower boundaries of a particular class.

(2–28) $i = B_{L(2)} - B_{L(1)}$
or $i = B_{U(2)} - B_{U(1)}$

Determining the class interval by the use of the lower (or upper) boundaries of adjoining classes.

(2–28) $i = L_{L(2)} - L_{L(1)}$
or $i = L_{U(2)} - L_{U(1)}$

Determining the class interval by the use of the lower (or upper) limits of adjoining classes.

(2–31) $\text{Midpt} = \dfrac{L_L + L_U}{2}$

Determining the class midpoint by using the upper and lower limits of a class.

(2–31) $\text{Midpt} = \dfrac{B_L + B_U}{2}$

Determining the class midpoint by using the upper and lower boundaries of a class.

(2–33) $\text{Midpt} = B_L + \frac{1}{2}i$

Determining the class midpoint by using the lower boundary and size of the class interval.

(2–35) $i = \text{midpt}_{(2)} - \text{midpt}_{(1)}$

An alternative formula for determining the class interval by using the midpoints of adjoining classes.

(3–4) $\bar{X} = \dfrac{\Sigma X}{n}$

Sample mean for ungrouped measurements.

(3–8) $\mu = \dfrac{\Sigma X}{N}$

Population mean for ungrouped measurements.

(3–9) $\bar{X} \text{ (or } \mu) = \dfrac{\Sigma fX}{\Sigma f}$

Mean for grouped data, for either a sample or a population.

(3–25) $\text{Med} = X_{n/2+\frac{1}{2}}$

Position of the median in an array of ungrouped values.

(3–32) $\text{Med} = B_L + \dfrac{n/2 - \text{cf}_B}{f_c} \, i$

Value of the median for grouped data.

(3–47) $Q_1 = X_{n/4+\frac{1}{2}}$
$Q_2 = X_{n/2+\frac{1}{2}}$
$Q_3 = X_{3n/4+\frac{1}{2}}$

Positions of the first, second, and third quartiles in an array of ungrouped measurements.

(3–50) $Q_1 = B_L + \dfrac{n/4 - \text{cf}_B}{f_c} \, i$

$Q_2 = B_L + \dfrac{n/2 - \text{cf}_B}{f_c} \, i$

$Q_3 = B_L + \dfrac{3n/4 - \text{cf}_B}{f_c} \, i$

Values of the first, second, and third quartiles for grouped data.

(3–54) $D_4 = X_{4n/10+\frac{1}{2}}$

Position of the fourth decile in an array of ungrouped measurements. Used to illustrate the modification of the formula for the median for the purpose of determining the values of deciles or percentiles.

(3-55) $D_4 = B_L + \dfrac{4n/10 - \mathrm{cf}_B}{f_c}\, i$

Value of the fourth decile for grouped data. Used to illustrate the modification of the formula for the median for the purpose of computing the values of deciles and percentiles.

(3-57) Mode = most frequent value

Mode for ungrouped data.

(3-61) Mode $= B_L + \dfrac{D_1}{D_1 + D_2}\, i$

Mode for grouped data.

(3-69) $N_e = \min$

The mathematical criterion for a "good" average that is satisfied by the mode.

(3-70) $\Sigma e = \min$

The mathematical criterion for a "good" average that is satisfied by the median.

(3-73) $\Sigma e^2 = \min$

The mathematical criterion for a "good" average that is satisfied by the mean. Referred to as the least-squares criterion.

(4-2) $R = H - L$

Range for ungrouped measurements.

(4-6) $R = B_U$ (highest class) $- B_L$ (lowest class)

Range for grouped data.

(4-9) $\mathrm{QD} = \dfrac{Q_3 - Q_1}{2}$

Quartile deviation.

(4-22) $x = X - \bar{X}$

The definition of a deviation value.

(4-26) $\mathrm{MD} = \dfrac{\Sigma|x|}{n}$

Mean deviation for ungrouped data.

(4-28) $\mathrm{MD} = \dfrac{\Sigma f|x|}{\Sigma f}$

Mean deviation for grouped data.

(4-34) $s = \sqrt{\dfrac{\Sigma x^2}{n}}$

Sample standard deviation for ungrouped data, deviation formula.

(4-36) $s = \sqrt{\dfrac{\Sigma f x^2}{\Sigma f}}$

Sample standard deviation for grouped data, deviation formula.

(4-44) $s = \sqrt{\dfrac{\Sigma X^2}{n} - \left(\dfrac{\Sigma X}{n}\right)^2}$

Sample standard deviation for ungrouped data, computational formula.

(4-51) $s = \sqrt{\dfrac{\Sigma f X^2}{\Sigma f} - \left(\dfrac{\Sigma f X}{\Sigma f}\right)^2}$

Sample standard deviation for grouped data, computational formula.

(4-69) $V = \dfrac{s}{\bar{X}}$

Coefficient of variation.

(4-79) $a_3 = \dfrac{m_3}{s^3}$ where $m_3 = \dfrac{\Sigma x^3}{n}$

A measure of skewness (with $a_3 = 0$ for a symmetrical distribution).

(4-82) $a_4 = \dfrac{m_4}{s^4}$ where $m_4 = \dfrac{\Sigma x^4}{n}$

A measure of kurtosis (with $a_4 = 3$ for a mesokurtic distribution).

(5-57) $P(A \text{ or } B) = P(A) + P(B)$

The probability of mutually exclusive outcomes A or B occurring in a single event.

(5-61)	$P(A \text{ or } B) = P(A) + P(B) - P(A,B)$	The probability of nonexclusive outcomes A *or* B occurring in a single event.
(5-71)	$P(A,B) = P(A)P(B)$	The probability of outcomes A *and* B occurring in two independent events.
(5-80)	$P(A,B) = P(A)P(B|A)$	The probability of outcomes A *and* B occurring in two dependent events.
(6-36)	$(q + p)^n$	The binomial whose expansion to various powers yields various binomial probability distributions.
(6-76)	$Z = \dfrac{X - \mu}{\sigma}$	Formula for transforming a measurement into a Z value, which indicates deviation from the mean in units of the standard deviation. Used in conjunction with Table A.1, "Table of Areas under the Normal Curve."
(7-80)	$\sigma_{\bar{X}} = \dfrac{\sigma}{\sqrt{n}}$	Standard error of the mean when the population standard deviation is known and the population is infinite in size (or $n < 5\%N$).
(7-84)	$\sigma_{\bar{X}} = \dfrac{\sigma}{\sqrt{n}}\sqrt{\dfrac{N-n}{N-1}}$	Standard error of the mean when the population standard deviation is known and the population is finite in size.
(7-93)	$s_{\bar{X}} = \dfrac{s}{\sqrt{n-1}}$	Standard error of the mean when a sample standard deviation is known and the population is infinite in size (or $n < 5\%N$).
(7-96)	$s_{\bar{X}} = \dfrac{s}{\sqrt{n-1}}\sqrt{\dfrac{N-n}{N-1}}$	Standard error of the mean when a sample standard deviation is known and the population is finite in size.
(8-39)	$\bar{X} \pm 1.96 s_{\bar{X}}$	The 95 percent confidence interval for estimating the population mean with the use of the normal probability distribution.
(8-43)	$\bar{X} \pm 1.64 s_{\bar{X}}$	The 90 percent confidence interval for estimating the population mean with the use of the normal probability distribution.
(8-43)	$\bar{X} \pm 2.58 s_{\bar{X}}$	The 99 percent confidence interval for estimating the population mean with the use of the normal probability distribution.
(8-53)	$N\bar{X} \pm NZs_{\bar{X}}$ or $N(\bar{X} \pm Zs_{\bar{X}})$	Confidence limits for estimating the total quantity in a population.
(8-58)	Point estimate $\pm Zs_{\text{stat}}$	The general formula for defining the confidence interval used in estimating any population parameter.
(8-63)	$s_{\bar{X}_1 - \bar{X}_2} = \sqrt{s_{\bar{X}_1}{}^2 + s_{\bar{X}_2}{}^2}$ $\sigma_{\bar{X}_1 - \bar{X}_2} = \sqrt{\sigma_{\bar{X}_1}{}^2 + \sigma_{\bar{X}_2}{}^2}$	Standard error of the difference between two means.
(8-67)	$(\bar{X}_1 - \bar{X}_2) \pm Zs_{\bar{X}_1 - \bar{X}_2}$	Confidence limits for estimating the difference between the means of two populations.

(8-80) $p \pm Z s_p$

Confidence limits for estimating a population proportion.

(8-81) $s_p = \sqrt{\dfrac{p(1-p)}{n}}$

Standard error of the proportion when the population is infinite in size or $n < 5\%N$.

(8-82) $s_p = \sqrt{\dfrac{p(1-p)}{n}} \sqrt{\dfrac{N-n}{N-1}}$

Standard error of the proportion when finite correction factor needs to be used.

(8-92) $N_p \pm NZs_p$
    or $N(p \pm Zs_p)$

Confidence limits for estimating the total number in a category of the population.

(8-94) $s_{p_1-p_2} = \sqrt{s_{p_1}{}^2 + s_{p_2}{}^2}$

Standard error of the difference between two proportions.

(8-95) $(p_1 - p_2) \pm Zs_{p_1-p_2}$

Confidence limits for estimating the difference between the proportions in two populations.

(9-25) $\mu_H \pm Zs_{\bar{x}}$

Formula for defining critical limits in testing a hypothesized value of the population mean.

(9-47) $Z = \dfrac{\bar{X} - \mu_H}{s_{\bar{x}}}$

Formula for testing a hypothesized value of the population mean which is based on transforming the value of the sample mean into a Z value. This is the procedure usually used.

(9-64) $Z_{CR} =$
$\dfrac{\text{observed value} - \text{expected value}}{\text{standard error of the statistic}}$

Critical ratio for testing any hypothesized (expected) population value.

(9-69) $Z_{CR} = \dfrac{\bar{X}_1 - \bar{X}_2}{s_{\bar{x}_1-\bar{x}_2}}$

Critical ratio for testing the significance of the difference between two means.

(9-84) $\sigma_p = \sqrt{\dfrac{\pi_H(1-\pi_H)}{n}}$

Standard error of a proportion, computed on the basis of a hypothesized population proportion. This is the standard error value normally used in hypothesis testing concerning a single proportion, rather than s_p.

(9-85) $Z_{CR} = \dfrac{p - \pi_H}{\sigma_p}$

Critical ratio for testing a hypothesized value of the population proportion.

(9-89) $Z_{CR} = \dfrac{p_1 - p_2}{s_{p_1} - p_2}$

Critical ratio for testing the significance of the difference between two proportions.

(10-24) $df = n - 1$

Degrees of freedom used in conjunction with Table A.3, "Table of Areas for t Distributions," when testing a hypothesis concerning a population mean or estimating its value. The use of the t distribution rather than the normal distribution is required when σ is unknown and $n < 30$.

(10-43) $\bar{X} \pm ts_{\bar{x}}$

Estimating the population mean by using the t distribution.

(10-52) $\bar{X}_1 - \bar{X}_2 \pm ts_{\bar{x}_1-\bar{x}_2}$

Estimating the difference between the means of two populations by using the t distribution.

(10–53) $\text{df} = n_1 + n_2 - 2$

Degrees of freedom used in conjunction with Table A.3, "Table of Areas for t Distributions," when testing a hypothesis concerning the difference between means or estimating the difference.

(10–60) $t_{\text{CR}} = \dfrac{\bar{X} - \mu_H}{s_{\bar{X}}}$

Testing a hypothesized value of the population mean by use of the t distribution.

(10–67) $t_{\text{CR}} = \dfrac{\bar{X}_1 - \bar{X}_2}{s_{\bar{X}_1 - \bar{X}_2}}$

Testing the difference between means by using the t distribution.

(11–16) $\chi^2 = \sum \dfrac{(f_o - f_e)^2}{f_e}$

The value of χ^2 (chi-square).

(11–20) $k - 1$

Degrees of freedom used in conjunction with the χ^2 test when the observed frequencies can be listed along a single dimension (one-way classification).

(11–36) $(r - 1)(k - 1)$

Degrees of freedom used in conjunction with the χ^2 test when the observed frequencies are entered in a contingency table (two-way classification).

(11–39) $f_e = \dfrac{\Sigma r \Sigma k}{\Sigma f}$

Determining expected frequencies for the cells of a contingency table.

(11–70) $\chi^2 = \dfrac{n(ad - bc)^2}{(a + b)(c + d)(a + c)(b + d)}$

Alternative formula for computing the value of χ^2 for 2 × 2 contingency tables. Does not require the separate computation of expected cell frequencies.

(11–80) $\chi^2 = \sum \dfrac{(|f_o - f_e| - 0.5)^2}{f_e}$

The formula for χ^2 which includes Yates' correction for continuity.

(12–21) $P(B) = P(A)P(B|A) + P(\sim A)P(B|\sim A)$

Determining the overall probability of an outcome in the second of two dependent events when the outcome of the first event is not known.

(12–35) $P(A|B) = \dfrac{P(A)P(B|A)}{P(B)}$

Bayes' formula for determining the value of the posterior probability.

(12–38) $P(A|B)$
$= \dfrac{P(A)\,P(B|A)}{P(A)P(B|A) + P(\sim A)P(B|\sim A)}$

The computational version of Bayes' formula for determining the value of the posterior probability.

(12–51) $\Sigma X P(X)$

The value of the expected payoff related to a decision act when the probabilities of the outcomes are known (decision making under conditions of risk).

(13–34) $Y_c = a + bX$

General equation for a straight line used in regression analysis in which a is the value of Y_c when X is equal to zero and b is the slope of the line.

(13–47) $b = \dfrac{\Sigma XY - n\bar{X}\bar{Y}}{\Sigma X^2 - n\bar{X}^2}$

The formula for b in the equation for the straight line which satisfies the least-squares criterion.

(13–47) $a = \bar{Y} - b\bar{X}$

The formula for a in the equation for the straight line which satisfies the least-squares criterion.

(13–80) $\sigma_{Y.X} = \sqrt{\dfrac{\Sigma(Y - Y_c)^2}{N}}$

Standard error of estimate for a population of values.

$(13\text{-}80)$ $\quad s_{Y.X} = \sqrt{\dfrac{\Sigma(Y - Y_c)^2}{n}}$

Standard error of estimate for a sample.

$(13\text{-}82)$ $\quad \hat{s}_{Y.X} = \sqrt{\dfrac{\Sigma(Y - Y_c)^2}{n - 2}}$

Estimated standard error of estimate for a population of values based on sample data.

$(13\text{-}89)$ $\quad Y_c \pm t\hat{s}_{Y.X}$
$\qquad$ or $Y_c \pm Z\hat{s}_{Y.X}$ $\quad$ if $n \geq 30$

Setting confidence limits for an estimate based on a regression equation.

$(14\text{-}17)$ $\quad r^2 = 1.00 - \dfrac{s_{Y.X}^2}{s_Y^2}$

The coefficient of determination (or the square of the coefficient of correlation) defined on the basis of the standard error of estimate being known. This formula is used to illustrate that r^2 represents the proportion of explained variance in the dependent variable, but it is seldom used for computational purposes as such.

$(14\text{-}25)$ $\quad r^2 = 1 - \dfrac{\text{unexplained variance}}{\text{total variance}}$

Verbal version of the formula in (14–17).

$(14\text{-}50)$ $\quad r = \dfrac{\Sigma Z_X Z_Y}{n}$

Pearson product-moment coefficient of correlation.

$(14\text{-}51)$ $\quad r = \dfrac{n\Sigma XY - \Sigma X \Sigma Y}{\sqrt{n\Sigma X^2 - (\Sigma X)^2}\sqrt{n\Sigma Y^2 - (\Sigma Y)^2}}$

Computational formula for the Pearson r. This is the formula usually used.

$(14\text{-}66)$ $\quad s_{Y.X} = s_Y \sqrt{1 - r^2}$

Sample standard error of estimate computed when r is known. This, rather than the formula in (13–80), is usually used.

$(14\text{-}67)$ $\quad \hat{s}_{Y.X} = s_Y \sqrt{1 - r^2} \sqrt{\dfrac{n}{n - 2}}$

Estimated standard error of estimate for a population of values based on sample data when r is known. This, rather than the formula in (13–82), is usually used.

$(14\text{-}71)$ $\quad Y_c = \left(\bar{Y} - r\dfrac{s_Y}{s_X}\bar{X}\right) + \left(r\dfrac{s_Y}{s_X}\right)X$

Solution of the values of a and b in the regression equation $Y_c = a + bX$, by utilizing the known value of r. The formulas in (13–47) are usually used rather than this one.

$(14\text{-}73)$ $\quad r_{\text{rank}} = 1 - \dfrac{6\Sigma D^2}{n(n^2 - 1)}$

The rank correlation coefficient.

$(14\text{-}81)$ $\quad R_{1.23}$

Symbol representing the coefficient of multiple correlation between the dependent variable, always indicated by 1, and two other variables, indicated by 2 and 3 in this case.

$(14\text{-}86)$ $\quad r_{14.23}$

Symbol representing the coefficient of partial correlation between variables 1 and 4, with variables 2 and 3 statistically held constant in this case.

$(15\text{-}16)$ $\quad Y = TSCI$

The most generally accepted model in time-series analysis, indicating the multiplicative relationship among the trend, seasonal, cyclical, and irregular components.

(15–17) $Y = T + S + C + I$

An alternative approach to time-series analysis which incorporates the assumption that effects are additive. Seldom used in practice.

(15–24) $CI = \dfrac{Y}{TS}$

An example of the decomposition of time-series data, by which the combined cyclical and irregular effects are identified as the residual.

(15–59) $S = \dfrac{TSCI}{TCI}$

Symbolic representation of the identification of the seasonal component of a time series by the ratio-to-moving-average method.

(15–72) $CI = \dfrac{Y}{T} = \dfrac{TCI}{T}$

Decomposition of annual time-series data for the purpose of identifying combined cyclical and irregular effects.

(15–80) $TCI = \dfrac{Y}{S} = \dfrac{TSCI}{S}$

Symbolic representation for the process of de-seasonalizing monthly or quarterly time-series values.

(15–83) $Y_c \text{ (monthly)} = \dfrac{a}{12} + \dfrac{b}{12} X$

The first step in changing the scale of the least-squares equation for the trend component from annual values to monthly values.

(15–85) $Y_c \text{ (monthly)} = \dfrac{a}{12} + \dfrac{b}{12}\dfrac{X}{12}$

The second step in changing the scale of the least-squares equation for trend. The X units now become coded months rather than coded years.

(15–86) $Y_c \text{ (monthly)} = \dfrac{a}{12} + \dfrac{b}{12}\left(\dfrac{X}{12} - 5.5\right)$

The final step in changing the scale of the least-squares equation for trend. $X = 0$ is now centered at January 15 of the year, rather than being located at July 1.

(15–91) $I = \dfrac{CI}{C}$

Identification of the irregular component of the time series by the residual method.

(16–19) $\dfrac{p_1}{p_0} \times 100$

A simple price index, or price relative.

(16–22) $\dfrac{q_1}{q_0} \times 100$

A simple quantity relative.

(16–24) $\dfrac{p_1 q_1}{p_0 q_0} \times 100$

A simple value relative.

(16–26) $\dfrac{\Sigma p_1 q_0}{\Sigma p_0 q_0} \times 100$

Laspeyres' index. The composite price index in which prices are weighted by base-year quantities.

(16–31) $\dfrac{\Sigma p_1 q_1}{\Sigma p_0 q_1} \times 100$

Paasche's index. The composite price index in which prices are weighted by given-year quantities.

(16–46) $\dfrac{\Sigma (p_0 q_0)(p_1/p_0 \times 100)}{\Sigma p_0 q_0}$

The weighted average of price relatives. A composite price index whose value is the same as for Laspeyres' index.

(16–61) $C_n = \dfrac{L_n C_{n-1}}{100}$

Formula for computing the chain index for periods that follow the designated base period.

(16–62) $C_{n-1} = \dfrac{C_n}{L_n} \times 100$

Formula for computing the chain index for periods that precede the designated base period.